METEOROLOGICAL OFFICE

Handbook of Aviation Meteorology

LONDON : HMSO

© *Crown copyright 1971*
Applications for reproduction should be made to HMSO
First published 1960
Second edition 1971
Second impression 1977
Third edition 1994

ISBN 0 11 400365 3

HMSO

HMSO publications are available from:

HMSO Publications Centre
(Mail, fax and telephone orders only)
PO Box 276, London, SW8 5DT
Telephone orders 071-873 9090
General enquiries 071-873 0011
(queuing system in operation for both numbers)
Fax orders 071-873 8200

HMSO Bookshops
49 High Holborn, London, WC1V 6HB
(counter service only)
071-873 0011 Fax 071-873 8200
258 Broad Street, Birmingham, B1 2HE
021-643 3740 Fax 021-643 6510
33 Wine Street, Bristol, BS1 2BQ
0272 264306 Fax 0272 294515
9-21 Princess Street, Manchester, M60 8AS
061-834 7201 Fax 061-833 0634
16 Arthur Street, Belfast, BT1 4GD
0232 238451 Fax 0232 235401
71 Lothian Road, Edinburgh, EH3 9AZ
031-228 4181 Fax 031-229 2734

HMSO's Accredited Agents
(see Yellow Pages)

and through good booksellers

PREFACE

The primary objective of this handbook is to provide a work suitable for use by pilots undergoing intermediate or advanced courses of instruction at flying training schools. Within these limits the subject is covered comprehensively, but an elementary knowledge of meteorology on the part of the reader will be an advantage. The presentation has been made reasonably simple and physical ideas explained as they arise; mathematical knowledge is not required beyond an ability to handle some simple formulae, but for the benefit of those readers familiar with elementary calculus, proofs of most of the formulae used are collected together in an appendix.

While the routine work of meteorology is in general performed by staff of state meteorological services throughout the world, the maximum value is obtainable from the services provided only if the users are equipped with an adequate knowledge and understanding of the many meteorological processes and phenomena that may affect aircraft operations, and if they are also aware of the means by which information on these matters is obtained by the meteorologist and made available to them. The range of subject matter necessary to meet these requirements is extensive; moreover it is still expanding as flying itself continues to develop. It is, however, neither possible nor desirable to confine the scope of this book to the precise needs of students attending a variety of courses and requiring to pass one or other of the several examinations open to them. Accordingly, with but very little widening of the scope, the book has a secondary object; that of the presentation of a general account of meteorology, including its theory and practice and its applications to aviation. It is hoped, therefore, that it will be found useful to any who are in one way or another concerned with the applications of meteorology to aviation and who require a non-mathematical account of the subject; included among these potential readers will no doubt be many meteorological personnel themselves, but more especially those under training.

The book is divided into five parts which are more or less independent. Part I contains a somewhat detailed account of the physical principles of the subject, together with their immediate applications to aviation. Part II gives a brief description of the raw material of meteorology — the observations, how they are made, distributed and charted. This leads on to a discussion of synoptic meteorology with an outline of the principles of weather forecasting in Part III. Part IV deals with the general circulation and world climatology on a very broad basis and contains guidance on how to use available climatological data for aviation purposes. It also includes brief notes on weather features affecting some routes. Part V is very short and deals briefly with the meteorological information and services available to users.

In the production of this third edition, the basic objectives of the handbook remain the same. However, in the process of revision, not only has existing material been updated and additions made as appropriate but an attempt has been made to give the handbook a more practical slant and this, it is hoped, will make the book of more use and of more interest to aviators. Only limited progress to this end was possible as it was not intended to rewrite the whole book and because it is still necessary for basic meteorological theory to be covered. However, one area in which significant change has been possible is in the presentation of examples. More emphasis is now placed upon the charts and products which an aviator might receive as flight documentation rather than upon those used by forecasters; examples are now given of the various charts and other products used for self briefing in an Annex at the back of the book. Any other material which is thought to be of an ephemeral nature, such as details of codes, will also be found there.

Some discussion is necessary of the philosophy that has been adopted as regards units. In general, the units adopted are those which are in use for practical meteorological and aviation purposes. These are mainly metric units but there are some exceptions. In particular, vertical distances are given in feet and wind speed is given in knots. The Celsius scale is used for temperature and hectopascals now replace millibars for pressure, although currently the latter unit continues to be used in the United Kingdom. In aeronautical transmissions and documentation, units are abbreviated in accordance with ICAO Doc. 8400 (Approved abbreviations and codes) and presented in a single type case, usually upper case. However, when used in this book, such abbreviations will generally be presented in the form found in scientific and technical texts, that is, in accordance with the convention approved by the Système International d'Unités (SI).

The original (1960) edition of the *Handbook of Aviation Meteorology* (Met.O.818) was prepared as a successor to the late Dr R.C. Sutcliffe's *Meteorology for Aviators* and as such naturally owes a very great deal to that earlier publication. The preparation was largely the work of Mr A.F. Crossley of the Meteorological Office with substantial assistance given by other members of the Meteorological Office staff — notably by Dr A.G. Forsdyke — and by colleagues of the Ministry of Transport and Civil Aviation. After revision by Mr F.D. Roberts of the Meteorological Office a second edition was issued in 1971. This present edition is founded upon a revised draft which was prepared in 1984, largely the work of Mr K. Bryant and Dr A.P. Cluley of the Meteorological Office; the further updating has been undertaken by Mr W.J.T. Norris, formerly of the Meteorological Office. The assistance received from Messrs F. Dalton and B.K. Lloyd of the Central Forecasting Division, former colleagues in the Central Forecasting Office and Mr D. Hendy and staff at London (Heathrow) Airport meteorological office is gratefully acknowledged.

CONTENTS

PART II

METEOROLOGICAL OBSERVATIONS

Chapter 11

SURFACE OBSERVATIONS

Chapter 17

OTHER DEPRESSIONS

Chapter 18

ANTICYCLONES

Chapter 19

ELEMENTS OF FORECASTING

PART IV

GENERAL CIRCULATION AND WORLD CLIMATE

Chapter 20
GENERAL CIRCULATION AND WORLD CLIMATE

PART V

METEOROLOGICAL INFORMATION FOR AVIATION

Chapter 21
METEOROLOGICAL INFORMATION FOR AVIATION

Appendix I
DERIVATION OF SOME FORMULAE INTRODUCED IN THE TEXT

Appendix II

Annex

PART I

PHYSICAL PRINCIPLES

CHAPTER 1

THE ATMOSPHERE

1.1 METEOROLOGY — A BRANCH OF PHYSICS

The meteorologist's principal concern is with the conditions within the atmosphere surrounding the earth, but the lithosphere (the earth's crust), and hydrosphere (the oceans), also need to be considered in so far as their condition interacts with that of the atmosphere. The whole surface of the earth and its atmosphere may be regarded as an enormous laboratory in which experiments are continually being performed, often on a grand scale and beyond the scope of human control, but still fundamentally the same as the experiments which the physicist performs and studies in his laboratory. The only sound foundation for an understanding of the subject is therefore a thorough grounding in the principles of physics, for example the laws of motion, of heating and cooling, and of condensation and evaporation. With such knowledge it is hoped that all the complex behaviour of the atmosphere can ultimately be explained. We shall therefore take the results of observation, and as far as is possible supply the physical explanations, in the belief that the aviator can assimilate those facts which are important to him only if he appreciates the reasons underlying them.

Before proceeding to the account of physical principles, it will be convenient to present a short description of the main atmospheric structure. This will show how the atmosphere may be regarded as consisting of several layers, and where those layers with which both weather and aviation are concerned stand in relation to the atmosphere as a whole. The lower layers are, for certain purposes, idealized into a standard atmosphere: some particulars of this are also included in this chapter. The foundations will have then been laid for the explanation of the physical processes and their application to aviation.

1.2 COMPOSITION OF THE ATMOSPHERE

The atmosphere, in its dry state, is a mixture of many gases of which nitrogen and oxygen are by far the most abundant, accounting for almost 99% of the whole in the proportion (by weight) of three parts of nitrogen to one of oxygen. Even though the density of the atmosphere decreases with height to a small fraction of its value at the earth's surface, analyses reveal no measurable variations in its composition up to a height of at least 60 km except in regard to ozone and some other trace gases which are affected by photochemical reactions in the stratosphere. From a height of about 70 km upwards, gravitational separation begins to be effective, and the atmospheric composition varies with height. However, for the levels with which we are mostly concerned in the study of weather, dry air may be taken to be a uniform mixture in the proportions given in Table 1.

Actually the atmosphere is never entirely dry; water vapour is invariably present, although in widely varying proportions. This vapour also behaves as a gas, and so long as it remains as vapour the assumption of dry air needs little modification.

3

TABLE 1. *Percentage composition of dry air (by volume)*

			------------------------ *traces only* ------------------------			
Nitrogen	(N_2)	78.09	Neon	(Ne)	Nitrous oxide	(N_2O)
Oxygen	(O_2)	20.95	Helium	(He)	Ozone	(O_3)
Argon	(A)	0.93	Krypton	(Kr)	Sulphur dioxide	(SO_2)
Carbon dioxide	(CO_2)	0.03	Xenon	(Xe)	Nitrogen dioxide	(NO_2)
			Hydrogen	(H)	Ammonia	(NH_4)
			Methane	(CH_4)	Carbon monoxide	(CO)
			Iodine	(I)		

Frequently though, the vapour condenses into liquid or solid form, as in fog, mist, cloud and precipitation. Much in meteorology is concerned with the impact of these changes of phase of water substance. Further, particles of dust, smoke and other impurities held in suspension affect the transparency of the atmosphere and will need to be given consideration in the appropriate place.

1.3 STRUCTURE OF THE ATMOSPHERE

Although the composition of the atmosphere remains unchanged up to great heights, there are certain changes in its physical conditions which enable various layers to be distinguished (see Fig. 1).

Troposphere
The lower layers are identified in the first instance by the rate of change of temperature with height. The average rate at which temperature decreases from the surface upwards is fairly uniform over the earth; this fall continues regularly until it ceases more or less abruptly at a height of several kilometres. This layer, characterized throughout by a marked fall of temperature with height, is called the troposphere and its upper boundary the tropopause.

The height of the tropopause varies with latitude, season and weather situation. In general, it is lowest (8–10 km) in Arctic regions in winter and highest (16–18 km) in tropical and equatorial regions; over southern England it averages about 11 km. Since air is compressible, the troposphere contains much the greater part of the whole mass of the atmosphere; over three-quarters in middle latitudes. The remaining fraction is spread out with ever increasing rarity over a height range some hundred times that of the troposphere.

Stratosphere
The stratosphere extends from the tropopause to a height of about 50 km above sea level and is characterized by a temperature which is steady or increases with height; this increase is more noticeable near the top of the layer where the average temperature is only a little below 0 °C. The upper boundary of the layer, where the temperature is at a maximum, is called the stratopause. The relatively high temperatures at these levels are due to the presence of small quantities of ozone (O_3), an isotope of oxygen which is a very strong absorber of ultraviolet radiation. If all of this radiation were allowed to pass it would prove highly injurious to life as it has developed on earth. Thus, these small quantities of ozone in the stratosphere,

4

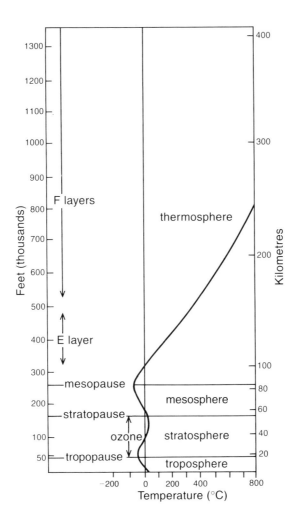

Figure 1. The atmosphere.

which would amount to an equivalent thickness of only 3 mm if brought to sea-level pressure, are nonetheless of vital importance. It has long been realized that there are small day-to-day variations in the total amount of ozone above any one place on the earth but interest (not to mention concern) has been heightened in recent years following the discovery by a British Antarctic Survey team in the late 1970s of the so-called 'ozone hole' during the Antarctic spring (Farman *et al.* 1985)*. Spatial variations in ozone concentrations have become increasingly under scrutiny and there are indications of a global-scale decrease. A working group of the Intergovernmental Panel on Climate Change (IPCC 1990), reporting in 1990, attributed the major ozone depletion of high southern latitudes to the effects of man-made chlorofluorocarbons (CFCs) and speculated that further reductions are likely during the coming decades as CFC abundances continue to increase.

---

* references cited in the text are listed alphabetically in a bibliography at the end of this book. The bibliography also contains other suggestions for further reading.

Mesosphere

This is the region of decreasing temperature above the stratopause. The mesosphere ends at the mesopause between 80 and 90 km where the lowest temperatures of the whole atmosphere are encountered (about 290 °C).

Thermosphere

Above the mesosphere lies the thermosphere; its upper limit is undefined. Temperature increases rapidly with height up to about 200 km and then increases more slowly or not at all. Above 200 km temperature varies widely with time, depending upon solar activity; it is about 600 °C when the sun is 'quiet' and possibly 2000 °C during times of sunspot maxima.

The lower part of the thermosphere contains the zone known as the ionosphere because here the tenuous atmosphere is highly ionized by the action of solar ultraviolet and X-ray radiations. The resulting concentration of ions and free electrons is high enough to cause reflection of radio waves, so making long-wave transmission possible over the earth's surface. The ionization reaches peak values at the levels known as the E, F_1 and F_2 layers at about 110, 160 and 250 km respectively, and associated with the names of Kennelly, Heaviside and Appleton. The ionosphere generally penetrates downwards into the upper part of the mesosphere.

The upper part of the thermosphere, roughly above 700 km, is known as the exosphere. Here the atmosphere is extremely tenuous and the mean free path of particles is so great that they can escape from the atmosphere. In this region it is not possible to define temperature in the usual way.

Whilst flight is limited to the troposphere and stratosphere, rockets fitted with recording instruments are not so restricted. Nevertheless, in regard both to the study of weather and to flight by aircraft it is unnecessary to consider the mesosphere and thermosphere further, and attention throughout subsequent chapters will be concentrated upon the troposphere and stratosphere.

1.4 STANDARD ATMOSPHERES

International standard atmosphere (ISA)

For many purposes, such as the graduation of pressure altimeters and the design and testing of aircraft, the average state of the atmosphere needs to be represented in definite terms which can be used as a basis of reference. Such a representation is termed a standard atmosphere; it aims to specify the average variation of temperature with height, from which the corresponding variations of pressure and density can also be deduced. It will be helpful to give details of a particular specification here although the general discussion of variations of temperature, pressure and density with height must be deferred to subsequent chapters.

The standard atmosphere as defined by the International Civil Aviation Organization (ICAO 1964) is now used internationally by aviation. The chief specifications of this ICAO Standard Atmosphere (or ISA) are shown in Table 2A.

More details are given in Table 2B.

Certain other standard atmospheres have been prepared to cover purposes such as aircraft design and testing for which the ISA specification may be inadequate.

TABLE 2A. *Chief specifications for the ISA*

At mean sea level (MSL)	pressure 1013.25 hPa, temperature 15 °C, density 1.225 kg m^{-3}.
From MSL to 11 km (36 090 ft)	a decrease of temperature with height of 6.5 °C per km, or 1.98 °C per 1000 ft.
From 11 km to 20 km (65 617 ft)	temperature constant at -56.5 °C.
From 20 km to 32 km (104 987 ft)	a rise of temperature with height of about 1 °C per km, or 0.3 °C per 1000 ft.

TABLE 2B. *The ICAO international standard atmosphere*
Surface density 1.225 kg m^{-3}

Height	Temper-ature	Pressure	Relative density	Height	Temper-ature	Pressure	Relative density
km	°C	hPa	%	feet	°C	hPa	%
32	-44.7	8.9	1.1	105 000	-44.7	8.9	1.1
30	-46.6	11.9	1.5	100 000	-46.2	11.1	1.4
27.5	-49.1	17.4	2.2	95 000	-47.7	13.9	1.8
25	-51.6	25.5	3.3	85 000	-50.7	22.2	2.8
22.5	-54.1	37.5	4.9	80 000	-52.2	28.0	3.6
20	-56.5	55.3	7.2	75 000	-53.7	35.4	4.5
17.5	-56.5	81.8	10.7	70 000	-55.2	44.9	5.8
15	-56.5	121.1	15.8	65 000	-56.5	56.9	7.4
12.5	-56.5	179.3	23.5	60 000	-56.5	72.3	9.5
10	-49.9	264.9	33.7	55 000	-56.5	91.8	12.0
7.5	-33.7	382.9	45.5	50 000	-56.5	116.6	15.3
5	-17.5	540.4	60.1	45 000	-56.5	148.2	19.5
2.5	-1.2	746.9	78.1	40 000	-56.5	188.2	24.7
1	8.5	898.7	90.7	35 000	-54.2	239.1	31.0
0.5	11.7	954.6	95.3	30 000	-44.3	301.5	37.5
0	15.0	1013.25	100.0	25 000	-34.5	376.5	44.8
-0.5	18.2	1074.8	104.9	20 000	-24.6	466.0	53.3
				15 000	-14.7	572.0	62.9
				10 000	-4.8	696.9	73.8
				5 000	5.1	843.1	86.2
				2 000	11.0	942.1	94.3
				0	15.0	1013.25	100.0
				$-1 000$	17.0	1050.4	103.0

CHAPTER 2

PRESSURE

2.1 INTRODUCTION

The study of atmospheric pressure may be said to form the foundation of the science of meteorology. Weather is closely dependent upon the distribution of pressure at the surface, and charts of sea-level pressure, supplemented by other charts for higher levels, constitute the basis of weather forecasting. Moreover, pressure differences provide the forces which are responsible for the generation of wind and the consequent changes in weather. The intimate connection between pressure and height is utilized in the pressure altimeter for the ready determination of height in the atmosphere.

Barometric pressure

The pressure of the atmosphere, as of any liquid or gaseous fluid, is the force exerted on a surface of unit area by the activity of the molecules composing the fluid. When the fluid in any region is at rest the motion of the molecules is entirely haphazard and the pressure is exerted uniformly in all directions; this is the static or barometric pressure. If the fluid were in motion, an additional pressure would be exerted on a surface of small area opposed to the direction of flow; this is termed the dynamic pressure, or more simply, in the atmosphere, the pressure of the wind. While meteorology is concerned mainly with the static pressure, the notion of dynamic pressure has some important applications including, in particular, the pitot tube by means of which the wind speed or the rate of movement of an object through the air may be measured. Generally when the word pressure is used without qualification it refers to the static or barometric pressure.

Pressure as the weight of air above

The atmosphere is held to the earth by gravitational attraction but is prevented from collapse by the molecular motions referred to above; hence any area of the earth's surface may be regarded as supporting the weight of the overlying air. The pressure of the atmosphere at a point on the earth's surface is therefore equivalent to the weight of the whole column of air standing on unit area at that point. Similarly, if one considers a point at some particular height above the surface, it is seen that the pressure at that height is equal to the weight of the air above. This rule is of general applicability, and it may be shown to remain true within very wide limits when the air is in motion; the only exceptions are concerned with the presence of very violent air currents such as may occur in thunderstorms, and even then any modification required is of theoretical rather than practical interest.

Units

The pressure unit which has been ordinarily used in meteorology is the millibar, one bar (=1000 millibars) being the pressure exerted by a force of 10^6 dynes per square centimetre; this corresponds very roughly to the average pressure at sea level.

Before the introduction of the millibar, pressure was measured in terms of the length of the column in a mercury barometer and was reported as so many millimetres or inches of mercury; the use of inches is still encountered in some parts of the world, notably in the USA.

In recent years however, the trend towards the adoption of SI (Système International d'Unités) units has been gathering pace. The SI unit of pressure is the pascal (Pa), defined as the pressure exerted by a force of one newton per square metre (N m^2), and many meteorological services already use this unit (or rather its derivative the hectopascal) in place of the millibar. No confusion arises — one hectopascal is simply one millibar. Recognizing this trend and anticipating eventual worldwide adoption of the SI unit, textual reference throughout the remainder of this book will be to hectopascals (hPa) though the millibar (mb or m.bar) will often be found in accompanying figures and tables. Indeed, it is likely to be many years before references to millibars disappear once and for all from meteorological charts and diagrams. Note that HPA and INS (for inches) are the abbreviations approved by ICAO for worldwide use in aeronautical communications (ICAO 1989).

The following equation summarizes the relationship between these various units:-

$$1000 \text{ mb} = 1000 \text{ hPa} = 10^5 \text{ N m}^2 = 750.1 \text{ mm Hg.} = 29.53 \text{ in Hg.}$$

2.2 PRESSURE AT MEAN SEA LEVEL

Isobars and pressure systems
In representing the distribution of pressure at a given time, it will be clear that on account of the marked reduction of pressure with height it is essential for the observations to be reduced to a common level (usually mean sea level). Isobars or lines of equal pressure, usually at intervals of 2 or 4 hPa, are drawn to fit the reduced observations to form a synoptic chart from which the pressure distribution may be perceived at a glance. Further details regarding the drawing of isobars are given in Chapter 19 while examples of synoptic charts are included in the Annex. Experience with synoptic charts shows that the isobars take up various configurations, each of which has its own characteristics in regard to wind and weather. From inspection of a sequence of synoptic charts the pressure systems are seen to undergo continuous modifications and to move from place to place; occasionally one disappears, or a new one is formed. These pressure systems are described briefly below and illustrated schematically in Fig. 2.

Depression or low (or occasionally 'cyclone', this last word being more commonly used in its adjectival form or reserved for tropical systems) (L in Fig. 2). A region of relatively low pressure depicted by more or less circular and concentric isobars surrounding the centre, where pressure is lowest. The size of the low circulation may vary from tens of metres in a tornado to some hundreds of kilometres in a tropical storm (when the term cyclone is more appropriate) and to well over 1500 kilometres in the larger systems of temperate latitudes. Lows are often described as vigorous, deep or intense, shallow or weak, but these are relative terms only. They may be said to develop, deepen, intensify, dissipate, decay or fill up.

Secondary depression (S in Fig. 2). A small low within the area covered by a larger, or primary, low and appearing rather as a satellite. The isobars need not

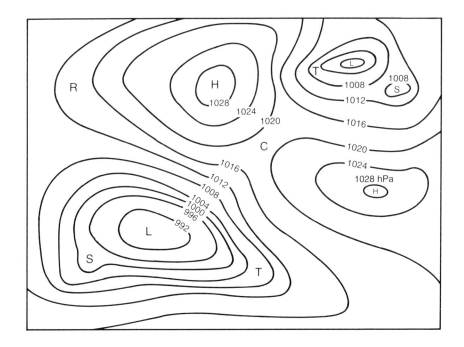

Figure 2.   Various types of pressure distribution.

show a closed centre, and the term may be applied to any small region of relatively low pressure which maintains its identity for a time.

Trough of low pressure (T in Fig. 2). Indicated by isobars extending outwards from an area of low pressure so that pressure is lower in the trough than at the two sides. When the isobars change suddenly in direction at the trough they may be described as V–shaped, although this name for a pressure type has largely fallen into disuse.

Anticyclone or high (H in Fig. 2). A region of relatively high pressure shown by more or less circular isobars similar to those of a low but with the highest pressure at the centre. The isobars are often more widely spaced than in the low, especially near the centre. Highs may be said to build, intensify, give way, weaken, decline or collapse.

Ridge, wedge or tongue of high pressure (R in Fig. 2). Indicated by isobars extending outwards from a high and always rounded, never V-shaped as sometimes occurs at a trough.

Col (C in Fig. 2). A region of almost uniform pressure between two highs and two lows.

Pressure gradients

The slope or gradient of the surface of the ground has its analogy in the field of pressure. The steepest slope on a contour map is at right angles to the contour lines, and is greater or less according as the lines are close or far apart; in exactly the same way we speak of the gradient of pressure as being directed at right angles to the isobars. A field of pressure is said to be flat when the differences are slight and the

10

isobars far apart; the gradient is said to be steep or tight when the isobars are close together.

Barometric tendency and isallobars
One of the elements plotted on a weather map is the tendency or change of pressure during the period of three hours preceding the time of observation. It is of great practical value in forecasting as it enables one to see at a glance in what areas pressure has been falling or rising. Just as the field of pressure is made to stand out clearly by drawing isobars, so the distribution of the pressure changes can be emphasized by drawing lines of equal tendency; these are known as isallobars. Regions of falling pressure may thus be shown by closed curves similar to the isobars of a depression, the greatest falls being at the centre. It is customary to describe such an area as an isallobaric low; similarly, an isallobaric high is a region where pressure has risen.

Diurnal variation of pressure
Changes of pressure occur almost continuously and have many causes; the movement and development of depressions, anticyclones and other weather systems is the most obvious cause, but superimposed on these irregular trends it is often possible to detect a rhythmical oscillation. In middle and high latitudes the irregular changes are usually sufficient to obliterate these oscillations, although they may be recognized during quiet, settled weather. Whereas in England the amplitude averages less than 1 hPa, it is about 4 hPa at the equator; in polar regions it is negligible. The oscillation may best be described as a double wave travelling round the earth following the sun, having minima at 0400 and 1600, with intermediate maxima at 1000 and 2200, all local time. There is, therefore, a semi-diurnal variation, but the changes are not perfectly symmetrical and they vary considerably with locality. The variations have little influence on other meteorological factors but their occurrence needs to be kept in mind when interpreting the three-hourly pressure tendencies plotted upon synoptic charts, otherwise the diurnal effect might give a false impression of the changes taking place. In the tropics and subtropics these regular variations are the predominant feature. In regions subject to tropical cyclones any departure from the regular oscillation is often the first indication of an approaching storm.

A definitive explanation of the semi-diurnal variation has proved difficult, but research indicates that its origin probably lies in a natural oscillation of the atmosphere which happens to have a period of almost exactly 12 hours. Such an oscillation would be excited and maintained by resonance produced by the 24-hour variation of temperature.

2.3 PRESSURE AND HEIGHT

Variation of pressure with height
From the observation given above to the effect that the pressure at a point is equal to the weight of air above, it follows that the pressure at any height above the surface of the earth is less than the pressure at the surface itself, by the weight of the column of air extending from the surface up to that height. It follows that pressure invariably decreases with height in the atmosphere. The amount of reduction up to a

given height, being simply the weight of the air column up to that height, depends upon the density or temperature of the air in the column. This is illustrated at Fig. 3 which represents an imaginary vertical section through the atmosphere. The pressure at ground level is taken to be uniform (p_0) but the air above A is supposed warmer than that over B (level for level). Up to some height h, the weight of the column AC is therefore less than that of BD, consequently the reduction of pressure from A to C is less than that from B to D, and pressure at C is greater than at D. Therefore at height h the pressure decreases from C to D, the higher pressure lying over the warmer air, and the lower pressure over the colder air. Further, if the pressure at C is p_1 this value of the pressure is reached at some lower level F in the cold air; and if the pressure at D is p_2 then this pressure is not attained in the warm air until some higher point E is reached. In this way we can indicate the lines of equal pressure CF, ED, etc. in a cross-section of the atmosphere, and we find that they are in general sloping (or curved) lines, even if the surface pressure should, exceptionally, happen to be uniform. The ideas of this paragraph will be found later to have an application to the variation of wind with height (Chapter 5).

The general fall of pressure with height in the international standard atmosphere may be noted from Table 2. It is also useful to know what increase of height corresponds with a fall of pressure of 1 hPa for any particular values of pressure and temperature. This is given by the equation (Appendix I):

$$\text{height difference for 1 hPa change of pressure} = 96\ T/p \text{ feet} \qquad (1)$$

where T is the kelvin temperature (degrees Celsius + 273) and p is the pressure in hectopascals. Selected values derived from this formula are given in Table 3. It is seen that a pressure change of 1 hPa in the international standard atmosphere is roughly equivalent to a height interval of 27 ft at 1000 hPa, 50 ft at 500 hPa and 100 ft at 200 hPa.

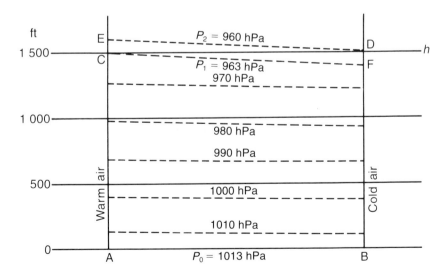

Figure 3.   Variation of pressure with height.

TABLE 3. *Height difference corresponding to a pressure difference of 1 hectopascal*

Temp.	Pressure (hPa)											
	1050	1000	900	800	700	600	500	400	300	200	100	50
°C					*feet*							
40	29	30	33	38	43	50	60	75	100	150	301	601
0	25	26	29	33	37	44	52	66	87	131	262	524
−40	21	22	25	28	32	37	45	56	74	112	224	448
−80	18	19	21	23	26	31	37	46	62	93	185	371

Another formula is required to express the difference between the heights h_1 and h_2 in terms of the corresponding pressures p_1 and p_2. When the temperature T is constant it may be shown that (Appendix I)

$$h_2 - h_1 = 221.1T(\log p_1 - \log p_2) \qquad (2)$$

where the heights are in feet and the temperature in kelvin. When the temperature is not constant, T may be regarded as the mean temperature of the layer. This equation may be used to determine either the change of pressure between two given heights or the change of height between two given pressures. Its use is illustrated in the following example.

Example of pressure–height calculation. Given the following observations of upper-air temperature: mean sea level 1016 hPa, 12 °C; 1000 hPa, 14 °C; 900 hPa, 9 °C; 800 hPa, 6 °C; 700 hPa, 2 °C; what is the height of the 700 hPa level?

To a close approximation this is best done by finding the arithmetic mean temperature of the columns of air between successive observations and then using equation (2) to obtain the thickness of each column, finally adding the results to give the height of the 700 hPa level above the surface. The mean temperature between 1016 and 1000 hPa is 13 °C or 286 K; hence by the formula the thickness of this layer is 436 feet. Similarly the mean temperatures of the succeeding 100 hPa layers are 284.5, 280.5 and 277 K and the thicknesses 2879, 3172 and 3552 feet respectively. The total of these, 10 039 feet, is the height of the 700 hPa level above mean sea level.

A quicker, but less accurate, method is to estimate the mean temperature of the whole column from the surface to 700 hPa and to use this figure in the formula with $p_1 = 1016$ hPa and $p_2 = 700$ hPa. To find the mean temperature for this purpose, the mean temperatures of the layers as determined above should be added together and divided by the number of layers; this gives 282.5 K, from which the total thickness is determined as 10 088 feet. The difference from the figure obtained by the more detailed method arises because the value used for the mean temperature of the whole air column is but an approximation.

An alternative method of calculating the height of a pressure surface will be described later in connection with the tephigram (Section 3.6).

Reduction of pressure to mean sea level
Surface observations are necessarily made at various heights above mean sea level (MSL). As a pressure difference of as little as one hPa is of consequence in the

13

construction of synoptic charts and may be caused by an elevation of less than 30 ft, it is clear that the pressures must be reduced to a common level. With the choice of mean sea level as the standard, the corrected pressure is in most cases a hypothetical value since it requires surface pressure to be increased by the weight of the supposed column of air between ground level and sea level. The correction is that appropriate to a certain standard temperature with an adjustment, depending on the air temperature at the time, which allows for variation from the standard. This gives reasonably consistent results for heights up to 1500 ft, but for higher levels the reduction becomes less reliable. British practice in such cases is to report the pressure reduced to station level, but over high plateau country such as East Africa some more appropriate standard level may be used.

2.4 ALTIMETRY

The close connection between pressure and height is made use of in the construction of the pressure altimeter which in principle is merely an instrument for measuring pressure, i.e. an aneroid barometer with its scale graduated to read height in feet instead of pressure. It has been seen in the previous section that the relationship between pressure and height is not invariable, but depends both on the surface pressure and on the weight or temperature of the air up to the height concerned, factors which are constantly changing with time and place. Accordingly the altimeter can indicate the height accurately only in certain specified conditions; whenever the temperature or pressure departs from these, either an adjustment to the setting or a correction to the reading, or both, must be made to obtain the true height. The instrument has a linear height-scale so designed as to indicate the correct height when the conditions are those of the ICAO standard atmosphere. As the instrument, of which there are various types, is in general use for the determination of height in aircraft, the effect of differences of pressure and temperature from standard will be considered at some length. For this purpose it will be assumed that the instrument is properly adjusted and properly exposed in an aircraft and that it is in fact responding correctly to the atmospheric pressure at the position of the aircraft. Instrumental errors will be considered later.

Zero correction for pressure variations
Aircraft altimeters are fitted with a sub-scale graduated in millibars or hectopascals (sometimes inches) which, when the indicated height is zero, reads the barometric pressure at the position of the instrument. This sub-scale can be adjusted so that the indicated height (for example, above ground or above sea level) is correct at time of take-off and can, if required, be readjusted during flight or in preparation for landing. Apart from a possible correction for temperature, the indicated height remains approximately correct after being 'set for zero' only so long as the surface or sea level pressure directly beneath the aircraft remains unchanged. In practice this is seldom the case. Although set correctly when commencing a flight, the altimeter may be noticeably in error on landing either at the same or some other airfield. These 'zero errors' arise as a result of spatial and temporal changes in the barometric pressure. The altimeter will over-read if the barometric pressure falls during the flight and under-read if it rises, the amount of the error being roughly 27 feet for each hectopascal change in surface pressure. To take an example,

suppose the altimeter was set to a sea level pressure of 1010 hPa; then if pressure has fallen to 1000 hPa on landing, a height of some 270 ft above sea level would be recorded, while if pressure has risen to 1020 hPa the indicated height will be some 270 ft below sea level. As a general rule it should be remembered that if the flight is towards an area of higher pressure the altimeter under-reads. On the other hand, when flying towards an area of lower pressure the altimeter over-reads; this case needs careful attention as the apparent clearance over ground or other obstacles may be more than the actual clearance by some hundreds of feet.

Suppose a flight is made at a constant indicated height without any change of sub-scale setting. Since the altimeter responds only to changes of pressure, it follows that the flight takes place at a constant pressure level and that there is a gain or loss of height above sea level according as the aircraft is flying towards an area of higher or lower barometric pressure. This is illustrated in Fig. 4 for an aircraft which leaves London with altimeter set to a sea-level pressure of 1019 hPa and flies at an indicated height of 4000 ft. Pressure is low to the north, and on arrival at Glasgow the sea-level pressure there has fallen to 991 hPa. This is 28 hPa less than at take-off, and the indicated height (ignoring differences of temperature from standard) over-reads by 770 ft. Results of this type can be related to the wind which is experienced. In the case discussed, the wind throughout the flight will have been blowing from port in accordance with Buys Ballot's law (see Section 5.2). The associated over-reading of the altimeter constitutes an example of the following practical rule: when flying with winds from port in the northern hemisphere, the altimeter tends to overread, and with winds from starboard to underread. The error increases with the strength of the wind and with the length of route. In the southern hemisphere the sign of the error is reversed.

Corrections for temperature variations
While the application of a correction for change of surface pressure ensures a correct indication of height at sea or ground level according to the setting, the

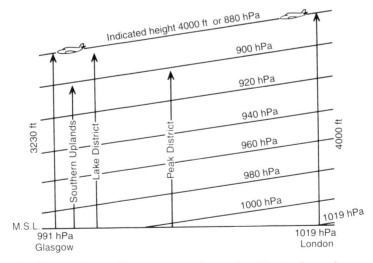

Figure 4.   Showing the need for zero correction to the altimeter for surface pressure variations. On arrival at Glasgow the indicated height overreads by 770 ft.

15

reading at other levels is still subject to error, although in many cases only a small one, depending on the difference between the actual and standard temperatures. In the conditions illustrated in Fig. 3, the indicated height will remain constant for a flight from B to A at 960 hPa (represented by the line DE) while the true height will increase, the difference corresponding to CE when the aircraft is over the point A where the air is warmer than at B (it is assumed that the surface pressure is uniform).

If the zero height corresponds to pressure p_0, and the height h to pressure p, then from equation (2) the true height at pressure p is given by

$$h = 221.1T(\log p_0 - \log p)$$

and the indicated height by

$$h' = 221.1T_i(\log p_0 - \log p)$$

where T is the mean temperature (kelvin) of the air column from p_0 to p and T_i is the mean standard temperature within this range of pressure. The true height is therefore given by

$$h = (T/T_i)h' = (1 + (T - T_i)/T_i))h'. \tag{3}$$

In practice, $T - T_i$ in this expression is replaced (as an estimate) by the difference between the observed and standard temperatures at the indicated height; if then the observed air temperature is set against the indicated height on a navigational computer the corrected height may be read off on another scale.

For example, if the temperature exceeds the standard temperature by 10 degC the indicated height requires to be increased by roughly 4%. Generally the correction is comparatively small for heights within a few hundred feet of the setting level, at least in comparison with the errors produced by variations in surface pressure, but since the temperature correction increases in proportion to the indicated height, the error at higher levels may be considerable; 5% at 15 000 ft amounts to 750 ft. For this reason alone it is desirable to pay close attention to the temperature correction at altitude and to maintain ample clearance when flying over mountainous country in bad weather.

Instrumental errors of the pressure altimeter
Apart from the errors of meteorological origin already described, the instrument is subject to other errors which may be summarized as follows:

Scale error. This is due to faulty calibration. It can be eliminated in the instrument workshops.

Friction error. This causes irregular and jumpy movements of the pointer even when pressure is changing uniformly. It may be overcome by gentle tapping or by the normal vibration of the instrument panel.

Hysteresis error. This shows as a lag in the indicated reading after a rapid climb or descent, and is due to imperfect elasticity of the aneroid capsule. The error increases both with rate of change of pressure (or height) and with the magnitude of the change. It assumes great importance for military aircraft when executing low-level attacks, particularly at night.

Temperature error. This is the change in reading due to a change in temperature of the instrument — not to be confused with a change in ambient air temperature. It is usually counteracted by the inclusion of a compensating bimetallic strip.

Position error. The instrument is connected to a static vent fitted to the surface of the aircraft where the pressure may differ from the true static pressure of the atmosphere.

Radio altimeters

Although these instruments record height independently of the meteorological conditions, it is convenient to refer to them here. There are two types in common use, one depending on the pulse radar system and the other on frequency modulation. With both types the height above the earth's surface is indicated in flights over the sea or level ground. The pulse radar type, often referred to simply as the radar altimeter, measures height over a range of the order of 1000 to 50 000 ft. The error in the absolute measurement is within ± 100 feet, but changes of height at an approximately constant level are measurable to within about ± 30 feet. The frequency modulation type, sometimes referred to as the radio altimeter, covers the range from zero to about 5000 ft; the error of this instrument is proportional to height and may amount to $\pm 3 \%$. Both types are needed to cover the whole range of flight levels.

Pressure altitude

This is defined as the height of a given level in the international standard atmosphere (ISA) above the level corresponding to a pressure of 1013.2 hPa. It is therefore the height indicated by a pressure altimeter with sub-scale set to 1013.2 hPa. Such a sub-scale setting is often referred to as 'standard altimeter setting' and is normally used for flying above the transition altitude. It will be realised that flight levels (FL) are simply pressure altitudes expressed in units of 100 feet; e.g. FL340 is a pressure altitude of 34 000 ft.

Altimeter correction

This is defined as the amount which must be added to the indicated height to obtain the true height above sea level h. When the sub-scale is set to 1013.2 hPa, the indicated height is the pressure altitude, h', and the altimeter correction is then the difference between the true height above sea level and the pressure altitude, or $h - h'$. When flying over the sea the altimeter correction will be given by the difference between simultaneous readings of the radio and pressure altimeters, the sub-scale of the latter being set to 1013.2 hPa; this correction is sometimes denoted by D and referred to as the D-value or D-factor. The D-value is positive when the radio altimeter reading (i.e. the true height) exceeds the pressure altimeter reading and negative when the pressure altimeter reading is the greater.

2.5 ALTIMETER SUB-SCALE SETTINGS

Some definitions

There are several different pressure values which may be set on an altimeter sub-scale in order to accommodate the effect of the difference between the actual state of the atmosphere and the state of the standard atmosphere which is assumed in the design of the pressure altimeter. The pressure which is set on the sub-scale is usually referred to by its abbreviation in the international Q Code; short definitions of the relevant groups are as follows:

> QFE   Atmospheric pressure at aerodrome elevation (or at runway threshold).
>
> QFF   Barometric pressure at a stated place, reduced to mean sea level.
>
> QNH   Altimeter sub-scale setting to obtain elevation when on the ground.
>
> QNE   The height indicated on landing at an aerodrome when the altimeter sub-scale is set to 1013.2 hPa.
>
> Forecast QNH   Forecast, valid for one hour, of lowest QNH expected in any part of a specified altimeter setting region (ASR).

The initial pressure measurement is carried out in the meteorological office (or perhaps in Air Traffic Control) to obtain what is known as 'the station-level pressure'. This value is applicable only to the particular height of the barometer. To determine the pressure value at any other level, corrections have to be applied; these are made according to standard practices as were described in Section 2.3. Paradoxically, the correction procedure is called 'reduction' to sea level (or aerodrome level as the case may be) even though the process almost always involves an addition to the station-level pressure.

QFE is the pressure reduced to the official aerodrome elevation; since the height difference between the barometer and the airfield is unlikely to be large, the correction involved is usually quite small.

QFF is the pressure obtained by reducing the station-level reading to sea level; it is this value which is plotted on 'surface' weather charts. Remembering that a height difference of only 27 feet is associated with a pressure change of about 1 hPa, it is clear that this correction will be considerable at higher-level aerodromes. Also, since the reduction procedure assumes an isothermal atmosphere between the station level and sea level any difference arising from the atmosphere's departure from ISA will tend to be magnified at higher-level sites.

QNH is also a pressure reduced to sea level, but in this case it is assumed that ISA conditions obtain in the column between station level and sea level. If h is the height of the aerodrome above mean sea level and h' is the height in the standard atmosphere which corresponds with the pressure at aerodrome level (QFE), then the altimeter, set to 1013.2 hPa, has an error of $(h' - h)$ (see Fig. 5). Since the height scale is linear, the value of QNH is then obtained as the pressure in the standard atmosphere which corresponds with this height $(h' - h)$. A table giving details of the standard atmosphere may be used for this purpose; alternatively a table may be easily prepared for any aerodrome giving the value of QNH directly from the reading of the barometer.

18

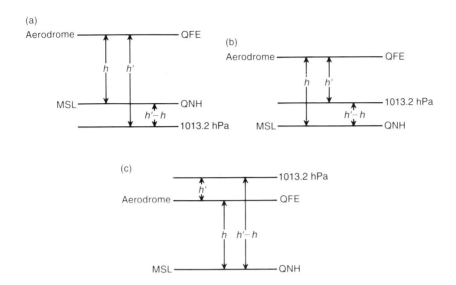

Figure 5.   Determination of QNH

h' is the height of QFE in the standard atmosphere and QNH is the pressure corresponding to the height $h' - h$.
  Example (a) — MSL pressure is less than 1013.2 hPa and $h' - h$ is positive.
  Example (b) — MSL pressure is greater than 1013.2 hPa and $h' - h$ is negative.
  Example (c) — both QFE and QNH are greater than 1013.2 hPa, and both h' and $h' - h$ are negative.

QNE was introduced as a substitute for QFE at high-level aerodromes to cover occasions when the sub-scale did not have sufficient range to set QFE. If, with the altimeter set to 1013.2 hPa, the pilot requests QNE, the reply states what height the altimeter will read on landing at the aerodrome concerned. This is simply the height in the standard atmosphere corresponding with the QFE.

Choice of altimeter setting
On occasion the pilot of an aircraft may be free to exercise his personal preference in choosing an altimeter setting, but at other times he will be required to adopt a setting prescribed by Air Traffic Control. In either case it is advisable that he should be aware of the advantages and disadvantages of whatever setting is used. The main considerations influencing the choice of setting are concerned with the phase of the flight, i.e. taking-off, cruising or landing, terrain clearance, and with maintenance of vertical separation in controlled airspace.
  An altimeter set to the QFE for an aerodrome reads zero (strictly the height of the altimeter above ground) when the aircraft is on the ground at that aerodrome; this is sometimes referred to as the 'zero' setting and for obvious reasons has been widely used. While in the air, the QFE setting gives approximately the height of the aircraft above the aerodrome level, but this information becomes of less use, or even misleading, when away from the aerodrome. Even when carrying out circuits and landings it may lead to difficulty, but still more so on a cross-country flight.

19

There is much to be said in favour of a setting which gives approximately the height above some more general level; mean sea level is an obvious choice. Such a setting would be provided by QFF, but as this is the pressure reduced to sea level in accordance with isothermal conditions it leads to inaccuracies when used with the pressure altimeter which, of course, assumes ISA conditions. The error in the indicated height would be small for heights near mean sea level, but the discrepancy increases in proportion to height and to the difference between standard and actual conditions.

These difficulties are minimized by the use of QNH, since with this setting the reduction is made according to the standard atmosphere and the instrument should therefore read the aerodrome elevation correctly on landing. It is the setting best suited to the construction of the pressure altimeter and gives the most satisfactory relation between indicated and true height under all circumstances, thereby providing a satisfactory measure of terrain clearance in transit.

Whatever altimeter setting is used, indicated altitudes in flight are subject to the effect of variations in temperature and pressure with time and place. Such variations are overcome in the United Kingdom by the regulation that aircraft cruising between certain heights within a flight information region (FIR) are required to use the forecast QNH value applicable to the particular altimeter setting region (ASR) and are to make the appropriate change of setting on crossing the boundary between one ASR and another. When commencing the approach to land, a change may be made to some other setting. Because forecast QNH (the lowest QNH expected) values are issued hourly for each ASR, these procedures adequately cover spatial and temporal changes of sea-level pressure throughout the ASR concerned.

A map of the United Kingdom altimeter setting regions will be found in the RAC section of the *UK Air Pilot* (CAP32) (CAA 1993).

CHAPTER 3

TEMPERATURE

3.1 INTRODUCTION

Temperature is commonly measured according to one of two scales which are arbitrarily fixed with reference to the melting point of ice (the ice point) and the boiling point of pure water (the steam point) at normal pressure. On the Celsius (or Centigrade) scale these fixed points are taken as 0 °C and 100 °C respectively; this scale has been adopted internationally and is in general use for scientific purposes and in aviation. The Fahrenheit scale is defined with the melting point at 32 °F and boiling point at 212 °F; use of this scale for meteorological and other purposes is confined to some English-speaking countries. No further use of Fahrenheit will be made in this book but, for the reader's benefit, a conversion table is included in Appendix II and the conversion formula $F = 9C/5 + 32$ may be noted, where F and C are temperatures in degrees Fahrenheit and Celsius respectively.

A third scale is used which has its zero based upon the following argument. Heat is a form of energy; as heat is extracted from a substance the internal energy must be reduced; this means that the random motions and vibrations of the constituent molecules are reduced, with the result that the molecules become arranged in a somewhat more orderly pattern than before. As more heat is extracted the cooling and rearrangement proceed further until eventually a state is reached at which the molecules have attained their maximum orderliness. In this state it is impossible to extract any more heat and the temperature has therefore reached its lowest possible value. Thermodynamic considerations show that this minimum temperature is the same for all substances, and it is accordingly referred to as the 'absolute zero'; its value is -273.16 °C (for meteorological purposes normally taken as -273 °C). The idea of an absolute zero is important for theoretical work and it forms the basis of the absolute or Kelvin scale on which the melting point of ice is approximately 273 K and the boiling point of water 373 K. Therefore the simple relationship $K = C + 273$ applies where K and C are temperatures in kelvin and degrees Celsius respectively.

This chapter not only includes a general description of the distribution of temperature and its variation with height, but attempts an explanation of how this distribution comes about. This requires some account to be given of the methods of heat transference in the atmosphere, especially by radiation and by adiabatic processes, while consideration of the latter makes this a convenient place to introduce the tephigram and to derive the basic criteria for vertical stability. The final section explains the direct effects of temperature upon aircraft operations.

3.2 RADIATION

The molten interior of the earth is enclosed within a solid crust through which heat penetrates only slowly by conduction, except here and there in volcanic eruptions and hot springs. The temperature increases downwards from the surface at an average rate of 1 degC per 100 feet, but the flow of heat upwards to the ground is insignificant compared with that received from the sun by day or lost by radiation at night. The temperature of the earth's surface and atmosphere depends in the last resort almost entirely upon heat received from the sun, only a negligible amount coming from the stars. There is now general agreement that inadvertent human intervention in the years since the industrial revolution is probably leading to a slow increase in the temperature of our atmosphere, though the magnitude of this so-called 'global warming' and its consequences remain a subject of much debate. In spite of this it is clear that throughout historical time earth's temperature has remained substantially unchanged and it follows that all the heat received from the sun must have been returned to space in the form of terrestrial radiation; the incoming solar radiation and the outgoing terrestrial radiation have been in balance.

In order to understand the processes of heating and cooling of the earth and atmosphere it is necessary to know something of the properties of radiation in general. Every body, whatever its state, emits radiation in the form of electromagnetic waves which travel through space at a uniform speed of 3×10^8 metres per second, the speed of light. By analogy with waves on the surface of water, the radiant waves are characterized both by their wavelength (or frequency), and by their energy of vibration (or amplitude). Since the velocity of propagation is constant, the wavelength is inversely proportional to the frequency: the number of waves passing any point in unit time. Most bodies emit radiation over a wide range of wavelengths simultaneously, the relation between energy and wavelength depending both upon the temperature and the nature of the source. The distribution of energy in the spectrum of a theoretically perfect radiator, the so-called 'black body', is illustrated in Fig. 6 for temperatures roughly appropriate to the solar and terrestrial surfaces, both of which radiate practically as black bodies. Note that the shape of the energy distribution curve is the same whatever the temperature of the radiation source but that the total energy emitted is proportional to the fourth power of the absolute temperature (Stefan's law). The total energy emitted by the earth at 300 K (27 °C) is about 460 W m^{-2} whereas the total emitted by the sun at about 6000 K is around 7.4×10^5 W m^{-2}.

The electromagnetic waves used in transmission by radio and radar are essentially of the same character as those concerned in solar and terrestrial radiation but they are of very much greater wavelength. The ranges of wavelength in the solar and terrestrial spectra are shown in Fig. 6; for radio transmissions the range of wavelengths is from a few millimetres to about 30 000 metres (frequency 10^5 MHz to 10 kHz) and for radar about 1 centimetre to 10 metres. Each of these varieties of electromagnetic radiation is affected to some extent and in varying degree by atmospheric conditions. The shortest waves, as we have seen, are of fundamental importance for heat transference; the radio waves have no significant effect on the atmosphere, but may be absorbed or refracted in the upper air (Section 1.3), while the behaviour of radar waves near the surface has given rise to the subject of 'radio meteorology' of which a brief account will be given in Section 10.8.

The dependence of the character of radiation on temperature may be illustrated by the behaviour of a piece of metal when heated. It first emits radiation which is invisible but which may be felt as heat; as the temperature rises the metal begins to glow with a dull red colour, and with further heating the colour brightens until ultimately the metal becomes white hot. These changes in colour indicate a

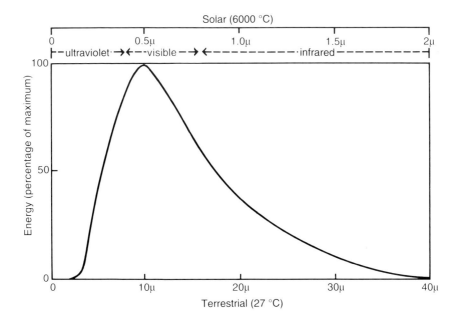

Figure 6.   Energy and wavelength in the black body spectrum at terrestrial and solar temperatures ($\mu = 10^{-6}$ m).

progressive reduction of wavelength; in general, the higher the temperature the shorter is the effective wavelength and the greater the intensity of the emitted radiation. Now the temperature of the surface of the sun being some 6000 °C, solar radiation is mainly in the form of short waves visible to the human eye, in other words ordinary light. Seen as a whole the sun's light appears white, but when the various wavelengths are separated, as by refraction through a prism, the white light is seen to be composite, the longest waves appearing red, the shortest violet, with intermediate colours completing the familiar rainbow spectrum. Although the greater part of solar radiation is comprised within this visible spectrum there is a part with wavelengths too short to be observed by the eye; this is beyond the violet end of the spectrum and is known as ultraviolet light. At the other extreme there is a fringe of waves too long to be visible and therefore known as the infrared. The complete solar radiation, comprising visible light, the ultraviolet and the infrared, is responsible for all the heat which the earth receives from outside and may be broadly described as short-wave radiation. This heat is lost again by radiation from the earth in the form of relatively long waves, for terrestrial temperatures are much too low to give visible radiation. The earth therefore receives heat by short-wave radiation from the sun but loses it by means of long waves.

Effect of solar radiation on the earth and atmosphere
Of the total radiation reaching the outer atmosphere from the sun, about one third is reflected back to space by the earth or by the upper surface of clouds and plays no further part in terrestrial affairs. This reflecting power is referred to as the 'albedo'

of the earth. Some of the radiation is absorbed in the upper atmosphere, particularly by ozone in the ultraviolet range of wavelengths, and a small proportion is absorbed by clouds, but in clear weather about 85% of the solar energy passes through the atmosphere to reach the earth's surface. Of this energy about 10% is usually reflected but over a snow surface reflection may amount to 80%; an equally large proportion may also be reflected from the sea surface at small angles of incidence. A further portion is taken up in the evaporation of water or in the melting of snow and ice. The remainder of the incoming radiation is absorbed and tends to raise the temperature of the surface. Because of the almost complete transparency of the air to solar radiation, absorption takes place mainly at the earth's surface, with the result, of great importance for meteorology, that the atmosphere is heated not directly from the sun but indirectly from the heated earth; it is heated from below and not from above.

3.3 TEMPERATURE AT AND NEAR THE EARTH'S SURFACE

In meteorology, the so-called 'surface temperature' is the temperature of the air measured at a height of 1.25 metres (4 feet) above the ground in a specially constructed louvred screen. While the variation of this air temperature on the whole follows closely that of the ground surface itself, there are on occasions large differences between the two. The primary influences controlling the variations of ground and air temperature are the incoming solar and outgoing terrestrial radiation, the nature of the surface, and the horizontal transference of heat by air movement.

Insolation
Solar radiation has its greatest heating effect when the sun is highest in the sky; firstly because it then passes through the atmosphere by the shortest path and suffers least loss by absorption and diffuse reflection; second, because the area of ground exposed to a beam of radiation increases with the obliquity of the path (if the ground is horizontal it varies with the cosecant of the angle of elevation of the sun above the horizon). There is a third effect, particularly over the sea: a much greater fraction of the incident radiation is reflected back to space when the sun is low in the sky than when it is high. The broad features of the distribution of average temperature over the earth's surface may be traced directly to the varying elevation of the sun, greatest in equatorial regions and decreasing towards the poles. The seasonal variations, warm in summer and cold in winter, may similarly be explained.

Nature of the surface
Of the solar radiation reaching the surface of the earth, that portion which undergoes reflection plays no part in raising the surface temperature, only the absorbed portion is concerned in this. Apart from the amount of heat lost or gained, the temperature attained by the ground depends upon the character of its surface. When heat is absorbed by a substance the increase of temperature is dependent on the thermal capacity or the amount of heat required to raise the temperature of the substance by 1 degC. By taking the thermal capacity of water as unity we may express that of any other substance as the ratio of its thermal capacity to that of

water; this ratio is known as the specific heat. From this it follows that, other things being equal, the rise in temperature is inversely proportional to the specific heat. Water, with a specific heat of unity, experiences relatively small temperature changes, but the solid materials of the earth's surface have a smaller specific heat and temperature changes are therefore greater.

A further factor is the amount of material which shares the loss or gain of heat. Over the solid earth it is the immediate surface which absorbs and radiates heat, and the change of temperature is spread downwards by the slow process of conduction. These effects will differ with various types of ground, but generally speaking changes of temperature over 24 hours affect only the first few centimetres, while even the seasonal changes affect only a few metres. Conditions over the sea are very different however, for some of the incoming radiation penetrates to a depth of several metres before being entirely absorbed so that the whole of this layer takes part in the temperature changes. Mixing of the surface waters of the sea also tends to spread any temperature changes through a considerable depth. The amount of heat available for raising the sea temperature is further considerably reduced by the transformation of some of the energy of radiation into latent heat of evaporation; this latter effect is also important over damp ground and vegetation, but it is almost negligible over deserts.

Temperature of surfaces exposed to direct sunshine
The solid ground or other objects exposed to strong sunshine may attain remarkably high temperatures during the middle part of the day if conditions are such that the absorbed heat is conducted but slowly downwards. For example, the surface of a runway or a steel rail under the influence of sunshine becomes much hotter than the air, whose temperature is measured in the conventional manner. As a rough rule, the maximum temperature of the exposed surface may be some 20 degC above the maximum shade temperature of the air measured at 1.25 metres above the ground, but wide variations from this figure must be expected according to the nature and thermal insulation of the exposed surface. Similarly, the surface of an aircraft standing on a runway may reach equally high temperatures. However, the take-off performance of an aircraft is related to the air temperature at the level of the engines, and this temperature is given with reasonable accuracy by that measured in the thermometer screen, since only an extremely shallow layer of air is affected by the abnormally high temperature of the ground and exposed surfaces.

Nocturnal radiation and water vapour
The loss of heat by long-wave radiation emitted from the earth's surface depends almost entirely upon the temperature of the surface, but this loss is in part offset by a downward stream of long-wave radiation from the atmosphere. The difference between these two streams is the net outgoing long-wave radiation; this can be readily measured at night, when the short-wave radiation is absent, and so has come to be known as the 'nocturnal' radiation although it actually takes place continuously and is usually greater by day when the surface temperature is higher. Dry air is practically transparent to the long waves, but they are partially absorbed by water vapour and carbon dioxide and these in turn emit long-wave radiation in all directions so that some radiation is returned to the ground in this way. Water vapour in the atmosphere therefore obstructs the free passage of radiation from

ground to space and so hinders the nocturnal cooling of the surface. However, the vapour is transparent to some wavelengths of the earth's radiation and the observed nocturnal cooling results mainly from this part of the radiation which escapes through the atmosphere, whatever the humidity, provided that the sky is clear. The lowest temperature on a radiation night is accordingly found at the ground itself whilst the screen temperature is commonly higher by amounts up to about 5 degC.

Diurnal variation of surface temperature
The differences already mentioned in the physical conditions of the surface result in diurnal temperature changes being much smaller over the sea than over land. In fact sea surface temperature shows a variation from day to night of less than 1 degC, and the air temperature near the sea surface is equally steady in quiet conditions. On land, however, the diurnal variation of air temperature may average as much as 20 degC over the interior of continents, where the moderating effect of the sea does not penetrate. Near the coast the diurnal variation depends on the direction of the wind; with a wind off the land the temperature changes will be almost as large near the coast as inland, but with a wind of any strength from the sea they become small. Even when there is no general wind off the sea the local sea-breezes which develop regularly on warm sunny days have a pronounced effect in tempering the heat of the day. In the absence of disturbing influences, surface temperatures are largely controlled by the difference between incoming and outgoing radiation. At night, cooling by long-wave radiation continues unchecked until the arrival of the refracted rays from the sun at dawn, when temperature is at a minimum; thereafter the incoming radiation continues in excess of the outgoing until two or three hours after midday, when balance is again reached and temperature is at its maximum. Cooling of the ground and air near the surface is then resumed and proceeds throughout the rest of the day and the following night.

Other things being equal, the diurnal variation is greatest when the wind is calm. With more wind, the surface air becomes mixed with the air above so that the gain in heat by day and the loss by night become spread through a layer of air which may be some 600 m (2000 ft) thick. In consequence the range of surface temperature is reduced; it may become quite small when the wind is strong.

Effect of clouds on surface temperature
When a cloud obscures the sun the decrease in the amount of heat received can be sensed immediately; a small proportion of the radiation is absorbed by the cloud and some diffuse radiation transmitted, but the major part is merely reflected back to space and is lost to the earth. The intensity of the reflection is apparent from the brightness of a cloud surface exposed to direct sunshine. A thin sheet of cirrostratus cloud cuts off a fair proportion of the sun's radiation, and a thick layer of lower cloud may be almost opaque. The heating of the earth by day is therefore considerably decreased by a layer of cloud or by what is essentially the same thing, a deep fog. The cooling of the earth by long-wave radiation is even more considerably decreased, sometimes to zero, for a cloud layer readily absorbs all the earth's radiation whilst radiation is emitted by the lower surface of the cloud back to earth.

The invisible water vapour, we have seen, absorbs and re-radiates some of the long waves but is transparent to others, so the cooling of the earth by radiation is not thereby entirely prevented; on the other hand a layer of cloud, by absorbing and re-radiating all the long waves, insulates the ground almost perfectly from above. A cloud radiates like a black body, and if the cloud layer is as warm as the earth it will send as much heat downwards as the earth radiates upwards with, consequently, no net loss from the ground. The diurnal variation of temperature at the ground becomes small when skies are obscured with low cloud; the lower the cloud the more nearly its temperature approaches that of the ground and the more effective it is in reducing nocturnal cooling.

If, as frequently happens at night, an initially clear sky clouds over after radiation has caused the air and soil at the surface to become cooler than the soil below, then a flux of heat upwards from the ground to the air produces a rise in temperature at the grass and screen levels.

Local differences in surface temperature

Because of the variable character of the earth's surface and differences in its topography, local differences in temperature arise which may be of significance to aviation. By day, upward convection currents may be set off over relatively warm ground: under the influence of the sun's radiation, bare rock, dry soil, metalled roadways and runways attain a relatively high temperature compared with grass-covered land and wooded areas. The cause is to be found mainly in the loss of heat by evaporation of moisture from vegetation. Water surfaces are particularly slow to heat up for reasons previously explained.

The differences which occur at night when the ground cools by radiation are largely a matter of exposure. In a sheltered position, particularly in a valley, the air becomes much colder than that over freely exposed ground mainly because the air is left undisturbed and is allowed to cool continuously. As it is then relatively heavy it remains as a pool of cold air in the valley, unaffected by any light winds above. Even slight depressions in the ground may allow cold air to collect in this way. The temperature differences are sometimes astounding, as is well known to the fruit grower concerned with the threat of night frosts.

The general effect of height should be allowed for in hilly country, the air above being on the whole colder by about 1 degC for each 500 feet, although there are marked variations and the low land is, as we have just seen, often the colder on a clear night.

Effect of the source of the air

The temperature of the air is not only dependent upon local conditions but varies widely according to the source of the air supply; if the wind blows from a warmer or colder region it retains its relatively high or low temperature for some considerable time. Generally speaking, air moving from high latitudes is perceived as cold, from low latitudes as warm, although there are marked variations due to the distribution of land and sea and the seasonal variation of temperature. Thus, over the British Isles a south-easterly wind in summer tends to be hot, but in winter it may be very cold, drawing air from the interior of the cold continent; similarly westerly winds are usually mild in winter but comparatively cool in summer. These broad effects are just as important as those produced by radiation but their fuller discussion must be deferred to later chapters.

3.4 TRANSFER OF HEAT BY LONG-WAVE RADIATION

The vertical distribution of temperature in the atmosphere is the result of several processes (see Fig. 7), one of which is the transfer of heat by radiation. In discussing the cooling of the earth it was noted that perfectly dry air is almost transparent to the long waves but that water vapour and carbon dioxide readily absorb radiation within certain wavelengths. The spectrum of terrestrial radiation may roughly be divided into two regions:

(i) that in which water vapour and carbon dioxide are transparent to radiation; this part of the radiation is transmitted directly through a cloudless atmosphere without in any way affecting the air temperature, and

(ii) that in which radiation is absorbed by water vapour and carbon dioxide.

The radiant heat which is absorbed tends to raise the temperature of the vapour and of the air; at the same time the vapour itself emits radiation in all directions. Apart from lateral radiation (which tends to balance out) the emissions from water vapour and CO_2 resolve into two main streams, one returning radiation back towards the earth, the other passing radiation upwards; the upward stream is augmented by the outgoing terrestrial radiation in the transparent wavebands, and provides for the radiative transmission of heat upwards through successive layers of the atmosphere and ultimately out to space.

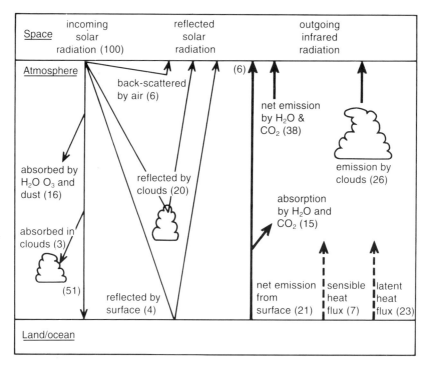

Figure 7.   Heat processes in the atmosphere. Figures in brackets represent global averages in relative energy units, the incoming radiation being taken as 100. Continuous thin lines represent short-wave radiation, continuous thick lines long-wave radiation, and dashed thick lines other methods of heat transfer.

At any height therefore the air tends to gain or lose heat in proportion to the net radiation absorbed or emitted by water vapour and CO_2. The consequential change in temperature from this cause is rather small, however, being estimated at about 1 degC in 24 hours. The direction of the net flux of heat is necessarily from high to low temperature, i.e. upwards in the normal state of the atmosphere. Further, the greater the concentration of vapour the less easily is the heat transferred. If radiation were the sole agent concerned in the transfer of heat, the vertical distribution of temperature would adjust itself to the distribution of vapour in such a way that the total outward flux of radiation would on the whole just balance the heat which the earth and atmosphere receive from the sun. The rate of fall of temperature with height in the troposphere that would result from such a radiative balance is however much greater than that which actually exists; it is clear that the temperature of the troposphere cannot be controlled by radiation alone.

Other methods of heat transference
Besides radiation, there are several other processes of heat transference in the atmosphere (see Fig. 7 and also Section 5.9). Since these are of comparable importance, it is desirable that they should be mentioned here although their fuller discussion cannot be given until later. Thus, vertical currents of thermal origin transfer heat upwards or downwards in the process known as *convection*, while the transfer of heat horizontally by wind is referred to as *advection*. The irregular eddying motion, or *turbulence*, of the atmosphere may effect a redistribution of heat in any direction, but most importantly in the vertical. When two bodies of differing temperature are in contact, heat passes from the hotter to the cooler body by *conduction*; this process is of little consequence in meteorology except for the flow of heat within the earth's surface and the exchange of heat between the surface and the air actually in contact with it. Lastly, the *latent heat* (see Section 3.5) which is absorbed by the melting of ice and by the evaporation of water, mostly at the earth's surface, may subsequently be released elsewhere in the atmosphere by the processes of condensation and freezing. In the troposphere, all the above processes of heat transference are effective along with long-wave radiation. In the stratosphere, neither convection nor latent heat have any influence but short-wave radiation becomes important on account of the presence of ozone (see Section 1.3).

3.5 ADIABATIC PROCESSES

Adiabatic processes in unsaturated air
It is a property of all gases that when they are compressed their temperature rises and when they are allowed to expand their temperature falls. Compression of the gas requires expenditure of energy, but in accordance with the principle of conservation, the energy is not lost but is transformed into molecular energy of motion within the gas and so raises its temperature. This property is applied in the diesel engine, the temperature of the air in the cylinders being raised by compression to a value above the firing point of the injected fuel oil; another popular illustration is provided from experience with a bicycle pump. Cooling by expansion is perhaps less familiar, but is the basis of a method of obtaining the extremely low temperatures required to liquefy certain gases and it is also applied in some household refrigerators.

When other effects, such as conduction and mixing, are eliminated so that the air is thermally insulated from its surroundings, then any change of temperature is said to be an 'adiabatic' change and its origin is said to be dynamical as opposed to thermal. The change of temperature (T_0 to T kelvin) can be calculated for a given change of pressure (p_0 to p) by the following formula (Appendix I):

$$\log T - \log T_0 = 0.287(\log p - \log p_0). \tag{4}$$

Large changes in temperature can be produced in this way; for example, if the initial temperature is 20 °C and pressure is reduced from 1000 hPa to 900 hPa, the final temperature is lower by 9 degC. The temperature so attained by air when it is compressed (or expanded) adiabatically to a pressure of 1000 hPa is known as the potential temperature (see Appendix I). By virtue of the definition, the potential temperature remains constant during any adiabatic change.

Now if a small mass of air is made to undergo a change of pressure by being moved fairly rapidly upwards or downwards, any transfer of heat by non-adiabatic processes (e.g. conduction, turbulent mixing, radiation) will be too slow to be effective except near the boundary of the displaced mass of air; the interior of the mass therefore changes temperature adiabatically. By expressing the right-hand side of equation (4) in terms of difference in height it may be shown that the temperature of the displaced air changes at the rate of 3 degC per 1000 ft, known as the dry adiabatic lapse rate (or DALR) (see Appendix I). So long as the sample of air remains unsaturated, it is therefore cooled by ascent and warmed by descent at this rate.

The above rule requires modification if the air becomes saturated (i.e. cloudy) during ascent, but understanding of this requires some explanation regarding the change of state between water vapour and liquid water substance.

Evaporation, condensation and latent heat
When water changes from the liquid to the vapour state, a certain quantity of heat must be supplied; to change boiling water into vapour (steam), more than five times as much heat is required as is needed to bring the same amount of ice-cold water up to the boil. Once boiling has begun, the temperature remains constant and the heat supplied during this stage is said to become latent; it is stored up in the vapour and released only when the vapour condenses. Boiling does not of course take place in meteorological processes but water may pass directly to the vapour state by evaporation, and the amount of latent heat to be provided is only to a small extent dependent on the temperature at which the change takes place. Cooling by evaporation is too familiar to call for illustration; it is made use of in the measurement of humidity by the dry-bulb and wet-bulb thermometers (Section 11.4). The importance of latent heat in the thermal processes of the atmosphere is also brought out by noting that roughly one third of the radiant heat absorbed at the surface of sea and land is taken up in the evaporation of water and that most of this heat is subsequently released at other levels in the atmosphere. Given a quantity of dry air at a certain temperature there is a definite limit to the amount of water vapour which it can be made to hold. When the air contains just this amount it is said to be saturated, and the amount of vapour present is known as the saturation vapour content. The saturation vapour content increases with the temperature, in

other words saturated warm air holds more vapour than does saturated cold air. If, therefore, air containing moisture, but not saturated, is cooled, it will ultimately reach a temperature at which it becomes saturated. Any cooling beyond this point — known as the dew-point — causes condensation of the surplus moisture which may then be deposited as dew or hoar-frost if the air is at the surface, or held in suspension as the water droplets or ice particles of cloud or fog.

Adiabatic processes in saturated air

When saturated air is made to rise the adiabatic contribution to cooling continues to operate as with dry air, but the cooling now causes condensation and is in part offset by the latent heat liberated. The rate of cooling of ascending saturated air, termed the saturated (or wet) adiabatic lapse rate (SALR), is therefore less than the dry adiabatic lapse rate. Unlike the latter, its value is not constant but depends on the amount of vapour condensed. If the temperature is low, saturated air can hold but little moisture and the latent heat released will be small; with warm saturated air, much more heat is set free in this way. As a rough value the saturated adiabatic lapse rate at low levels in temperate latitudes may be taken as half the dry adiabatic rate, or 1.5 degC per 1000 ft, but the figure may fall to about 1 degC per 1000 ft in the warm saturated air of tropical regions and may exceed 2 degC per 1000 ft when the temperature falls much below freezing-point, ultimately approaching the dry adiabatic value.

The result is very different when saturated air is made to descend, provided little or no condensed water is held in suspension, for adiabatic warming then causes the air to become unsaturated almost immediately and thereafter it warms at the dry adiabatic lapse rate. On the other hand, if all the water condensed out on ascent were to be retained, the effect of descent would be gradually to evaporate the droplets so that the vapour would remain saturated and the temperature would increase at the saturated adiabatic lapse rate. In practice the larger droplets, if any are formed, fall out as precipitation, while the remaining cloud particles are rapidly evaporated by warming, so that descending cloudy air is generally assumed to clear rapidly and to warm at the dry adiabatic lapse rate.

The further discussion of upper-air temperature and lapse rates is greatly facilitated by the use of special diagrams, the principles of which will now be introduced.

3.6 THE TEPHIGRAM

When observations of temperature and humidity are obtained at a series of heights above a point on the earth, it is convenient to plot the data on a diagram so that the vertical distribution may be appreciated at a glance. A Cartesian diagram of temperature against height would go some way to meet this aim. Such a diagram is shown in Fig. 8. It may be regarded as a rectangular grid consisting of two sets of lines: horizontal lines on each of which the height is constant, and vertical lines on each of which the temperature is constant; the latter may be called isotherms. The line ABC represents temperatures measured during a specimen sounding and is referred to as the environment curve. This environment curve shows an increase of temperature, i.e. an inversion, from the surface at A to 400 m at B and a general fall of temperature with height up to C, apart from two shallow isothermal layers around

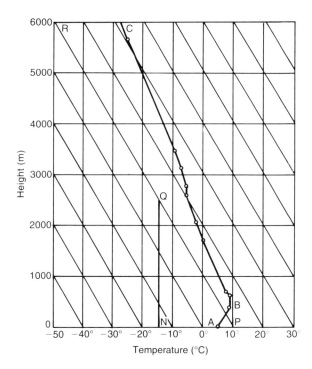

Figure 8. Temperature–height diagram showing dry adiabatics. ABC represents a specimen environment curve.

500 and 2700 m. With a framework of this kind, the variations of lapse rate of a temperature sounding become clear. However, interpretation can be further improved by the incorporation of additional lines into the diagram. One such set is provided by the 'dry adiabatics'. We have seen how the dry adiabatic lapse rate has the constant value of 3 degC per 1000 ft or about 1 degC (actually 0.98 degC) per 100 m.

Let us now consider a sample of dry air represented by the point P (10 °C at zero height). If the sample ascends adiabatically, the point which represents its temperature and height moves along the straight line PR which slopes upwards at about 1 degC for each 100 m of height. For example, if the air is lifted to 2500 m its temperature at that height is given by the ordinate QN through the point Q where PR intersects the 2500 m height line, i.e. −15 °C. Descent of air is treated in a similar manner. Thus the result of any adiabatic displacement of dry air may be obtained by following the dry adiabatic line through the point representing the initial temperature. A series of such lines, the dry adiabatics, is incorporated in Fig. 8.

Such a temperature–height diagram is not well suited to meteorological observations since temperatures are usually recorded, not at fixed heights but at fixed pressure levels. Consequently it is more convenient to take the pressure as one of the co-ordinates, or better still, the logarithm of pressure since this is more simply related to the height (cf. Chapter 2, equation. (2)). There are in fact many types of diagram which can be used for the analysis of upper-air soundings, but the only one that need be described here in detail is that known as the 'tephigram'. This is in general use throughout the United Kingdom meteorological service; the current edition is reproduced in the Annex and part of it is shown in a simplified form in Fig. 9. The diagram has as its rectangular axes the temperature and a function known as entropy (see Appendix I) but for convenience in plotting the results of upper-air soundings the axes are rotated anticlockwise through 45 degrees so that the isotherms slope upwards from left to right and the lines of equal entropy downwards from left to right. Now the entropy of dry air may be expressed in terms of potential temperature and since the latter remains constant during an adiabatic change it follows that the lines of equal entropy are the dry adiabatics; they are labelled with values of the potential temperature at intervals of 10 degC. Thus the framework of the diagram is the rectangular lattice formed by the isotherms and the dry adiabatics. The lines running almost horizontally across the diagram are the isobars. The faint, pecked lines sloping from left to right are lines of equal humidity mixing ratio (see Section 6.1). The remaining full lines are the saturated adiabatics, curved lines which for the most part slope upwards from right to left; these indicate the relationship between the pressure and temperature of a saturated mass of air as it

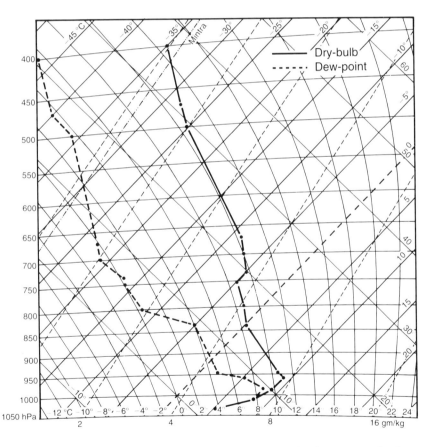

Figure 9. Section of a tephigram, simplified and reduced, and showing an example of an environmental curve.

ascends under conditions which may be described as pseudo-adiabatic since latent heat of condensation is released during the ascent. Since the condensed water is presumed to fall out as it forms, then on descent the air would immediately become unsaturated and its representative point would move along a dry adiabatic; for this reason the saturated adiabatics are said to be irreversible.

The tephigram derives its name from the use of temperature (T) and the entropy (now denoted by S but formerly represented by ϕ or 'phi') as basic co-ordinates. In ordinary use it may be regarded simply as a distorted pressure–temperature diagram in which the axes are inclined. The complete diagram should be carefully studied. Although at first sight it may seem complicated, it is easy to use once familiarity has been acquired. It will be found to have several important applications which will be described in due course, including the evaluation of height which now follows.

Height and the tephigram
Equation (2) in Section 2.3 relates a difference of height to the corresponding difference in pressure when the intervening temperature distribution is isothermal. Values of layer thickness computed from this equation are marked on the tephigram (not the simplified Fig. 9) for each 100 hPa layer from 1000 hPa to 300 hPa and for 50 hPa layers above 300 hPa; the values are entered along the isobar in the middle of each layer. For example (Fig. 10), the layer from 800–700 hPa with an isothermal temperature of -11.7 °C (261.5 K) has a thickness, by interpolation, of 1023 m. Whatever the actual distribution of temperature, the temperature of an isothermal layer of identical thickness may be obtained by application of the equal-area rule. Here, if ABC represents the observed distribution of temperature between pressure levels DA and CE, the equivalent isothermal temperature is given by that isotherm DBE for which the areas ABD and CBE are equal; for a layer extending between consecutive 100 hPa isobars, the thickness is then interpolated for this temperature from the height figures quoted on the diagram. This method of determining height from observations of temperature and pressure is theoretically exact for dry air; if the example in Section 2.3 is reworked in this way it will be seen that the two results agree to within a few metres.

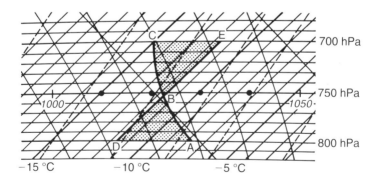

Figure 10.   Height and the tephigram. The isothermal DBE is drawn so that the areas ABD and CBE are equal. By interpolation, the thickness of the layer AC is 1023 metres.

When the limiting pressure levels are not multiples of 100 hPa the height interval may usually be determined with sufficient accuracy by interpolation or extrapolation of the nearest 100 hPa layer, or by use of equation (1) (Section 2.3) with appropriate values for temperature and pressure. ISA heights in feet and metres are entered on the left of the tephigram at pressure intervals of 50 hPa, zero height corresponding to 1013.2 hPa. A tephigram is included in the Annex.

3.7 STABILITY AND INSTABILITY

The equilibrium of a fluid at rest is determined in theory by giving an element of the fluid a small displacement and noting whether the forces then acting on the element tend to return it to its original position or to increase its displacement. In the former case the fluid is said to be in a state of stable equilibrium and in the latter case, an unstable state — any small disturbance then continues to grow and the original state breaks down, perhaps violently. Similar remarks apply if the fluid is in motion, the supposed displacement being then relative to the original motion. Since vertical displacements in the atmosphere usually take place adiabatically, the vertical stability can be readily considered with the aid of a diagram such as the tephigram. Consider then a sample of air represented by the point P on a tephigram (Fig. 11) and suppose it is lifted adiabatically until its pressure falls to that of the isobar AB. If the air is unsaturated, the point representing the sample as it ascends will start to move along the dry adiabatic PA; if the air at P is saturated, its path will lie along the saturated adiabatic PB. We need to consider the supposed adiabatic displacement of the sample in relation to the observed or environmental lapse rate. Three cases may be distinguished.

Absolute instability — observed lapse rate (as PP₁) exceeding the dry adiabatic   If the air is unsaturated the temperature of the displaced element at A is higher than that of the environment at P₁ at the same pressure level. The displaced element is therefore lighter, i.e. of lower density than its environment, and its buoyancy tends

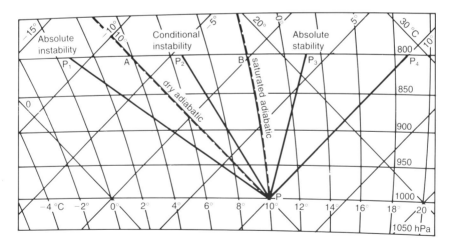

Figure 11.   Stability and instability in relation to lapse rate.

35

to increase the displacement still further. Similarly if the air at P is saturated, the displaced sample at B is again warmer than the environment at P_1 and therefore buoyant. Hence if the lapse rate exceeds the dry adiabatic, any small upward displacement will lead to further ascent because of the buoyancy acquired by the displaced air whether the sample be saturated or not. This case is referred to as absolute instability.

Conditional instability — observed lapse rate between dry and saturated adiabatics (as PP_2) If the air at P is unsaturated, then when moved adiabatically to A it becomes colder and therefore denser than its environment P_2; it consequently tends to sink back to P and the lapse rate is stable. On the other hand, saturated air at P would rise to the point B where it would be warmer than the environment P_2 and therefore unstable. The lapse rate PP_2 is therefore stable if the air is unsaturated, but unstable if it is saturated. This case is referred to as conditional instability.

Absolute stability — observed lapse rate less than the saturated adiabatic (as PP_3) The displaced air at either A or B is then cooler than the environment at P_3 and tends to fall back to its original level. This is referred to as absolute stability. The degree of stability increases as the point P_3 lies further to the right from B, so that with an isothermal lapse rate PP_4, or still more with an inversion of temperature, the stability is very marked and any vertical displacements are short lived. Any lapse rate less steep than the saturated adiabatic may be described as a stable lapse rate.

Neutral equilibrium
If the observed lapse rate coincides with the dry adiabatic when the air is unsaturated, or with the saturated adiabatic when the air is saturated, then an element displaced upwards remains in its new position and the equilibrium is said to be indifferent or neutral.

Superadiabatic lapse rate
From the preceding considerations it follows that in the free air the lapse rate cannot much exceed the dry adiabatic for then the atmosphere would be unstable and vertical currents would redistribute the heat until a dry adiabatic lapse rate was established. Similarly in saturated or cloudy air, the lapse rate cannot for long exceed the saturated adiabatic. A different situation occurs at the surface when the ground is exposed to strong sunshine (Section 3.3). The rate at which heat is then absorbed by the air at the surface may be greater than the rate at which the heat could be conveyed upwards if the lapse rate were dry adiabatic; in consequence a superadiabatic lapse rate, many times the value of the dry adiabatic, is set up but at most this extends only a few feet above the ground.

Some further aspects of instability will be considered later in relation to the convective development of cloud and precipitation (Section 6.5).

3.8 VERTICAL DISTRIBUTION OF TEMPERATURE

Convection
With the observed temperature curve AB shown in Fig. 12, consider what happens when the surface air is heated. As the temperature is increased from A to X, the air

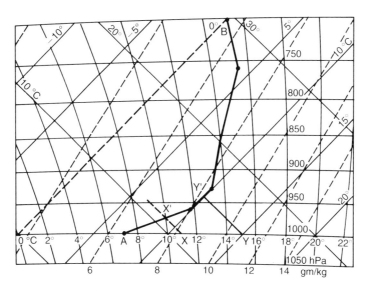

Figure 12.   Surface heating and convection.

becomes buoyant and begins to rise adiabatically. When it reaches the level where the dry adiabatic through X meets the environment curve at X′, its temperature is reduced to that of the environment and so it rises no further but mixes with its surroundings. If the surface temperature is further increased to Y, then the air would rise along the dry adiabatic through Y to the level of Y′. With continued heating of the surface, as at the ground on a sunny morning, successive small masses of air rise upwards in this way, their place at the surface being taken by air which has descended and is in turn heated by contact with the ground. The rising masses of air convey heat upwards from the surface, an example of the process known as convection. It is clear that the height, or rather the pressure level, to which the heated parcels of air can rise depends both on the rise of temperature at the surface and on the environmental lapse rate. When the lapse rate is stable, the surface air cannot rise far before being cooled to the temperature of the environment; with a steeper lapse rate or with intensified surface heating, the ascent may proceed far enough to produce saturation and cloud formation; these cases will be discussed in Chapter 6. It should be emphasized also that convection of unsaturated air tends to produce a dry adiabatic lapse rate, so long as the air remains unsaturated; thus in Fig. 12, by the time the surface temperature has increased to Y the original stable lapse rate or inversion AY′ has been changed into the dry adiabatic YY′, the part of the curve above Y′ remaining so far unaffected.

Diurnal variation of lapse rate in the lowest layers
The effect of sunshine in producing convection and a steep lapse rate near the ground has just been noted. On hot afternoons the lapse rate may become dry adiabatic up to a height of a few thousand feet, or up to the base of the cloud, where it is replaced by the saturated adiabatic. After the surface temperature has passed its maximum the effect of radiative cooling of the ground begins to spread upwards by conduction and vertical mixing, but as the greatest fall of temperature takes place at

the ground itself the lapse rate becomes progressively more stable until vertical currents are finally damped out. This stabilizing process is, however, liable to be interfered with by wind since this produces vertical mixing (turbulence) near the surface and so tends to keep the lapse rate steep (Section 5.3). In quiet conditions surface cooling is confined to the lowest levels and it commonly proceeds until a marked inversion has formed; on a clear night over land the depth of the surface inversion may exceed 500 feet. Sunshine usually destroys the inversion rapidly during the following morning, although if fog or a cloud layer hinders solar heating the change will be delayed.

It will be clear that the regular change of temperature from day to night which is characteristic of conditions near the surface is to some extent propagated upwards by conduction and mixing. Observations, however, show that the diurnal variation of temperature decreases rapidly as height increases and that it ceases to be of practical significance above about 3000 ft.

Temperature and lapse rates in the upper air
The average distribution of temperature in the vertical was described in Section 1.3 and Fig. 1. This is now amplified by Fig. 13 which shows the variation with latitude in the troposphere and stratosphere. The representation is considerably smoothed as the mean temperature is far from uniform along the parallels of latitude. From the surface upwards the temperature decreases at a rate of about 2 degC per 1000 ft, largely independent of height or latitude; this may be considered to be the average or normal lapse rate. The decrease continues regularly throughout the troposphere but is succeeded in the stratosphere by a layer with practically uniform temperature, except in tropical latitudes where the lapse rate quickly reverses sign. The height of the tropopause shows a marked variation with latitude and the part over the tropics is not always continuous with the parts over middle latitudes; sometimes, especially in winter, both may be recognizable at different heights in subtropical latitudes. In such cases of overlapping tropopauses it is safest to assume that the characteristic

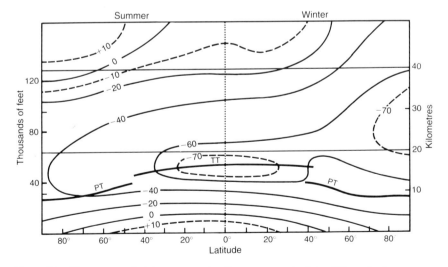

Figure 13.   Temperature–height cross-section for summer and winter. PT = polar tropopause and TT = tropical tropopause. Isotherms are in degrees Celsius.

properties of tropospheric air are to be found only below the lower tropopause, and those of stratospheric air to be found only above the upper tropopause; the intervening air should be regarded as having a transitional character. Because the tropopause is at a greater height over the equator the depth of troposphere through which the temperature decreases with height is greater and thus the temperature at the equatorial tropopause is lower than that at the polar tropopause; in fact the temperatures in the lower stratosphere over the equator are comparable with those at the same height near the winter pole. From Fig. 13 it is seen that within the troposphere the temperature increases from the polar regions to the equator. In the stratosphere the temperature increases from the equator towards the pole in summer, but in winter in the lower stratosphere the highest temperature occurs in middle latitudes and from there temperature decreases both towards the equator and the pole. In the upper stratosphere there is a continuous increase in temperature from the winter polar regions through the equatorial region to the summer polar regions.

3.9 TEMPERATURE AND AVIATION

The indirect importance of temperature in aviation will be abundantly clear from the preceding sections since it is in many ways directly related to the development of weather. Apart from the forecasting aspect, the aircraft constructor must allow for all possible variations in temperature up to the ceiling height of the aircraft in connection with aircraft performance and cooling systems. The air temperature again is intimately related to the risk of ice accretion during flight, a problem which will be addressed in a later chapter.

Temperature and aircraft performance
Air temperature has a profound effect upon aircraft performance. At a given pressure, high temperature implies low density and so has an adverse effect on both piston-engined and jet aircraft; this effect is usually greatest during take-off, but it also needs to be considered at other stages of flight, especially for jet aircraft. The efficiency of a jet engine depends in part on the difference between the outside air temperature and the maximum temperature (limited for safe operation) attainable in the combustion chamber. When the air temperature increases above a certain value, depending on altitude, both efficiency and true airspeed fall off (other things being equal) and the aircraft's operating height is reduced at the expense of an increase in fuel consumption.

Temperature accountability
The effects of temperature need to be considered in the compilation of aircraft performance data. Details of performance in terms of temperature, pressure, altitude, all-up weight, etc. are given in the appropriate aeroplane flight manual; for instance, for civil flying, approved operational requirements regulate the maximum weight at which an aircraft shall operate at take-off, *en route* and on landing, for particular altitudes and temperatures. The temperature used here is to some extent at the choice of the operator; it may be either the air (or 'ambient') temperature at the time (actual or forecast) or some prearranged or 'declared' value. The declared temperature is intended to give, on average, a calculated risk equivalent to that arising with the use of ambient temperatures. It will vary according to

circumstances; for example, for an aeroplane operating to a requirement which allows for failure of one engine at take-off, the declared temperature might be the mean monthly temperature plus a certain factor of the standard deviation* of hourly temperatures from this mean. If the factor was one half and the mean temperature of a certain month at a given airfield 19 °C and its standard deviation 4 degC, then the declared temperature would be 21 °C. A particular advantage of using a declared temperature computed on a monthly basis is that it simplifies greatly the long-term planning of operations; its use enables payloads to be assessed for an indefinite period ahead, although it may well be the practice of operators to use the ambient temperatures when actually engaged on operations. A declared temperature may be based on the mean monthly temperature and corresponding standard deviation either for the whole 24 hours or for any part of the day; consequently if the mean and standard deviation are available for different hours of the day, the timing of departures and arrivals may be planned to minimize the adverse effects of high temperatures and to take full advantage of low temperatures.

---

*The standard deviation of a set of observations is a measure of their variability. It is the square root of the average of the squares of the individual deviations from the mean.

CHAPTER 4

DENSITY

4.1 INTRODUCTION

The density of the atmosphere, defined as the mass of air contained in unit volume, is a property which enters into many of the theoretical problems of meteorology, instances of which will be found from time to time throughout this book. In several ways it is of direct practical concern for the performance of aircraft, because the level of maximum efficiency, lift, ceiling height and airspeed all depend upon it to a marked extent. If density is low at the surface engine thrust is reduced and both landing and take-off speeds are greater; allowance has to be made for these effects in planning the length of runways and in determining the take-off performance and maximum all-up weight of an aircraft.

Units
The SI unit for density is the kilogram per cubic metre (kg m^{-3}) though the former c.g.s. unit (g m^{-3}) will often be encountered in meteorological texts and tables. It is normally sufficient, however, to specify density as a percentage of the standard surface value. Alternatively a 'density altitude' may be used, defined as that altitude in the standard atmosphere to which the actual density corresponds.

4.2 DENSITY OF DRY AND MOIST AIR

Density of dry air
The value of the density of dry air, denoted by ρ, is most easily obtained by substitution of observed values of the pressure and temperature in the fundamental gas equation in the form:

$$\rho = p/RT \quad \text{(see Appendix I).} \tag{5}$$

R is the gas constant and has the value 2.87 when p is the pressure in hectopascals and T the kelvin temperature. For ISA conditions, where p is 1013.25 hPa and T is 288 K, the equation gives the corresponding density as 1.225 kg m^{-3}. The density for any other pressure and temperature is accordingly given by

$$\rho = (1.225 \times 288)/1013.25 \times p/T$$

$$= .3482 \, p/T \, \text{kg m}^{-3}. \tag{6}$$

Density of moist air
Equation (6) applies to perfectly dry air. In the atmosphere some water vapour is always present; being a gas, water vapour also obeys the fundamental gas equation but the value of the gas constant for water vapour is about 1.6 times that for dry air. Now the total pressure p of moist air may be regarded as the sum of the partial

pressures which would be exerted by the dry air and by the water vapour if each acted independently of the other. If the partial pressure of the vapour is denoted by e, then the density (or concentration) of the vapour is given from the gas equation by the expression $.622e/RT$. Further, the partial pressure of the dry air is $(p - e)$ so that the density of the dry air must now be written $(p - e)/RT$. The density of the moist air is the sum of the densities of the dry air and water vapour and may therefore be written

$$\text{density of moist air} = .3482(p - .378e)/T \text{ kg m}^{-3}. \tag{7}$$

Thus moist air has a lower density than dry air in similar conditions of pressure and temperature.

If the density of moist air is to differ from the density of dry air by less than 1%, then $.378e$ must be less than about 10 hPa at surface levels, that is e must be less than about 27 hPa, which is the vapour pressure in saturated air at 22 °C. Such high humidities occur commonly in moist tropical climates, and in such cases should be taken into account in determining density; in temperate and high latitudes, in dry climates, or at high-level aerodromes even in the tropics, the effect of humidity on density is small and can usually be ignored for the requirements of aviation. It may be noted that a decrease of density of about 1% would also be produced by a fall of pressure of 10 hPa, by a temperature increase of 3 degC, or by a height increase of 300 ft.

4.3 VARIATIONS IN DENSITY AT THE SURFACE

It has been seen that computation of the density of dry or of moist air for any given pressure and temperature is not difficult. At a given pressure, density is inversely proportional to the kelvin temperature so that warm air is comparatively light and cold air heavy. The relative values for dry air at different levels in the ICAO standard atmosphere (ISA) were included in Table 2. In regard to conditions at an aerodrome, the average and minimum densities occurring in any month may be provided for the use of operators since they indicate the average and most adverse effects of density variations upon take-off and landing speeds and on payloads. Such information is commonly required in terms of density altitude which can be obtained from a detailed table of the standard atmosphere; there is then available a direct comparison between conditions on the aerodrome and at the equivalent height in the ISA. The average value of the density for a given period may be obtained approximately by inserting average values of pressure and temperature (and, if necessary, vapour pressure e) at aerodrome level in equation (6) or (7). The minimum density may occur with exceptionally low pressure, exceptionally high temperature, or with a combination of both. In tropical countries the effect of temperature is usually the more important and it is sufficient to combine maximum temperature with average pressure in the equation. In regions liable to disturbance by deep depressions, low barometric pressure may be the chief cause of low density. Since very low pressure rarely occurs at the same time as high temperature a reasonable estimate is obtained by combining the lowest pressure with the average temperature for the time of the year.

For comparative purposes, the global variation of sea level density may be derived from charts of mean temperature and pressure. The results indicate a mean density in the neighbourhood of 1.2 kg m^{-3} at sea level in equatorial regions, increasing polewards to as much as 1.55 kg m^{-3} over Siberia in winter, where low temperature is combined with high pressure. In the northern summer, high temperature and relatively low pressure over south-western Asia and northern Africa produce a fall to below 1.15 kg m^{-3}. Variations during the course of a day arise mainly from the diurnal variation of temperature, the lowest densities occurring in early afternoon and the highest at night. Seasonal changes result from variations in both temperature and pressure. As already noted, the density decreases by about 1% for every 3 degC rise of temperature or 10 hPa fall of pressure.

4.4 VARIATION OF DENSITY WITH HEIGHT

Reference to Table 2 shows that throughout the troposphere pressure falls off upward much more rapidly than does the temperature, indicating a decrease of density with height at all levels. The decrease at lower levels is given very closely by subtracting 3% of the value for any given level to obtain the value 1000 ft higher; successive applications of this rule give good approximations up to about 20 000 ft. It is also useful to remember that in the standard atmosphere the density has roughly half its surface value at 20 000 ft, a quarter at 40 000 ft, and one tenth at about 60 000 ft.

In the upper atmosphere the density at any point fluctuates through a proportionate range similar in magnitude to that at the surface. A variation as much as 10% from the average value, a very unlikely extreme, would be equivalent to a change of height of about 3000 ft and apart from a possible temperature effect would alter the ceiling height of an aircraft by a comparable amount. At sea level we have seen that the mean density is lowest near the equator and highest in high latitudes; a similar distribution is at first maintained aloft but as the reduction of pressure with height is more rapid in cold areas than in warm, the latitudinal variation diminishes until by about 26 000 ft the density is almost uniform over the globe in all seasons. At this level, density does not depart by more than 2% from ISA regardless of season or location. A second level of minimum departure from standard occurs near 80 000 ft but the amount of departure is more variable than at 26 000 ft. Between these two minima there is a level of maximum departure from standard at about 50 000 ft where density becomes greater over the tropics than over the poles. This reversal implies that while certain aircraft have a comparatively low ceiling in the tropics because the air density in the lower atmosphere is less there than in higher latitudes, the performance relative to that in higher latitudes nevertheless improves with height; at about 26 000 ft there is little difference across the globe, while at higher levels and particularly in the lower stratosphere the air has more lift in low latitudes. For record high-altitude flying, conditions should therefore be more suitable in tropical countries than in other latitudes, and, in any other locality, more favourable during the summer season than at other times of the year.

4.5 AIR DENSITY AND AIRCRAFT PERFORMANCE

Both the lift and drag of an aircraft are directly proportional to the air density; other things being equal, an aircraft must fly faster to maintain height when the density is reduced. Since density decreases rapidly with increase of height in the atmosphere, flight at high levels necessitates an increase in either wing area or airspeed; the latter is made possible with modern engines and the greater airspeed is moreover facilitated by the reduced drag at these levels. However, at about two-thirds the speed of sound (speed of sound = about 574 knots in the ISA stratosphere) a marked increase in drag begins to develop, connected with an increase of density caused by compression as the air impinges upon the aircraft. The same effect operates on the tips of propeller blades even at much lower aircraft speeds; as the thrust of propellers also falls off as density decreases or as height increases, it will be appreciated that this type of propulsion becomes less and less efficient at speeds over about 400 knots and so is more suited to low-level flight. On the other hand, the jet-powered aircraft approaches its maximum efficiency at speeds of this order, but it should be mentioned that with these aircraft the performance does not depend on density alone, since temperature itself has a direct effect (Section 3.9).

With the internal combustion engine, the amount of oxygen drawn into the cylinders at each piston stroke is determined by the air density; with increase of height the oxygen intake sooner or later becomes inadequate to maintain the required power and supercharging is then necessary; similarly with jet engines the intake of air must ultimately decrease with height, in spite of increased air speed.

CHAPTER 5

MOTION OF THE ATMOSPHERE

5.1 INTRODUCTION

The motion of the atmosphere embraces the whole range of phenomena from the major currents of the atmosphere down to the random molecular motions. The various types of motion, vertical as well as horizontal, are all intimately connected with weather in one way or another and most of them are of direct importance to the flight of aircraft. We use the term 'wind' to refer to sustained horizontal air movement; on the large scale, wind is closely related to the horizontal variation of pressure and so to the ever changing pattern of cyclonic and anticyclonic pressure systems over the earth. Superimposed on this broad flow of air there may be smaller secondary disturbances which sometimes are too local or too transient to show up on the isobaric chart, while the wind itself consists of a succession of gusts and lulls, the effects of which may be seen on the detailed record of a suitable instrument. Finally, the motion may be broken down to that of the molecules of the various gases of which air is composed. Although this haphazard molecular activity does not require detailed discussion in this chapter, it nevertheless plays an essential part in many processes. It is by such activity that the pressure of the atmosphere is exerted; it is connected with the property of internal friction or viscosity which causes wind energy to be continually dissipated and transformed into heat energy; it accounts for the 'skin-friction' to which an aerofoil is subject as it moves through the air; it is the means by which heat is exchanged between the earth's surface and the air in contact with it; and it is in part responsible for frictional turbulence. The main concern of this chapter is first with the relation between wind and pressure, both at the surface and at higher levels, secondly with the modifications exerted by topography, third with the various types of vertical motion, fourthly with the role of wind in heat transference, and finally with some applications to aviation. This last includes the effects of wind shear and turbulence on aircraft and the use of wind data for flight planning purposes.

Units
The SI unit of speed is the metre per second (m s^{-1}) and this unit is used for wind speed in the scientific literature. It is also used for meteorological purposes within some of the countries of eastern Europe. More generally however, the unit adopted for operational purposes in both aviation and meteorology is the knot (nautical mile per hour). The SI abbreviation for the knot is kn and this will often be encountered in technical literature, but the approved ICAO abbreviation for use in aeronautical transmissions is KT. The knot and its abbreviation KT will be used for horizontal wind speed throughout the remainder of this book. Surface wind speed is sometimes described in subjective terms such as 'fresh', or 'gale force': such terms relate to the scale devised by Admiral Beaufort in the 19th century for use at sea. The Beaufort scale, adapted for use over land and with wind speed equivalents, is included in Chapter 11 (Table 9).

The following conversion factors may be noted:

$$1 \text{ knot} = 0.5144 \text{ m s}^{-1} \text{ (MPS*)} = 1.852 \text{ km h}^{-1} \text{ (KMH*)} = 1.15 \text{ miles h}^{-1}.$$

*ICAO approved abbreviations.

Different units are used for the expression of vertical velocity. Since the foot is widely used in aviation circles as the unit of height, vertical velocity will usually be expressed in terms of feet per second or feet per minute: the latter, abbreviated FPM, is used in meteorological messages warning of marked vertical motions (e.g. SIGMET messages, see Chapter 21).

5.2 PRESSURE AND WIND

Relationship between isobars and wind, Buys Ballot's law
Perhaps the most striking feature of any synoptic chart is the obvious relationship between the wind direction and the isobars, a relationship which is known as Buys Ballot's law:

> If an observer stands with his back to the wind, then the lower pressure is on his left in the northern hemisphere, on his right in the southern hemisphere.

The general validity of this law may be confirmed on any weather map, although not without some reservations. A few cases do not apparently fit the rule at all well, while, as illustrated at Fig. 14, the surface wind in general blows obliquely across the isobars from high pressure to low and in consequence the direction of lowest pressure is not precisely at right angles to the direction of the surface wind. It is also evident from examination of the charts that strong winds occur when the isobars are near together and light winds when they are far apart.

These relationships do not concern surface winds alone. When upper-air observations are studied it becomes apparent that the wind at some 2000 ft above the surface is directed almost exactly along the surface isobars with the lower pressure on the left (in the northern hemisphere) in accordance with Buys Ballot's law, while its speed is greater than that of the surface wind and inversely proportional to the distance between the isobars. This is true of the wind at any height in the free atmosphere, in relation to the distribution of pressure at that height.

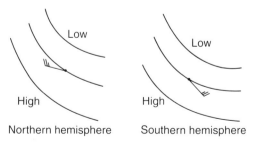

Figure 14.   Typical surface wind arrows.

The importance of these rules cannot be exaggerated for they enable the forecaster to give an estimate of wind from isobars alone, and if he can anticipate the changes in the field of pressure he can anticipate also the changes in the wind. The reasons for this close connection between wind and pressure must now be considered.

Primary cause of wind

This may be traced to variations in density arising from temperature differences which result from the effects of solar and terrestrial radiation. The sole external force operating on the air is gravity, but this acts in the vertical direction and can produce horizontal motion only indirectly through the agency of pressure differences. Thus if air has come to rest locally, it cannot begin to move again until, on account of density variations, a pressure difference is set up; the air is then acted on by a force perpendicular to the isobars towards the low-pressure side. The magnitude of this force is given by the pressure gradient G which may be taken as the difference of pressure between consecutive isobars divided by the distance between them. However, observations show that in the free air a steady wind is directed not across but along the isobars. This characteristic is explained in the succeeding paragraphs.

Effect of the earth's rotation

Once a body has been set in motion it will continue to move indefinitely at constant speed in the same straight line in space so long as there is no resultant force acting upon it. If a body is set in motion over the earth's surface, the action of gravity tends to prevent its leaving the surface; for example, an object set moving horizontally over the earth at not too great a speed might be expected (in the absence of friction) to continue indefinitely along a great circle and eventually to pass through the starting place again. In reality, rotation of the earth causes any great circle (other than the equator) to be continuously changing its orientation in space, and since the moving object tends to maintain a fixed direction in space, it must depart from a great circle track. It may be shown that any body moving relative to the rotating earth is subject to an apparent force which is known as the 'geostrophic' or, after its discoverer, as the 'Coriolis' force. This force acts at right angles to the relative velocity and, in horizontal motion, is directed towards the right in the northern hemisphere and towards the left in the southern hemisphere. For a unit volume of air, the magnitude of the force is $2\Omega\rho V \sin \phi$ where Ω is the angular velocity of the earth (one revolution a day or $2\pi/24$ radians per hour), ρ is the density, V the wind speed and ϕ the latitude. The formula shows that the Coriolis force is greatest at the poles and falls to zero at the equator (see Appendix I).

Geostrophic wind

It has been explained that air moving over the earth's surface is subject to forces due to the pressure gradient and to the earth's rotation. Away from the equator, say at latitudes greater than about 15°, where the Coriolis force is of a significant magnitude, if we consider motion along a great circle, then these two forces are the only ones acting in a horizontal plane. If the motion is to be steady these forces must therefore be equal and opposite. Writing the wind speed in this case as V_g and equating the expressions for the two forces,

$$2\Omega\rho V_g \sin\phi = G \quad \text{or} \quad V_g = G/2\Omega\rho\sin\phi. \tag{8}$$

The wind V_g defined in this way is termed the geostrophic wind. Since the Coriolis force acts at right angles to the wind direction, the pressure gradient must also be at right angles to the wind, so that the geostrophic wind therefore blows along the isobars with the lower pressure on its left in agreement with Buys Ballot's law. In the southern hemisphere the Coriolis force is reversed and the wind blows with the low pressure to the right.

It follows from the formula that the speed of the geostrophic wind is proportional to the pressure gradient or inversely proportional to the distance between the isobars — the closer the isobars, the stronger the wind. The speed is also inversely proportional to the sine of the latitude. The implication is that as the equator is approached ($\sin\phi$ tends to zero) the velocity increases indefinitely. This is not so of course: it shows that the steady balanced flow postulated above does not occur at these low latitudes. In practice then, use of the formula is limited to extratropical latitudes where it gives in general a useful estimate of wind speed in the free atmosphere.

Table 4 shows the speeds in various latitudes which correspond with that pressure gradient which gives a speed of 30 KT in latitude 45°, the density being assumed constant. From this table it is seen that a pressure gradient which corresponds with only moderate winds in middle latitudes gives speeds of double or more in low latitudes, but appreciably lower speeds near the pole. Allowance should therefore be made for this effect when interpreting weather maps. Pressure gradients generally are much more open in low than in high latitudes, and within the tropics steep gradients and strong winds occur as a rule only in tropical cyclones.

TABLE 4. *Geostrophic wind speeds at various latitudes for the same pressure gradient*

Latitude	90°	75°	60°	45°	30°	15°
Speed (knots)	21	22	25	30	42	82

For other pressure gradients the wind speeds are in the same ratio

Limitations of the geostrophic rule
The geostrophic wind is a precise measure of the true wind only when a balance is struck between the pressure gradient and the Coriolis force. This is an exacting condition, and is strictly fulfilled only with straight, parallel isobars. If the isobars are curved or if the pressure distribution is changing with time then additional forces are involved which may make the geostrophic formula inapplicable. Apart from the effect of curvature of the isobars, appreciable departures from the geostrophic rule arise with unsteadiness of the motion or with the introduction of a vertical component. Thus with transitory disturbances such as gusts and squalls the forces operating are unbalanced, so that these irregularities have little relation to the geostrophic wind. Similarly, with local winds such as land and sea breezes there is seldom sufficient time for a balance to be reached, so that as a rule they differ in both direction and speed from the wind which would normally be associated with the pressure gradient.

For these reasons there are many local or even general variations from Buys Ballot's law and the geostrophic rule. Nevertheless the geostrophic wind is fundamental in weather forecasting since often enough it gives a satisfactory approximation to the actual wind, while cases of serious departure from it are easily recognized in advance.

Geostrophic scale

The geostrophic wind is measured with the aid of a suitable scale engraved on transparent material and placed across the isobars. Apart from variations in density which can usually be ignored, the geostrophic speed in a given latitude depends only on the distance between the isobars, and the scale is merely a method of converting this distance into units of speed according to equation (8). Types of geostrophic scale applicable over a range of latitudes are shown in Fig. 15. The use

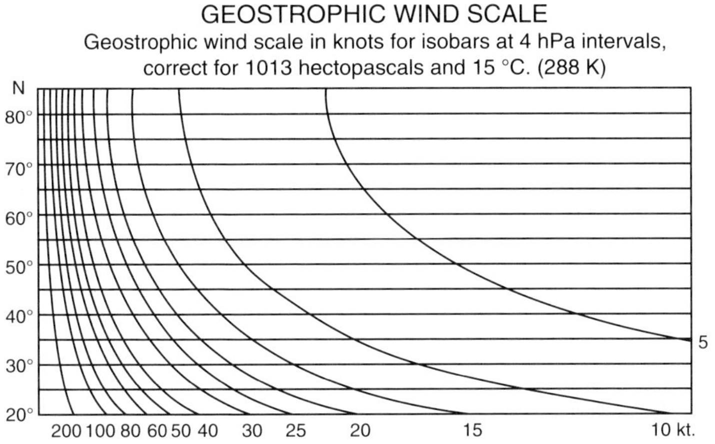

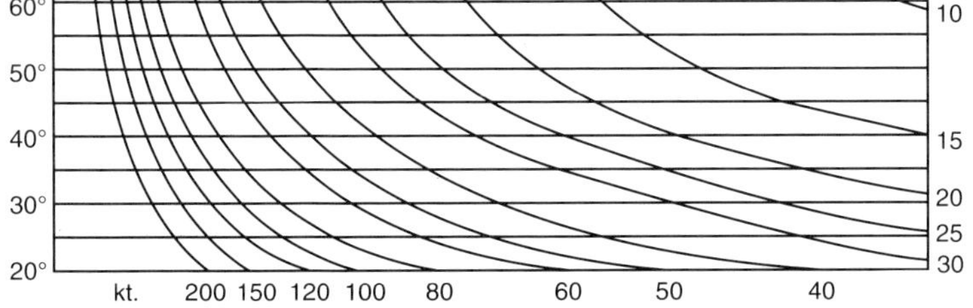

GEOSTROPHIC WIND SCALE
Geostrophic wind scale in knots for isobars at 4 hPa intervals, correct for 1013 hectopascals and 15 °C. (288 K)

GEOSTROPHIC WIND SCALE
Geostrophic wind scale in knots for contours at 120 geopotential metre intervals

Figure 15. Geostrophic wind scales. These examples are for use with charts constructed on the polar stereographic projection with one standard parallel at 60° N, where the natural scale is 1:20 000 000.

of the upper-air scale is described in section 5.4. Fig. 16 illustrates the use of a single-latitude scale which is placed across the isobars at right angles with the left-hand extremity on one isobar; the speed is read off at the point where the next isobar crosses the scale. Clearly the spacing of the graduations depends upon the scale of the chart in use as well as on the interval of pressure between consecutive isobars and both must be allowed for when using the scale; for example if the scale is constructed for use with 4 hPa intervals on a chart of scale 1:20 million the reading should be halved when used with 4 hPa intervals at a scale of 1:10 million.

Component of geostrophic wind in any direction
If, in Fig. 17, PQ is drawn normal to consecutive isobars PP′ and QQ′ then the geostrophic wind blows at right angles to PQ with a speed inversely proportional to

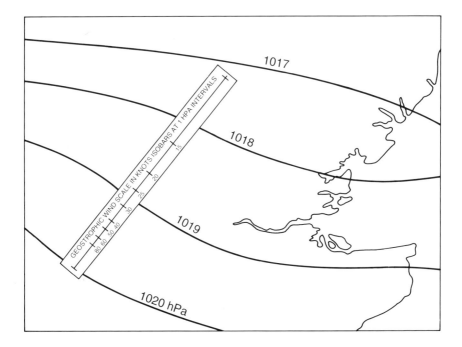

Figure 16.   Use of the geostrophic wind scale. In the case shown, the reading is 27 KT.

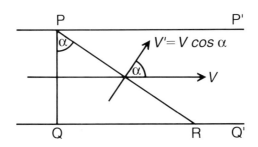

Figure 17.   Component of the geostrophic wind speed.

50

PQ, say, $V = k/\text{PQ}$. If now the geostrophic formula is applied to a line PR intercepted by the same isobars and inclined at an angle α to PQ, the speed obtained is

$$V' = k/\text{PR} = V\,(\text{PQ/PR})$$

or $V' = V \cos \alpha$, which is the component of the geostrophic wind at right angles to PR. Hence the component of the geostrophic wind perpendicular to any line is obtained by laying the geostrophic scale along that line and reading off the speed in the usual way.

Cyclostrophic wind
Since air is seldom constrained to follow a great circle, consideration must be given to the effect of the centripetal force which is necessary if air is to move on a path which is curved relative to the earth. If the air is moving steadily on a circular track of radius r and with a horizontal velocity V it has an acceleration to the centre of V^2/r and the centripetal force acting on unit volume of air is $\rho V^2/r$. If the Coriolis force is negligible this must be provided by the pressure gradient. Hence

$$\rho V^2/r = G \ \text{ and } \ V = (Gr/\rho)^{0.5}. \tag{9}$$

Motion under these circumstances is described as cyclostrophic, and equation (9) gives the value of the cyclostrophic wind. In certain types of motion, as for example near the centre of a tropical cyclone or in a circular tornado, the equation gives a close approximation to the actual wind.

Gradient wind
Generally, when isobars are curved, both geostrophic and cyclostrophic effects should be considered. If air is moving steadily round a centre of low pressure on its left in the northern hemisphere (Fig. 18(a)), the centripetal force acting inwards must be provided by the difference between the pressure gradient directed inwards towards low pressure and the Coriolis force directed outwards. Since the latter is at right angles to the wind it follows that all three forces must lie along the radius of curvature. Therefore

$$\rho\, V^2/r = G \ - \ 2\Omega\rho\, V \sin \phi \tag{10}$$

and dividing by $2\Omega\rho \sin \phi$

$$V = G\,/(2\,\Omega\rho \sin \phi) - V^2/(2r\, \Omega \sin \phi),$$

$$\text{or } V = V_\text{g} - V^2/(2r\, \Omega \sin \phi) \tag{11}$$

where V_g is the geostrophic wind.

In anticyclonic motion the centripetal force, acting towards high pressure this time, must be provided by the difference between the Coriolis force directed inwards towards high pressure and the pressure gradient directed outwards (Fig. 18(b)). Thus in anticyclonic motion the actual wind velocity will be greater

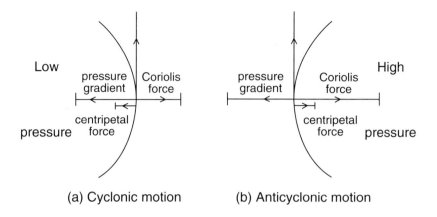

Figure 18.   Gradient wind and balance of forces in the northern hemisphere.

than the geostrophic for the same pressure gradient. The expression for the velocity now becomes

$$V = V_g + V^2/(2r \, \Omega \sin \phi). \tag{12}$$

The value of V obtained from equations (11) and (12), which allows for both cyclostrophic and geostrophic terms, is known as the 'gradient' wind. It depends not only on the pressure gradient but also on the curvature of the isobars and accurately represents the true wind only in steady and uniform circular motion.

The precise determination of the gradient wind is somewhat involved; the correction from geostrophic to gradient wind differs in magnitude as well as sign according as the curvature of the isobars is cyclonic or anticyclonic, while with moving systems it is the curvature of the trajectory of the air that is involved, not the curvature of the isobars. In practice, the geostrophic wind is determined in the usual way, and then, if required, reference to a table or diagram gives the correction to be applied to obtain the gradient wind. For example, suppose in a stationary system the geostrophic wind is 40 KT, radius of curvature of isobars 800 km and latitude 45°; then the gradient wind will be found to be 34 KT in cyclonic motion and 58 KT in anticyclonic motion. Again, if the radius of curvature is 1600 km, the values of the gradient wind are 36 KT and 46 KT respectively. The percentage correction to the geostrophic wind to obtain the gradient wind increases with the geostrophic wind speed, decreases with increasing radius of curvature, and decreases with increasing latitude. When the isobars are straight and parallel the gradient wind equals the geostrophic wind. When, as in low latitudes, the Coriolis term is negligible (equation (10) with small ϕ) the gradient wind is equal to the cyclostrophic wind.

The geostrophic formula, being the easiest to apply, is the most widely used and usually gives a useful approximation outside the tropics when the curvature is not too great. In other cases, for example near the centre of a pressure system where the radius of curvature of the isobars is small, it should be remembered that the geostrophic formula overestimates the speed in cyclonic motion and underestimates it in anticyclonic motion. Near the centre of a tropical cyclone the radius of curvature is small, as also is the Coriolis effect because of the low latitude; the cyclostrophic formula then gives a reasonable estimate of the wind. This is even more true of the tornado (Section 17.7) where the effects of small radius of curvature, steep pressure gradient and strong wind combine to render the Coriolis term relatively insignificant.

Effect of surface friction
The primary effect of friction with the earth's surface is to reduce the rate of flow in the lowest layers. The thickness of the layer affected, the so-called friction layer, is variable; it depends primarily on wind speed, lapse rate of temperature and roughness of the surface. Since throughout this layer the wind speed increases from the surface upwards, the geostrophic wind as determined from the isobars at sea level is considered to apply to the unretarded air just above the friction layer, i.e. at a height of about 2000–3000 ft above the ground. Within the friction layer the wind is slowed down and the Coriolis force, being reduced in proportion, is no longer sufficient to balance the pressure gradient. For this reason the wind near the surface blows somewhat across the isobars towards the side of low pressure. Both the reduction in speed of the surface wind and its inclination to the isobars vary considerably with circumstances; very rough rules are that over the sea, where friction is small, the surface wind blows at about 15 degrees to the isobars at a speed of about two thirds of the geostrophic value; over land, where friction is greater, the inclination to the isobars is about 25 degrees and the speed about one third to one half of the geostrophic value.

5.3 WIND NEAR THE EARTH'S SURFACE

In this section are considered the main features of the motion of the atmosphere within the layer affected by surface friction, the depth of which is usually between about 1500 and 3000 ft although at times less than 500 ft.

Turbulence and gustiness
The short-period and small-scale oscillations in wind which are classed under the general term turbulence are indicated very clearly on the records from an anemograph (Fig. 19). The speed and direction pens each record traces of varying width caused by a series of oscillations in rapid succession which follow no obvious regularity but spread as a whole over a reasonably well-defined range. It is usually possible to imagine the position of a mean line through each trace and so to determine the mean wind at any time. The width of the trace is an indication of the degree of gustiness and a gustiness factor may be defined:

$$\text{gustiness factor} = \frac{\text{range of fluctuation in gusts and lulls.}}{\text{mean wind speed}}$$

The range is determined from the highest gusts and lowest lulls over a period such as an hour, ignoring any very exceptional variations. The factor is conveniently given as a percentage; for example, if the mean wind is 30 KT with gusts up to 45 KT and lulls down to 15 KT then the range is 30 KT and the factor is 100%.

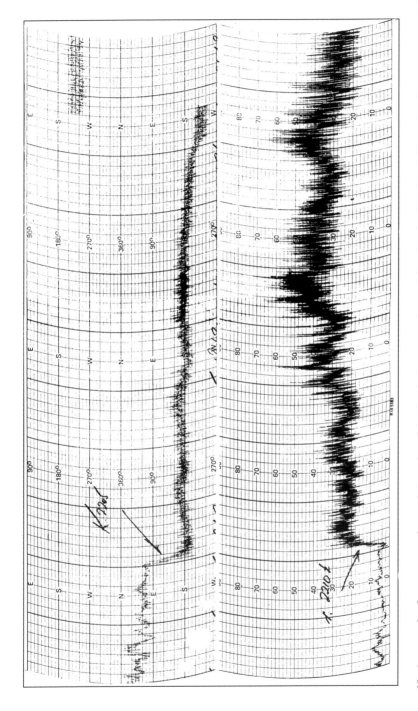

Figure 19. An example of an anemograph record. A section of the electrical anemograph record from London (Heathrow) Airport (north-east anemometer) from 2000 UTC on 15 October 1987 to 0700 UTC on 16 October 1987.

Another measure of gustiness is the gust ratio. This is the ratio of the maximum gust to the mean wind speed, usually measured over an hour. On occasions of strong wind, typical gust ratios range between 1.3 over open sea, to 1.6 over flat, open country and 2.1 near the centre of large cities. Individual gust ratios of 2.5 to 2.9 were recorded at city centre sites during the 'Great Storm' of 16 October 1987.

Two types of turbulence
There are two distinct types of turbulence or gustiness, distinguished by the terms frictional and thermal. Each type comprises both vertical and horizontal fluctuations of wind, these being practically inseparable. The frictional type of turbulence is a characteristic property of fluid flow in the neighbourhood of a boundary when certain conditions are realized. Fluid actually in contact with a stationary boundary is itself at rest, while throughout the friction layer the mean speed increases with distance from the boundary until the unretarded free stream is reached. When, for a given fluid and type of boundary, the speed of the free stream is sufficiently low, the flow remains smooth or laminar, but when the free speed surpasses a certain limit the flow becomes unstable and breaks down into turbulent motion; eddies then form near the boundary, drift away into the stream, and cause the friction layer to become much deeper in turbulent than in laminar flow.

The thermal type of turbulence results from convection currents set up by surface heating (Section 3.8). The heating may result from insolation over the land or from the passage of a relatively cool mass of air over a warmer land or sea surface.

Some factors affecting turbulence
The flow of air over the earth's surface is usually, although not invariably, turbulent, and the degree of turbulence and the thickness of the friction layer vary from one situation to another. Frictional turbulence is widespread, largely because the earth's surface is rough, dynamically speaking; moreover, gustiness is accentuated by flow over buildings, trees or rugged country. Since with either type of turbulence the eddies involve vertical as well as horizontal velocities, they develop more easily as the lapse rate become steeper. Factors unfavourable to the development of frictional turbulence are flow over open sea or relatively smooth ground, light wind or calm and a stable lapse rate; factors unfavourable to thermal turbulence are surface cooling and stable lapse rates. Over land there is in consequence a diurnal variation in turbulence which is most vigorous by day when the lapse rate is steep and least on a clear night with an inversion of temperature. The difference in degree of turbulence over land and sea is revealed by the gustiness factor derived from anemometer records; thus statistics show the factor for a site near London to be 100%, while for Falmouth (Cornwall) with winds off the sea it is only 25%. When the character of the surface in the neighbourhood of an aerodrome varies according to direction, as at a coastal site, then the gustiness varies with wind direction, often to a marked extent.

Surface turbulence and aircraft
To the occupants of an aircraft, turbulence is recognized as bumpiness, and the difference between flying at low level over land and sea in this respect is well known. Strong winds are habitually turbulent but again the degree of turbulence increases with the roughness of the surface and is generally more marked over land

than over sea. In turbulent conditions the landing and take-off of aircraft may be difficult, for sudden changes of wind speed or direction can cause loss of control when the aircraft is only just airborne.

Effect of turbulence on lapse rate of temperature

Turbulent mixing has the effect of steepening the lapse rate in the friction layer. If the lapse rate is stable to begin with, then air brought down to the surface from the upper part of the layer is warmed adiabatically to a temperature above that of the surface; similarly air carried upwards is cooled below the temperature of the upper layers. As mixing proceeds, the effect is to warm the lower layers and to cool the upper layers until the lapse rate becomes dry adiabatic, assuming the air remains unsaturated. Thus in Fig. 20, if the lapse rate is initially given by ABC, the result of mixing would be, ideally, to replace the portion AB by the dry adiabatic A'B' where BB' corresponds to the top of the mixing layer. The position of A'B' is such as to leave the mean temperature of the mixing layer unaltered. It is seen that a sharp inversion of temperature is formed at the top of the friction layer, although in practice it is likely to be rounded off as suggested by the broken curve B'C. Often the wind is not strong enough to produce complete mixing, in which case the final temperature curve will be intermediate between AB and A'B'. The case when the rising air becomes saturated will be discussed under the heading of turbulence cloud in Section 6.3.

Thermal eddies

The eddies of thermal origin are often of larger dimensions and productive of stronger gusts than those produced frictionally. Therefore thermal currents are more noticeable as a rule to occupants of an aircraft than are frictional eddies; they may

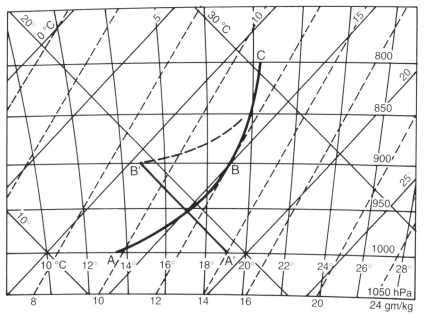

Figure 20. The effect of turbulence on the lapse rate of dry air. ABC is the initial lapse rate and A'B'C' the lapse rate after mixing.

56

extend to considerable heights when the lapse rate is favourable, and they are effective in mixing the surface air with that of the upper layers.

Near the surface, extreme gusts occur when some of the faster-moving air above the friction layer is brought down to the surface by the thermal eddies; in consequence the maximum gust speed in these circumstances may well exceed the speed of the geostrophic wind.

Squalls

In certain conditions thermal currents develop into large systems extending some kilometres horizontally and several thousand feet vertically; in these circumstances they may take many minutes to pass over a station and are no longer to be classed as turbulence or gustiness but are rather to be regarded as distinct secondary disturbances; the variations in wind take the form of squalls rather than gusts although rapid variations are superimposed by smaller eddies carried along in the system. The strongest gusts recorded are usually associated with such squalls. In the British Isles gusts of over 70 KT occur occasionally at almost any well exposed station and recorded speeds have exceeded 90 KT from time to time. The strongest gusts are in many respects more important than the mean wind for they may be the cause of severe structural damage. A parked aircraft may easily ride out a gale (defined as a mean wind of force 8 or more (34 KT or over)), but the hazard is greatly increased if a single gust rises to say 60 KT even though the mean wind may not reach gale force.

The essential difference between gusts and squalls lies in the time factor. A gust is a transient increase in speed lasting perhaps a few seconds; the squall is an increase in mean wind lasting usually for some minutes and then dying away again. A squall may be accompanied by a marked drop in temperature, a characteristic squall cloud and precipitation. Both speed and direction at the time of a squall may differ markedly from the prevailing geostrophic values.

Diurnal variation of wind

When the field of pressure is steady, there is a noticeable difference in the surface wind as between day and night. It has been seen how the surface wind is reduced in speed compared with the free wind at a height of about 2000 ft and backed or veered according to the hemisphere. For a given pressure gradient, the precise value of the surface wind depends on the degree of turbulence, since this controls the mixing process in the friction layer. If this is vigorous the friction layer is deep, if weak it is confined to a shallow layer. The diurnal variation in turbulence due to thermal eddies over land entails therefore a diurnal variation in surface wind, resulting in lighter winds and greater deviation from the isobars at night, stronger with less deviation by day. In the upper levels of the friction layer the variation is in the opposite direction. During the night when turbulence is weak the undisturbed wind is reached at a lower height, perhaps 500 or 1000 ft, whereas by day these layers are well within the friction layer and are subject to reduction in speed and deviation in direction. Turbulent mixing has, in other words, the effect of smoothing out the differences in wind between the surface and the free air; in the daytime the difference is small, at night it is large.

Diurnal variations of wind depending on variations in convection, are to be expected only when thermal eddies develop by day and die away at night through diurnal changes in surface temperature and lapse rate. There is therefore no observable diurnal variation over the open sea, while over land it fails to appear when skies are continuously overcast. It is more apparent in fine weather with clear nights and sunny days. In these conditions a light wind of say 10 KT by day may fall practically calm at night. The diurnal variation should be kept in mind whenever a precise estimate of speed and direction of surface wind is required, or when it is desired to estimate the upper-wind conditions above an aerodrome. Thus, if the wind at an aerodrome on a clear night is only 5 KT, the speed at 2000 ft may be as much as 20 KT, but with the same surface wind on a sunny day the upper wind would be unlikely to exceed 10 KT. It is impossible to lay down precise rules, as variations depend on various meteorological factors and particularly on local conditions. A veer in direction of 20 degrees and an increase in speed of the surface wind of 50 per cent from night to day is not uncommon; with light winds the percentage variation may be very much greater.

Wind and topography
The direction of the wind at low levels tends to some extent to conform with the contours of the land. A stream of air flowing towards a mountain range tends to be deflected parallel with it, and in general the wind tends to flow round an obstruction if possible rather than over it; however, if the lapse rate is comparatively steep, upward motion takes place more readily and flow over high ground is facilitated with possibly the development of orographic cloud and precipitation as consequences. Should the range be broken by a pass or valley the air will be forced through with enhanced velocity, and gale force may be reached locally. In narrow valleys the wind flows almost invariably from one direction or the other along the valley and gives no reliable indication of the general direction of the wind in the free atmosphere; a small change in the pressure distribution may cause the wind in the valley to swing to the opposite point of the compass. This constriction of wind through valleys is spoken of as 'funnel effect' or 'canalization'; it is responsible for the great speed attained by the mistral of the Rhône valley (Fig. 21). Some characteristic types of wind which owe their existence to topography will now be considered.

Föhn wind
Mountain ranges, as opposed to individual mountains, can form complete barriers to the flow of air or can significantly modify the properties of the air. The term 'föhn wind' is used to describe any wind which is blowing down a mountainside and is warmer and drier than the air at the same height on the upwind side of the mountain. The original explanation of this phenomenon was that moist air on the windward side of the mountain ascended with consequent condensation and eventual precipitation of some of the water, cooling at the saturated adiabatic lapse rate once condensation had started. On descent on the leeward side of the mountain, evaporation of the water droplets retained in the cloud would take place very quickly and warming thereafter would be at the dry adiabatic lapse rate, resulting in the air at a given level becoming warmer and drier than the air on the windward side. However, research shows that this explanation does not entirely satisfy the facts. Föhn winds and associated temperature rises have been observed without the formation of precipitation on the windward side. It now seems more likely that the

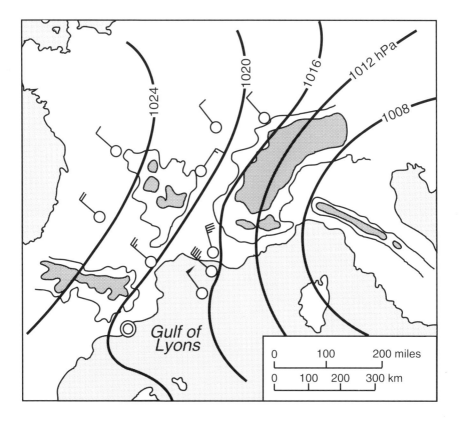

Figure 21. Funnelling through the Rhône Valley producing a mistral. Generalized contours are at 500 and 1000 metres; land above 1000 metres is stippled. Wind arrows are depicted conventionally.

descent of air on the lee side is often a result of subsidence of upper-level air, airflow at lower levels being blocked by the mountains, and the subsidence being materially assisted by the descending portion of large amplitude lee waves (Section 5.5).

There may be a delay in the onset of a föhn wind in a mountain valley because of the reluctance of the cold, denser air to clear and the warm föhn may blow over a valley at considerable strength without affecting the lower altitudes at all. However, if the warm wind is strong a 'swilling out' may suddenly take place and the cold air is then displaced very quickly. When this happens the valley wind can increase from zero to gale force within minutes, the time of onset being very difficult to predict. Taking the saturated lapse rate as half the dry lapse rate of 3 degC per 1000 ft, an ascent of saturated air and subsequent equal descent at the dry adiabatic rate gives an increase of temperature of 1.5 degC for each 1000 ft of displacement. High mountains may therefore produce warming of some 10 degC or more.

The term föhn wind has been adopted in meteorological terminology as a general name for the phenomenon wherever it exists. The chinook of the Rocky Mountains is another example, although it is not necessary to look so far afield for an illustration of the effect; it is noticeable on the lee side of high ground even in the British Isles, and accounts, for example, for the clear warm air sometimes found on the east coast of Scotland when moist south-westerly winds pass over the mountains.

Anabatic and katabatic winds

When the surface of the ground has an appreciable slope there is frequently a tendency for the wind to drift up or down the slope. If the slope is heated by the sun the air in contact with it becomes warmer than the free air at the same level; it is therefore lighter and tends to ascend. Such ascending winds are called anabatic winds. They are masked by irregular convection, and may not show clearly as a definite current of wind except perhaps where they are intensified by the funnel effect of a valley when the term 'valley wind' would be more appropriate. Except near a coastline where an upslope wind is augmented by the sea-breeze, anabatic winds are seldom of much significance.

The reverse, or katabatic, effect is also found over sloping ground in favourable circumstances (Fig. 22). The necessary condition is that the air over the slope shall be colder than air at the same level in the free atmosphere, so that it will tend to sink; the condition is therefore present when the ground is relatively cold. As surface cooling takes place by radiation at night, katabatic winds are normally a nocturnal phenomenon. Even in gently sloping country with no great elevation a downward drift of cold air occurs on a clear quiet night; the speed of the wind may be no more than a few knots, but it aids the formation of pools of cold air on low-lying ground and is one factor controlling the local incidence of frost, fog and mist. On mountain slopes the effect is increased, and if the ground is snow covered it may occur during the day as well as at night. A well known case of a vigorous wind of this type is the 'bora', an off-shore wind on the northern shores of the Adriatic. It normally sets in suddenly, and frequently reaches well over gale force with gusts of over 100 KT not unknown; it is extremely dangerous to shipping and to low-flying aircraft. In this and in several similar cases the wind is not purely katabatic, for it is influenced by the general pressure distribution and is locally intensified by the funnel effect down valleys extending towards the coast. Other examples may be found; on the coasts of Greenland and the shore of the Black Sea they are well known.

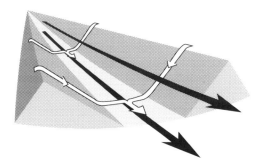

Figure 22.   Katabatic winds. Anabatic winds are in the opposite direction and are usually lighter.

The distinction between föhn and katabatic effects should not be overlooked. Both give downcurrents off high ground, but the former results from the general pressure distribution and is warm and dry, while the latter is a local development where surface cooling is more effective than adiabatic warming so that the wind is relatively cold even when it reaches sea level.

Ravine winds

These occur in and near ravines or narrow valleys which penetrate a mountain barrier. When there is a pressure difference, level for level, between the two sides of the barrier, air is impelled through the ravine by the pressure gradient. Such winds may be very strong not only in the ravine but after leaving its mouth, where they flow out into open country. Examples are the ravine wind at Genoa due to the difference of pressure between the Po valley and the Gulf of Genoa, the kosava of the Danube south-east of Belgrade which sometimes exceeds 35 KT, and the vardar winds near Salonika.

Land-breezes and sea-breezes

In coastal districts large diurnal changes of wind are a characteristic feature and are most marked in quiet conditions with sunny days and clear nights. The wind blows from the sea during the day, often setting in rather abruptly during the morning. If however there is a light off-shore wind to be overcome, its onset is delayed, perhaps even until the afternoon, but then takes place suddenly and may be accompanied by a minor squall with a sharp fall of temperature and an increase of humidity. The strength of a pure sea-breeze rarely exceeds 10 KT in the British Isles; above about 500 ft the speed rapidly decreases to become negligible in most cases by about 1000 ft. The sea-breeze sets in first near the coast, often being observed a kilometre or so out to sea, and the area affected gradually broadens both inland and seawards during the day. As a rule the breeze does not extend more than 15–25 km either side of the coastline, although there are numerous cases of much greater penetration over the land, which are probably to be explained by the effects of topography or by inflow caused by diurnal pressure fall inland. In temperate latitudes there is often sufficient pressure gradient to modify these local developments, and the diurnal variation in the vicinity of the coast then becomes complicated or even obliterated. It is necessary to make a special study of each section of coastline in order to forecast accurately the diurnal variation of wind.

At first, the sea-breeze is directly onshore, but the Coriolis effect gradually becomes more apparent as the air arrives after a longer track over the sea and the flow then tends to align itself with the coastline with land to the left (in the northern hemisphere). This process takes time and may not be reached until evening when the diurnal decline of the sea-breeze has already begun. The sea-breeze normally falls light soon after sunset, and after some hours may be replaced by an opposite drift from the land — the land-breeze. In the British Isles the land-breeze is rarely more than light, a few knots at most, and does not develop with any marked regularity; since it occurs only in stable conditions, its direction over the land follows the ground contours closely; it is also shallower than the sea-breeze, probably not exceeding a few hundred feet.

On account of the greater intensity of insolation, the sea-breeze in lower latitudes may reach in excess of 20 KT; throughout most of the tropics and subtropics, where prevailing winds are normally light, it is of very regular occurrence.

The explanation of land- and sea-breezes rests on the diurnal differences of temperature between the surfaces of land and sea. The increase of the land temperature by day warms and expands the overlying air, slightly lifting the overlying pressure surfaces so that at any particular upper level, say 500 ft, the weight of the air above (i.e. the pressure) is increased. In this way the pressure aloft over the land becomes slightly greater than before, while that over the sea is initially unchanged. Thus a drift of upper air commences from the land towards the sea. This in turn produces a slight increase of surface pressure over the sea and a reduction over the land; in consequence a flow of surface air sets in from sea to land and this constitutes the sea-breeze. At night the temperature difference is reversed owing to radiative cooling over the land and a contrary flow is induced at the surface. In both cases the upper return flow of air is spread over so great a depth that it is no more than a gentle drift, with scarcely any observable wind; but if the sea-breeze has established itself against a light offshore wind, then this offshore flow may still be found above the sea-breeze at a height of perhaps 1000 ft or more.

On some occasions the effect of the sea-breeze extends to 3000 or even 5000 ft. The warmer land air is lifted over the cooler air from the sea and the transition zone between the two types of air is often marked by a line of horizontal convergence of wind and vigorous convection. This transition zone may progress slowly inland as a sea-breeze front. It has small dimensions and although of great interest to glider pilots, its effect would normally be unnoticed by powered aircraft.

A cross section of a well-developed sea-breeze is shown in Fig. 23.

5.4 WIND IN THE FREE ATMOSPHERE

Wind in relation to pressure contours
It has been explained in Section 5.2 how the wind just above the friction layer, i.e. at about 2000 ft, is related to the distribution of pressure at the surface. Both wind

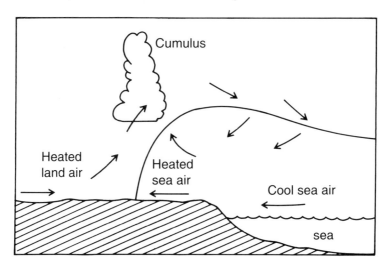

Figure 23.   Sea-breeze cross-section.

62

and pressure should strictly refer to the same level, and the relationship then holds good not only at 2000 ft but at any greater height. Thus, for example, at 20 000 ft the equation (8) for the geostrophic wind remains true, but since the density at this height is reduced to about half its surface value, the geostrophic speed at 20 000 ft is approximately double that at the surface for the same pressure gradient. Consequently allowance must always be made for the density if winds are derived from isobaric charts for the upper air, and the allowance will differ for each level.

There are considerable advantages to be gained from an alternative method of representing the distribution of pressure in the upper air. Consider a fixed pressure level of say, 500 hPa, with the heights at which this pressure occurs plotted on a chart, using simultaneous observations from a network of upper air stations. The heights will, of course, vary from place to place and the variation may be conveniently shown by drawing lines of equal height, or contour lines, usually at intervals of 60 metres. The completed contour chart shows the variations in height of the chosen pressure surface in exactly the same way that height of ground is indicated on an ordinary topographical map (see Fig. 24).

Any contour line is by definition horizontal and the pressure is the same at all points; it therefore satisfies the definition of an isobar on a horizontal surface. Thus in Fig. 24 the contour line for, say 5520 m, is an isobar in the horizontal surface at that height. Consequently the direction of the geostrophic wind is along the contours, and it is easily seen that it blows with the lower contour values on the left in the northern hemisphere and on the right in the southern hemisphere.

The speed of the geostrophic wind is determined by a formula which is even simpler than that which applies to an isobaric chart. The upper part of Fig. 25 illustrates a portion of a contour chart for 500 hPa in which PBQ is drawn normal to the contours; the lower part shows a vertical section through PQ. By applying equation (8), the geostrophic wind at B is given as

$$V = (2\,\Omega\rho\sin\phi)^{-1} \times (p_C - p_A)/AC.$$

Now the pressure at C exceeds 500 hPa by the weight of the column of air of unit cross-section represented by Q'C, therefore

$$p_C - 500 = g\rho\,(h_Q - h_C).$$

Similarly the pressure at A is less than 500 hPa by the weight of the column P'A, and

$$500 - p_A = g\rho(h_A - h_P).$$

By addition, since $h_A = h_C$,

$$p_C - p_A = g\rho(h_Q - h_P).$$

If this is substituted in the above expression then, since AC = PQ, the equation for the geostrophic wind in terms of the contours becomes

$$V = g(2\,\Omega\rho\sin\phi)^{-1} \times (h_Q - h_P)/PQ. \tag{13}$$

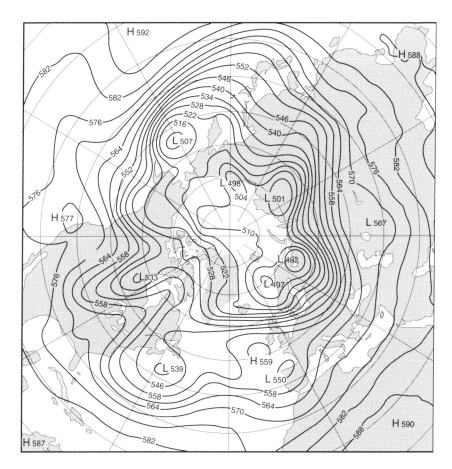

Figure 24.   Contours of the 500 hPa isobaric surface (in decametres).

The density does not appear in this equation and the second factor is simply the gradient of the contours, i.e. the difference in height between two contours divided by the horizontal distance between them, analogous to the pressure gradient on an isobaric chart. In a given latitude, the geostrophic speed varies only with the gradient of the contours. By the aid of this equation, a geostrophic scale for use with contour charts may be constructed similar to that in use with isobaric charts; since the equation does not contain the density, the same scale applies directly to contour charts at any pressure level. The scale is illustrated in Fig. 15.

The relation of the geostrophic wind to the contours on a pressure surface may now be stated by the following rule:

The geostrophic wind blows along the contours of a pressure surface with a speed which is proportional to the gradient of the contours and independent of the density; the direction is such that the lower contours are on the left in the northern hemisphere and on the right in the southern hemisphere.

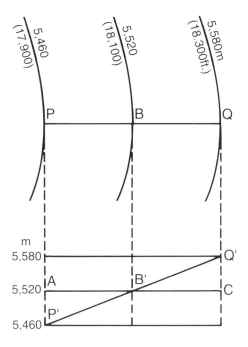

Figure 25. Vertical section through a pressure surface. The upper part of the figure shows contours of the 500 hPa surface and the lower part shows the vertical section. The vertical scale is greatly exaggerated.

As was explained in connection with isobars (Section 5.2), it follows that equation (13) gives the component of geostrophic wind at right angles to PQ, even when PQ is not normal to the contours.

The cyclostrophic and gradient winds may be determined from contour charts in the same way as from isobaric charts as already described, and there is no need to repeat the argument. In general, the limitations of the geostrophic wind derived from the surface chart, as discussed above, apply equally to the upper-air charts except that any effects due to the proximity of an irregular land surface are absent save in the vicinity of the highest ground. It should be remembered too that the geostrophic equation is in any case inapplicable near the equator and therefore alternative methods of analysis to those of producing contour charts need to be used.

Thermal wind

The general nature of the variation of wind with height may be envisaged by considering how the pressure field at the surface becomes modified at higher levels; this was discussed in Section 2.3 where the conclusion was reached that in areas where the temperature is high, the pressure in the upper air tends also to be high, and where the temperature is low the upper-air pressure also tends to be low. In terms of contours of a given pressure surface, we should say that they are relatively low over cold places and high over warm places. In either case it has been shown

65

that the wind at high levels tends to orient itself with the lower temperature on the left (in the northern hemisphere).

This connection between wind and temperature becomes more precise when it is noted that the ratio of the pressures between two heights depends only on the mean temperature of the intervening column of air, in accordance with equation (2) (Section 2.3). To take the simplest case, when there is no pressure gradient and therefore no wind at the surface, the pressure distribution and hence the geostrophic wind at an upper level is determined solely from the horizontal distribution of mean temperature. This we can now generalize into the statement that the vector difference of wind between two levels depends only on the horizontal distribution of mean temperature of the intervening layer of air. The thermal wind in a layer is defined as that wind which must be added vectorially to the geostrophic wind at the lower level in order to obtain the geostrophic wind at the upper level (Fig. 26).

Thus the thermal wind depends only on the horizontal distribution of mean temperature of the layer. The latter may be represented by drawing isotherms, and the relation of these to the thermal wind is given by the following rule:

The direction of the thermal wind is along the isotherms of mean temperature with the lower temperature on the left in the northern hemisphere, on the right in the southern hemisphere; the speed of the thermal wind is proportional to the temperature gradient.

Thickness charts
Isotherms of mean temperature, on which the thermal wind in a layer depends, are not normally drawn directly, but when contour charts are prepared it is usual to construct further charts showing the difference in height between pairs of standard pressure levels, e.g. 1000 and 500 hPa. As at any point the difference in height depends only on the mean temperature of the intervening air column, isopleths of the difference coincide with isotherms of mean temperature. Such charts are called 'thickness charts' and the 1000–500 hPa thickness chart is referred to as the 'total thickness'; by representing how the thickness of the given layer varies from place to place, they show how its mean temperature varies in the horizontal, and from this the distribution of the thermal wind is evident.

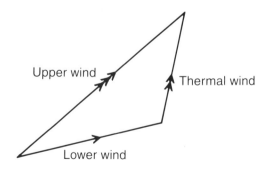

Figure 26.   Vector diagram illustrating thermal wind.

Variation of wind with height

The average variation of wind with height within the friction layer has already been described; the present section describes the variation within the remainder of the troposphere and in the stratosphere. The notion of the thermal wind enables some immediate conclusions to be deduced as to the distribution of wind in the upper levels. It has been seen (Fig. 13) that temperatures in the troposphere for the most part decrease from the equator towards the poles. The average thermal wind throughout most of the troposphere accordingly blows from the west and the usual variation of wind with height is such that the westerly component increases throughout the troposphere. In the upper troposphere the winds are in consequence predominantly westerly. In terms of pressure this implies that at levels high enough for the surface distribution to be overcome there is a depression over each pole, while pressure is relatively high in the subtropics. Within the tropics such inferences cannot be made since there the formulae for the geostrophic, and consequently the thermal, winds break down. The actual distribution of wind in the tropics consists in the main of a belt of easterly winds extending up to at least 40 000 ft and covering about 10–20 degrees of latitude but varying in position according to the season.

Outside the tropics, as already implied, low-level westerly winds usually increase with height with little change of direction, while easterlies tend to decrease and eventually give way to westerlies. On this account easterlies are often shallow, the reversal of direction perhaps taking place by 3000 ft although at other times they may persist to great heights; further, the reversal of direction may take place rapidly with a shallow calm layer separating the two currents, or by a gradual backing or veering spread over several thousands of feet. A westerly thermal wind also implies that northerly winds would be expected to back with height and southerly winds to veer.

5.5 VERTICAL MOTION OF THE ATMOSPHERE

Vertical motion of the atmosphere ranges in type from irregular local gusts and lulls with a period of a few seconds, to widespread and sustained, although slow, movements lasting for days at a time; the vertical velocity, according to the type of motion, ranges from zero to many tens of feet per second. Such motions are of immediate concern for aircraft flight and of fundamental importance to weather. The irregular upward and downward currents are responsible for bumpiness, while the more persistent local currents may cause aircraft to undergo marked vertical displacements or may adversely affect the rate of climb. They make difficulties for powered aircraft but for the glider pilot they are the very means of sustained flight when used skilfully. The effects of all forms of vertical motion on weather are far reaching; in particular, upward motion is an essential prerequisite to the formation of clouds and precipitation, while downward motion is often associated with clear skies. These different types of vertical motion will now be described, but their consequences with regard to cloud and precipitation are reserved for the next chapter. The first part of this section deals with scales and intensities of vertical motion likely to affect aircraft operations. Later, the vertical motions that are characteristic of synoptic-scale features are discussed.

Vertical currents produced by ground contours
In describing the flow of wind near the ground (Section 5.3), the turbulent character of the motion has been emphasized as a regular feature, even over a level surface. Individual eddies include upward and downward movements as well as horizontal variations in speed and direction; they may be of frictional or thermal origin, and when the size of the eddies is comparable with that of an aircraft, they are felt as short-period bumpiness. When there are obstacles in the path of the wind, such as trees or buildings or changes in the ground contours, then the character of the wind flow undergoes a change. This takes place in one or more of the following ways: by a general deflection of the stream in order to get round or over the obstacle, by the development or intensification of turbulence, and by the formation of lee waves. The extent to which any of these changes takes place depends on several factors which include the wind speed and its variation with height, the lapse rate of temperature, the size and shape of the obstructions and their orientation relative to the wind.

Flow disturbance due to isolated topography
The effects of complex terrain on airflow are difficult to predict. Only in the case of well defined topography (i.e. an isolated symmetric hill or a long ridge of uniform cross section) can changes in the undisturbed flow pattern be determined. Even in these rather idealized cases our understanding relates largely to numerical simulations as there are very few experimental data available, except for standing or lee waves. The evidence suggests that there are two types of disturbance that can be produced in the mean flow by such isolated topography. These are conveniently described in relation to the horizontal dimensions of the topography. For topography, typically less than a few kilometres in horizontal extent, the effects of buoyancy can be largely ignored and the flow perturbations can be considered a consequence of topography alone. Flow perturbations caused by large-scale topography are influenced by the atmospheric stability. These two cases are now discussed.

Disturbance due to small-scale topography
In these cases the amplitude of the vertical velocities is determined by the slope of the topography and the basic undisturbed upwind horizontal wind speed (U_0). Three cases may be distinguished, with the same flow characteristics being observed for unstable, neutral and slightly stable lapse rates. A schematic representation of the flow for these three cases is given in Fig. 27. The magnitude of the vertical velocity is roughly $U_0 \tan \alpha$ where α is the slope of the ground, with the magnitude limited to U_0 for slopes greater than 45°. For slopes less than 1 in 5 (α about 10°) the flow remains attached to the topography on both sides of the hill but as the slope becomes steeper there is flow separation with recirculating eddies behind the hill. When the slopes are 1 in 3 (α = about 18°) or greater there are recirculating eddies upstream and downstream of the hill. The regions containing eddies are highly turbulent.

With steep topography, the turbulent region may be extended down wind by trailing vortex circulations in which there are vertical velocities similar to U_0. In the particular case of 'rotor streaming' severe turbulence may be encountered in the layer about level with the hill top and extending some distance down wind; the requirements for this type of formation are that the air mass is stable, the low-level

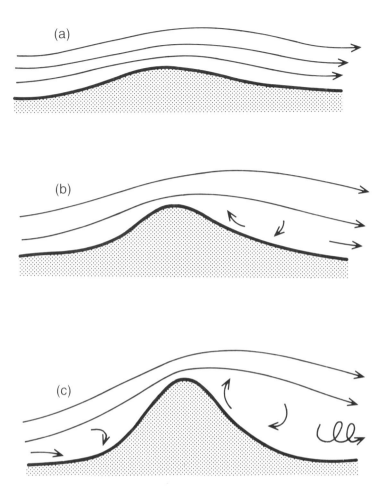

Figure 27. Flow over small-scale topography. Similar characteristics apply for unstable, neutral or slightly stable lapse rates. (a) Ground slopes less than 1 in 5 (approximately 11°), (b) ground slopes about 1 in 3 (approximately 18°) and (c) ground slopes greater than 1 in 3.

wind component across the hills is 20 KT or more, and that this component decreases sharply, or even reverses, at about one and a half to twice the height of the hills (Fig. 28). As the vertical velocities in these cases are roughly related to the undisturbed upstream flow the severity of the turbulence is seen to be wind-speed dependent. For strong winds and steep topography the turbulence can have serious impact upon aircraft operations, as illustrated by the following example. A research aircraft, operated by the United Kingdom Meteorological Office and instrumented specifically to measure turbulent fluctuations, experienced several rapid changes in vertical velocity of up to 60 ft s^{-1} in a period of 2 to 3 seconds. The aircraft was flying at about 1300 ft downwind of an isolated 1300 ft ridge and had to be grounded for stress checks. The low-level wind speed upstream of the ridge was 40 KT.

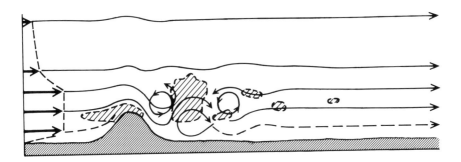

Figure 28.   Rotor streaming (after Forchtgott). The vertical profile of the wind is shown by the bold arrows on the left.

Disturbance due to larger-scale topography
In suitable conditions extensive waves occur to the lee of hills or mountains. The waves remain in a fixed position with the air moving through them: they can be regarded as oscillations about the stable state of the undisturbed airstream with the mountain providing the source of the disturbance and gravity providing the restoring force.

Over the mountain the flow is deflected by the high ground and in the lower layers it tends to follow the profile of the ground. Beyond the mountain a lee wave flow is established which has regular undulations bearing little relationship to the ground below (Fig. 29).

Vertical currents may be quite extensive and vigorous; for ridges with heights greater than about a kilometre the vertical velocities are comparable with U_0. The amplitude of the wave varies with height; in general it decreases with height after reaching a maximum somewhere in the lower to mid-troposphere. On occasions, however, extreme motions reach the lower stratosphere.

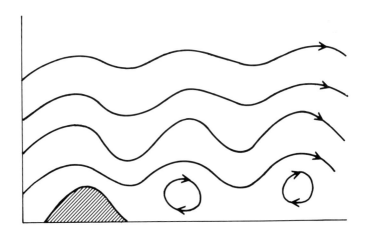

Figure 29.   Flow over a ridge, with lee waves.

The existence of lee waves requires certain conditions to be fulfilled regarding the distribution of wind and temperature with height. For strong wave development the airstream must consist of a deep current of air in which wind direction changes little with height and speeds increase upwards through the troposphere. The wind must blow within about 30° of the perpendicular to the ridge and the speed at the crest must be above 15 KT for small mountains and above 30 KT for large mountains. Powerful waves develop when, at levels where the airstream is disturbed by the mountain, there is a layer of marked stability, such as an inversion or an isothermal layer, bounded by less stable air above and below.

Fig. 30 shows computed streamlines for a hill of about 2000 ft where a stable layer extends from 4000 to 9000 ft above the low ground and the wind speed increases with height throughout the layer in which the lapse rate is stable. A phenomenon which is sometimes observed in well developed lee wave situations is the 'rotor'. This is not to be confused with the rotor streaming described above; the vertical wind profiles for the two phenomena are quite different. The rotor is a large, closed, eddy with a horizontal axis, which forms in the lee of a well defined escarpment; it may be manifest as a long roll of ragged cumulus or stratocumulus oriented parallel with the ridge; the line of cloud may display an apparent motion about the axis of the eddy but does not move away from the escarpment. Turbulence may be extreme in and above the rotor. Marked rotor development occurs in the lee of the Sierra Nevada in California; in the United Kingdom the 'helm bar' of Cross Fell is perhaps the best known example.

Wavelength and amplitude of lee waves
The natural wavelength of an airstream is a function of wind speed and atmospheric stability and is commonly a few kilometres, although it may be anything up to about 50 km. Light winds or marked stability through a substantial depth make for a short wavelength, whilst strong winds and slight stability are associated with a long wavelength. Wave motions are damped out in an unstable airstream. Motions

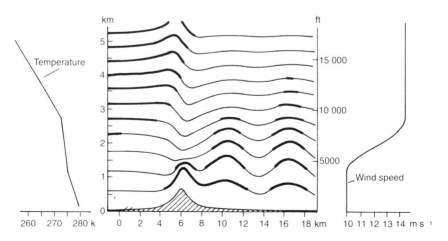

Figure 30. Conditions favourable for standing waves. Computed streamlines over a ridge (after R.S. Scorer). Vertical profiles are shown for wind speed (left) and temperature (right).

corresponding to the natural wavelength are likely to be found in any stable airstream. The presence of a hill or obstacle results in more pronounced waves.

The amplitude of the waves depends largely upon the size and shape of the high ground. In general, the higher the mountain the greater the amplitude of the lee waves, but in addition the width of the mountain is relevant. For a given airstream and height of hill, the lee waves of largest amplitude are generated by those hills having a cross-section which coincides with the natural wavelength of the airstream. A ridge whose wavelength matches the one natural to the airstream will give lee waves of larger amplitude than will another much larger hill.

Clouds and topography
The vertical motion induced in the airflow by topography can result in cloud formation anywhere between the surface and, in extreme conditions, 30 km (100 000 ft). In particular, a favoured region for cloud development is in the crest of lee waves. The clouds form in the ascending air and evaporate further downstream where the air descends, resulting in lines of cloud parallel with and downwind from the mountain ridge. In general, the presence of orographic clouds indicates regions of ascending air and possible turbulence. The absence of such cloud does not however imply smooth, undisturbed flow.

Icing
The displacement of air in mountain waves allows little chance of entrainment; the ascending motion is therefore very nearly adiabatic. In stable air the height of the 0 °C isotherm is lowered by the passage of air over high ground and the supercooled water content of the air may increase. For these reasons mountain waves are likely to increase the severity of ice accretion on aircraft in cloud. (The nature of aircraft icing is discussed more fully in Chapter 8.)

Safety heights over high ground
When mountain waves are occurring, the safety height for an aircraft overflying the high ground should be increased to allow for possible downdraughts and, whenever possible, to avoid the most turbulent zones. The additional height margin will vary widely according to different circumstances; methods of calculating it can be found in the relevant civil aviation information circulars. In a mountainous area such as the Alps where air flows over a succession of ridges, wave systems from one crest may interfere with those from the following crest. In some cases the waves may tend to cancel out but in others, where the waves are in phase, enhanced vertical motions may result.

Convection currents
Thermal currents resulting from the heating of the atmosphere at the ground were noted in Section 3.8. They often appear in the form of small irregular eddies which, rising from the ground and being carried along by the wind, are practically indistinguishable from the eddies of frictional turbulence, or they may take the form of more pronounced upward and downward currents, possibly arranged in a regular pattern. Differential heating of the ground has the effect of localizing vertical currents; upward currents tend to originate over the warmer parts of the ground such as dry soil, rock or sand, while downward currents tend to be associated with relatively cooler patches such as grassland, wooded areas and especially water

surfaces. The 'bumps' so produced are often marked and their association with variations in terrain is familiar to pilots. Convection currents and bumpiness also occur at other levels in the troposphere, usually in association with cloud formation, whenever the lapse rate becomes unstable.

The height to which convection currents extend is controlled largely by the lapse rate of temperature. A marked inversion with base at a height of a few thousand feet limits the upward penetration of convection currents originating at the surface. In such cases considerable, even intense, bumpiness may be experienced from ground level up to the base of the inversion, while the air above remains smooth. On the other hand, when the lapse rate in the free atmosphere is less stable, or if the surface heating is sufficient to overcome the stable tendency, the vertical currents may become very strong and perhaps extend through the entire troposphere. Wherever upward currents exist there must be compensating downcurrents in the vicinity, but these are usually spread over a wider area and so are less intense; these downcurrents are often found in the clear air between the clouds. The bumpiness accompanying extreme currents is severe; even the downdraughts may cause an aircraft to lose height rapidly. In these conditions ample clearance must be allowed above ground, particularly when flying over hilly country, while conditions for landing and take-off become difficult, especially for light aircraft.

Downcurrents frequently continue below the base of active cumulonimbus clouds. When the cloud base is below about 2000 ft these currents are gradually changed from near-vertical to become near-horizontal closer to the ground, the flow extending radially outward from the cloud. This effect may produce low-level wind shear which can prove hazardous during take-off and landing. Wind shear is examined in more detail in the Section 5.6.

Pronounced ascending currents, as well as many of less intensity, are responsible for the development of convection clouds and will be further considered in the next chapter.

Widespread vertical motion

So far we have considered the vertical motion associated with disturbances of relatively small horizontal dimensions caused by turbulence, ground contour or local convection currents and covering areas of at most a few tens of kilometres in extent. We now consider more widespread vertical motion. Even the largest types of pressure systems, the large anticyclones and depressions, involve vertical as well as horizontal motion, but being spread across extensive areas, the upward or downward velocity is very small, being of the order of a few feet per minute (as against feet per second for some other vertical motions), and its direct effect on aircraft is insignificant. The importance of this type of motion lies in its effects on the weather, for the motion may continue for several days and, though slow, may cause large masses of air to rise or fall through many thousands of feet. The problem is bound up with the general theory of depressions and anticyclones and is discussed in this connection in later chapters, but it is appropriate to consider some of the more general characteristics at this stage.

Divergence and convergence

Fig. 31 illustrates the types of motions known respectively as divergence and convergence. Air moving towards the point C from opposite sides constitutes an example of horizontal convergence, while in the vicinity of A there is horizontal divergence. There is in such cases a tendency for air to accumulate at C which must be exactly counterbalanced by vertical motion at these points; if the horizontal flow is taking place in the lower levels, the vertical motion must necessarily be upwards. Similarly at A the net effect of horizontal motion is to remove air, its place being taken by air descending from above. The figure also shows schematically that vertical motion at the surface is linked to divergence and convergence in the upper air; convergence aloft being associated with divergence at the surface and vice versa. Opposing motion is not essential for the production of convergence or divergence, as may be seen from the conditions of Fig. 31 by superimposing a horizontal wind strong enough to overcome the flow in one direction. An example is provided by wind blowing from the sea over a low-lying land surface. As the air passes over the land, the wind speed is reduced by the greater friction with the result that air arrives at the coastline faster than it is removed inland; the air is forced upwards and sometimes results in a line of cloud parallel with the shore.

The association of convergence with ascending motion and of divergence with descent of air holds not only near the surface but also at higher levels. In fact dynamical considerations indicate, and it is certainly found in practice, that the large-scale movements of convergence, ascending motion and cyclonic circulation are usually linked together in one system and divergence, descent and anticyclonic motion in another.

Vertical motion on a large scale may have marked effects on the lapse rate of temperature. Thus descending air is subject to adiabatic heating; moreover the air must at some level spread out horizontally, or diverge. The lower layers of the subsided air accordingly become warm and dry compared with that air immediately below which has not taken part in the descent. In this way an inversion of

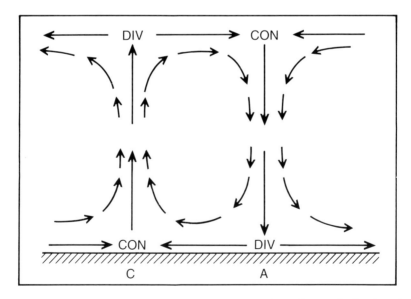

Figure 31.   Horizontal convergence and divergence near the surface, and related vertical motion.

temperature is formed, known as a 'subsidence inversion'; it is usually recognizable from the results of an upper-air sounding by the presence of dry air above the inversion. On the other hand, general ascending motion often leads to a steepening of the lapse rate, but since in this case condensation and cloud formation are usually involved, its discussion will be deferred to a later chapter (Section 6.5)

Non-divergence of geostrophic wind

Suppose PQ, P'Q' (Fig. 32) are two neighbouring isobars, not necessarily straight and parallel, and that the flow of air between them is geostrophic at all points. The rate at which air is transported across the section PP', supposed of unit vertical thickness, is $V_1 \times \rho_1 \times PP'$ where V_1 is the geostrophic wind speed at this point, while the transport across QQ' is $V_2 \times \rho_2 \times QQ'$. By the geostrophic equation (8), if the pressure is p on PQ and p' on P'Q'

$$V_1 = (p - p')/(PP' \times 2\Omega \sin \phi)$$

with a similar expression for V_2; therefore

$$V_1 \rho_1 \times PP' = (p - p')/(2\Omega \sin \phi) = V_2 \rho_2 \times QQ'.$$

The mass of air carried across PP' is thus identical with the flow across QQ', and since in geostrophic motion there is no flow across the isobars, there can be no tendency to accumulate air within the area PQQ'P'. The motion therefore remains horizontal, and this is always so when the winds are geostrophic. This result is expressed by saying that geostrophic winds are non-divergent. Thus the spreading apart or closing together of isobars do not by themselves imply the existence of divergence or convergence. The terms 'diffluence' and 'confluence' respectively have been introduced to denote such changes in the pattern not only of the isobars but also of isopleths such as streamlines and thickness lines.

It follows from this result that when vertical motion is present the horizontal wind cannot be exactly geostrophic. The importance of vertical motion for cloud and precipitation has been emphasised and it must follow that such conditions are necessarily related to departures from geostrophic flow. Regions in which the wind is not geostrophic and in which vertical motion occurs can be recognized with the aid of synoptic charts, as will be explained in Chapter 19, but quantitatively the problem is one of great difficulty. This is because the geostrophic departure — the

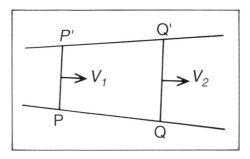

Figure 32.   Non-divergence of geostrophic wind.

'ageostrophic' component (Greek prefix 'a' meaning 'not') — and the associated vertical component are frequently too small to be directly measured.

Divergence and convergence due to surface friction
One effect of surface friction is to reduce the air flow near the surface to below the geostrophic value and to cause a flow of air across the isobars (ageostrophic) towards the side of lower pressure. When the total flow across a closed isobar is considered, it is seen (as in Fig. 33) to lead to convergence towards the centre of a low-pressure system and divergence away from the centre of a high. However, this type of convergence is confined to the friction layer and calculation shows that the effect is not of much importance. While it may perhaps account for a certain amount of cloud in depressions, frictional convergence is entirely inadequate to explain any but the lightest rainfall, so that other causes of vertical motion must be sought.

Divergence and convergence due to changing pressure
The geostrophic wind results from a state of balance between the pressure gradient and Coriolis force, but this balance is not achieved instantaneously. Consider air which is accelerated from rest by the pressure gradient resulting from a local fall of pressure; the Coriolis force, being proportional to the wind speed, is small at first and the deviating effect slight, so that in the early stages the wind is directed across the isobars towards the region of falling pressure. If the rate of fall of pressure is maintained, the lag in the adjustment of wind to pressure gradient continues and an ageostrophic component continues to flow towards the region of falling pressure. Similarly wind may be shown to have a component directed outwards from an area of rising pressure. The speed of these ageostrophic components not uncommonly amounts to about 10 KT; unlike divergence or convergence due to surface friction, they may affect a great depth of atmosphere. The upward motion associated with such convergence is sufficient to produce thick masses of cloud and continuous precipitation but even so the magnitude of the vertical currents, which are spread over a large area, is far too small to have any noticeable direct effect on the flight of aircraft.

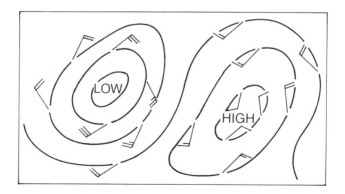

Figure 33.   Convergence and divergence due to friction.

5.6 WIND SHEAR

Definitions

Before considering the occurrence of wind shear in an aviation context, it is necessary to define some of the terms. Strictly speaking, wind shear is the rate of change of the wind in space, considered as a vector. Wind shear can therefore arise from changes in wind speed or wind direction or in simultaneous changes in both. This leads to the following definitions:

Vertical shear is the change in the wind velocity with height; for example, as would be measured by two anemometers mounted at different heights on a single tower. A typical value at low levels might be 1 knot per 100 feet.

Horizontal shear is the change in the wind with horizontal distance normal to flow; for example, as might be measured by two anemometers at the same height along a runway. A typical value at low levels would be 1 knot per 1000 feet.

Updraught or downdraught shear is the change in vertical air motions with horizontal distance.

Aviation aspects

Wind shear has always been a factor for consideration during take-off and in the final phases of landing but it has become a greater hazard for modern jet aircraft. This is primarily because their greater inertia causes them to maintain their speed relative to the ground when changing winds are encountered, resulting in air speed and lift variations which may be critical. Jet engines are slower to respond to changes in throttle setting; with a propeller-driven aircraft a sudden increase of power increases airflow over the wings to give immediate extra lift. Furthermore, the higher approach speeds of modern aircraft increase the suddenness of any wind shear effects, leaving the pilots less time to interpret such visual clues as there may be and to respond appropriately. Since most modern aircraft types approach at near minimum-drag speed any sudden change in air speed will increase drag and complicate recovery.

The significance of wind variations to aircraft handling depends critically on the spatial scale of the variations. Short-term fluctuations in the wind are common at low altitudes and are often self cancelling; they will simply result in bumpiness and are unlikely to cause prolonged excursions from the intended flight path and target air speed; they may be described as turbulence (Section 5.3). Variations over large distances will not give rise to difficulties and may not even be noticed. It is variations over the intermediate distances which produce the phenomenon of potentially hazardous wind shear.

For aviation purposes the following definitions have been formulated to distinguish between wind shear and turbulence:

Wind shear: Variations in the wind along the aircraft flight path of a pattern, intensity and duration that displace an aircraft abruptly from its intended path such that substantial control action is required.

Turbulence: Variations in the wind along the aircraft flight path of a pattern, intensity and duration that disturb the aircraft's attitude about its major axis but do not significantly alter its flight path.

For a landing aircraft a continuously decreasing head-wind component, if not counteracted, will cause the aircraft to drop below the target descent path and to land short of the threshold; a continuously increasing head-wind component will cause it to go above the planned descent path leading to a late touchdown and possible overrun. On take-off, a continuously decreasing head-wind will result in the climb-out gradient being reduced and in extreme cases loss of lift may be enough to cause the aircraft to fly into the ground; a continuously increasing head-wind component will, of course, present no problem.

These linear wind shears are not, however, the most hazardous. Situations are possible in which the head-wind component begins to increase, stops increasing and then decreases to below the original value. It will be appreciated that in this case any actions taken by the pilot to counter the effects of the initial shear may need to be reversed as a result of the later encounter and in such a situation the subsequent actions required of the pilot will call for larger changes of attitude and power than would have been required by the first encounter. This type of occurrence is sometimes referred to as a 'ramp pair' or 'double ramp' and constitutes a particularly hazardous situation.

Occurrence of wind shear
In any strong wind situation there will be an appreciable shear between the free flow at the top of the friction layer and the retarded wind flow close to the ground. This may be regarded as the normal state of affairs and with knowledge of the gradient and surface wind speeds the presence of wind shear may be anticipated and allowed for; a landing aircraft will often experience a continuously decreasing head-wind component. However, even this simple situation may be aggravated by fluctuations of wind speed and/or direction which owe their origin to disturbance of the flow near the ground by topographical features which may be natural or man-made; large hangars on airfield perimeters are an obvious hazard. Less predictable shears may be associated with the passage of sharp frontal boundaries or such apparently minor features as sea-breeze fronts. However, the most hazardous wind shear situations occur in association with thunderstorms and a particularly dangerous phenomenon is the microburst.

The microburst
The flow near the base of a cumulonimbus cloud is always likely to be turbulent but in some cases the flow becomes organized in such a way that strong thunderstorm downdraughts spread out horizontally just above the ground to form a sharply defined 'gust front' or 'microburst'. It is in such circumstances that the 'ramp pair' may be encountered, head-wind component increasing suddenly as the gust front is encountered, being replaced by a vertical downdraught beneath the storm cloud, and finally changing to a tail-wind component as the aircraft heads away from the downdraught (Fig. 34). Microbursts do occur in the British Isles but the more spectacular examples are usually associated with the severe thunderstorms of warmer climes. There is a high concentration of microburst incident reports from the USA, probably related to the higher incidence of aircraft movements as much as to the incidence of the phenomenon itself. A special investigation of 75 USA microburst incidents revealed a typical horizontal dimension of 1–3 km, and a lifetime of 5–15 minutes with a period of most severe wind lasting 2–4 minutes. It

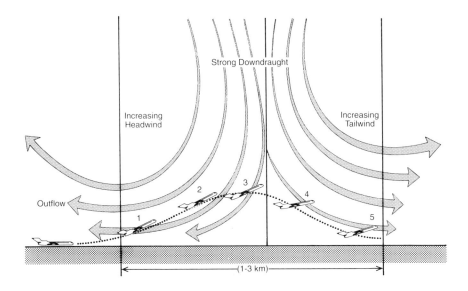

Figure 34. Flight through a microburst. An aircraft flying into the outflow encounters increasing headwind (1, 2), which boosts air speed and increases lift. The aircraft is buffeted by downdraught (3) and ultimately encounters tail wind (4, 5), reducing air speed and lift. (McCarthy and Serafin 1984.)

was found that microbursts tended to intensify in the first 5 minutes after downdraught impact with the ground. The average wind differential (i.e. head-wind to tail-wind shear) for an aircraft in flight through a microburst was found to be 25 m s^{-1} (about 50 KT) and the maximum 48 m s^{-1} (about 93 KT).

Wind-shear detection
Identification of the microburst as a factor in a number of fatal air accidents has prompted ongoing research into methods of detection. Low-level wind-shear alert systems (LLWAS) have been devised which detect sudden changes from an array of strategically sited sensors in the airfield vicinity. Such systems have proved effective in recognizing ground-level wind changes but since the sensors are ground-based, the systems lack the capability to forewarn of impending dangers from mid-air shears such as precede the microburst.

5.7 JET STREAMS

Jet streams are strong, narrow currents of air, characterized by strong vertical and lateral wind shears. The velocity at the centre of such streams is commonly about 100 KT and may reach 200 KT at times over Europe and the North Atlantic, while speeds approaching 300 KT have been recorded near the western Pacific seaboard. Typically, a jet stream is some thousands of kilometres in length, a few hundred kilometres wide and some 10 000 feet in depth. The wind velocity in jet streams results mainly from large latitudinal temperature gradients extending through a great depth of the atmosphere contributing a large thermal wind component.

Two major areas of jet stream occurrence in the upper troposphere are the subtropical jet streams near latitudes 30° and the jet streams associated from time to time with the polar frontal zones of middle latitudes in each hemisphere (frontal zones are discussed fully in Chapter 16). These jet streams have a generally westerly flow, but marked deviation from west can occur. There is also evidence for a jet stream with a predominantly easterly flow in equatorial latitudes, mainly in those longitudes where the upper easterlies are displaced some 10° or so from the equator. In all of these jet streams the maximum speeds are usually reached just below the level of the tropopause, i.e. the equatorial jet at about 100 hPa, the subtropical jet at about 200 hPa and the polar-front jets at about 250–300 hPa. In addition, there is a belt of very strong westerly winds (the 'polar night jet') in the stratosphere above 50 hPa over high latitudes in winter.

Jet streams of mid-latitudes
The mid-latitude jet streams, like many other features of the atmosphere, show great variation between one jet and another, and any one jet stream displays variations from day to day and place to place. Though jet streams result invariably from the existence of powerful thermal gradients, corresponding surface fronts are not always easily identified, and the location of the jet axis with respect to surface fronts varies from case to case. As a rule though the jet may be expected to lie more or less parallel with the surface fronts and over the surface cold air. Fig. 35 shows

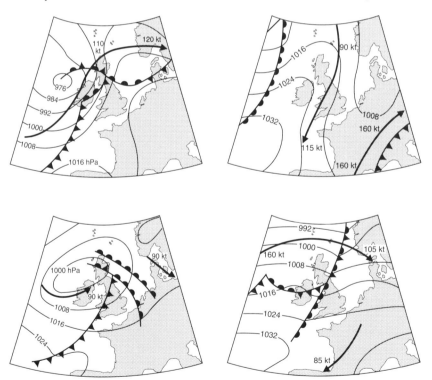

Figure 35.   Association of jet stream with surface fronts. Broad arrows depict a typical jet-stream configuration at 300 hPa. Wind speeds are in knots, and the contours are at 1000 hPa.

some typical jet-stream locations with respect to surface fronts over the British Isles.

A cross-section of a polar-front jet stream is shown at Fig. 36. Note that the vertical scale is much exaggerated; drawn strictly to scale the jet core would appear as a narrow ribbon of strong winds. The horizontal gradient throughout the troposphere can be clearly seen. The tropopause is higher above the warm air than above the cold air and the core of strong winds lies beneath the warm tropopause. Above the jet core the horizontal temperature gradient, and hence the thermal wind, reverses and the wind speed diminishes with further increase of height. It will be noted that the decrease of speed towards the colder tropospheric side of the jet is very well marked.

Large variations of wind speed occur along the jet axis. Within the jet core separate jet maxima may often be recognized; these 'jet streaks' may retain their identity for some time as they move downstream, i.e. along the jet axis.

Subtropical jet stream

The subtropical jet is located entirely within the tropical air mass and is not associated with any surface fronts. Its core lies near the 200 hPa level below the tropical tropopause and often in the vicinity of the break between this and the tropopause of middle latitudes. The position of the subtropical jet is less variable than that of the polar-front jet; the strong westerly flow shows up well on the mean charts from 500 hPa to 100 hPa over Eurasia in January, with the strongest mean winds over Japan at the 200 hPa level. In the southern hemisphere, the mean position of the jet is at 20 °S and on mean charts for July this westerly stream is seen to have a maximum of 90 KT over central Australia at 200 hPa.

5.8 CLEAR AIR TURBULENCE

The occurrence of turbulence within the first few thousand feet of the earth's surface has already been seen to have a dual origin, frictional and thermal (Section 5.3). The former type depends on friction with the ground and is confined to the friction layer. The thermal type on the other hand, while often originating in convection currents at the surface, can develop upwards to a height which depends on the lapse rate of temperature and, when extending to a high level, is always associated with convective clouds. Turbulence of a convective nature may also originate occasionally from thermal instability in the upper air, but again its presence is revealed by cloud. Nevertheless flying conditions in the upper air may be bumpy even in the absence of clouds. This type of clear air turbulence (or CAT) appears to arise from internal friction of the atmosphere which leads to a breakdown of smooth flow either when the rate of change of wind with height surpasses a certain limit dependent upon the lapse rate, or when the rate of change of wind in the horizontal becomes sufficiently great.

Attention was first drawn to the occurrence of clear air turbulence in the upper troposphere, though it seems that it can occur at any height, merging in the lower layers into the more familiar types. It is, however, most important at high altitudes because there, in clear air, it is relatively unexpected, being encountered without any visual warning such as would be provided by the presence of cloud. Turbulence

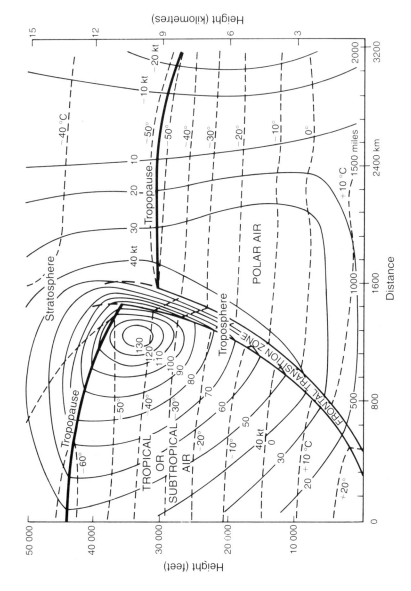

Figure 36. Cross-section across a polar front jet stream. Solid lines are isotachs (knots) and broken lines isotherms (°C). Positive wind speeds have a component out of the plane of the page.

(of whatever origin) is important to aviation for several reasons. It may cause fracture of some part of the aircraft, due either to particularly severe gusts or to more moderate gustiness continued over a long period; also at high altitudes a severe gust may be the cause of a stall, and the resulting loss of control can be dangerous, especially for a large aircraft; finally, air travel is uncomfortable in turbulent conditions.

Observations of clear air turbulence are made either qualitatively by an observer in an aircraft or by use of an accelerometer. The severity of the turbulence affecting an aircraft is proportional to the air speed but depends also to some extent on other characteristics of the aircraft as well as on the nature of the turbulence itself. The accelerometer records only the vertical displacement of the aircraft; the record is interpreted in terms of a vertical gust. More precisely it is expressed in terms of the equivalent velocity of a sharp-edged gust; this is defined as that instantaneous vertical velocity which superimposed on a steady horizontal wind would produce the measured acceleration of the aircraft. The acceleration is then directly proportional to the equivalent gust velocity and to the air speed.

Much more needs to be known about the cause and incidence of clear air turbulence. Although it decreases with height above the tropopause, it does not necessarily become negligible in the stratosphere.

Turbulence is associated with strong vertical and horizontal wind shear. High-level turbulence appears to occur in patches with horizontal dimensions of about 50 km or more and an average vertical extent around 2000 ft, although it is sometimes as little as 50 to 100 ft.

Clear air turbulence is frequently associated with a jet stream; a preferred region appears to be near or below the jet axis on the low-pressure side with a secondary maximum above the axis on the anticyclonic side. However, not all jet streams are turbulent. Clear air turbulence may also occur at high levels in standing waves over mountains and hills. Jet streams passing over mountains usually produce waves of considerable amplitude and thus increase the risk of turbulence. Turbulence is also associated with sharp upper troughs and occasionally with upper ridges. It is associated with cumulonimbus clouds and is to be expected above cumulonimbus tops.

Most of the reports of CAT are of light or moderate character; a study of about 4500 North Atlantic flights found that slight or greater turbulence was present during 10%, moderate or greater during 1.25% and severe during 0.013% of the time flown. A reporting scale for the intensity of turbulence is included in Chapter 12.

5.9 WIND AND HEAT TRANSFERENCE

The processes by which heat is first absorbed in the atmosphere, then redistributed horizontally and vertically and finally re-radiated to space are of considerable theoretical interest and are intimately related both to day-to-day motion of the atmosphere and to the general circulation. The radiative balance of the atmosphere as a whole was discussed in Section 3.4; on average the atmosphere neither gains nor loses heat, and since the only means of heat exchange with outer space is by radiation, the absorption of short-wave radiation from the sun must be exactly balanced by the long-wave radiation escaping from the earth's surface and atmosphere. We have seen how the absorption of solar radiation takes place for the most part at the earth's surface; on account of the small declination of the sun in low latitudes, much more radiation is absorbed per unit area of the earth's surface in low latitudes than in high, when averaged over the year. Investigation shows that the outgoing terrestrial radiation is only a little greater in low than in high latitudes. Consequently between the equator and about latitude 35° more radiation is absorbed than is emitted, while in higher latitudes there is on average a net loss of heat by radiation.

Thus, there is a source of heat near the surface in low latitudes but a 'sink' or area from which most of the heat is lost, is found in the polar regions. In order that a steady distribution of temperature should be maintained, the excess heat must somehow be conveyed from the tropical source to the polar sink. This transference is brought about mainly by wind, that is to say, by advection. Heat is transported polewards by streams of relatively warm air, but these displacements must be compensated by the movement equatorwards of air from high latitudes; hence in middle latitudes both warm and cold air masses are brought into proximity and their interaction creates the variable cyclonic and anticyclonic circulations which are a characteristic feature of those regions. Another effect of the wind is to generate ocean currents and these also make appreciable contribution to the poleward flux of heat.

Apart from the effects of radiation, exchanges of heat in the vertical direction are brought about directly or indirectly by means of vertical currents. In this respect the effect of molecular motions is negligible except for the transfer of heat between the earth's surface and air actually in contact with it, i.e. by conduction. A more effective agent for the vertical transfer of heat is turbulence and even more effective, when conditions are suitable, is convection. The turbulent transfer of heat, which also operates horizontally, is nevertheless a small-scale process seldom appreciably affecting layers of air more than a few thousand feet in thickness; on the other hand convection may affect the whole depth of the troposphere. Both horizontal and vertical currents also produce a redistribution of heat by the transport of water vapour; thus latent heat absorbed by evaporation at the surface in one place is released by condensation in the upper air at some other place. The whole process of the redistribution of heat in the atmosphere, including the exchanges between the atmosphere and the earth's surface, is extremely complicated but in many ways of fundamental importance for the understanding of weather.

5.10 FLIGHT PLANNING

In order that the time of flight of an aircraft on a given route can be determined, the ground speed must be known at each point and this depends on the wind speed and direction at each point. A knowledge of the expected upper-air winds is therefore required, whether a single flight is to be made (forecast winds required) or whether planning the setting up of a new route (climatological winds needed). One other important meteorological parameter which is required for flight planning is the temperature along the route. The performance of jet engines depends markedly on temperature and therefore a knowledge of the expected temperature is required to calculate the likely fuel consumption. The most efficient height at which to fly on a given route depends not only on the meteorological factors of wind and temperature, but also on the aircraft weight and its performance characteristics.

Equivalent headwinds
One method of handling calculations of the effect of the wind is by use of the equivalent headwind concept. The ground speed at each point along the flight track depends on the wind components along and at right angles to the track. The amount by which air speed exceeds the ground speed at any point of a track is known as the equivalent headwind at that point. When this concept is applied to the route as a whole it leads to the following definition:

> The equivalent headwind over a route is defined as that constant wind which, blowing along the track at all points, results in the same average ground speed as that produced by the actual distribution of wind at the time of flight.

The wind information for the route, when expressed in this way, is thus reduced to a single figure, as far as the average speed and time of flight are affected. A negative value of the equivalent headwind is to be interpreted as an equivalent tailwind. It should be noted that there is no single value of equivalent headwind for a route as the result depends on the air speed and therefore on the particular aircraft concerned.

The above ideas lead to great simplification in preparing statistics for a given route when approximately the same track is to be flown on each occasion. From the frequency distribution of wind strength and direction at points of the route in the neighbourhood of the operating height, it is possible to deduce the frequency distribution of equivalent headwinds, whence a table or diagram may be prepared showing, for example, how often any particular value of equivalent headwind or tailwind is likely to be exceeded in a given period. Such a diagram is illustrated in Fig. 37 for a great circle route London to New York in December. Typical air speeds have been used in the computation; the values used are shown at the right-hand side of the diagram. An operator planning a regular service on this route may readily assess the frequency of headwinds that are within the performance capability of a particular aircraft. At 30 000 ft an aircraft needs the endurance to cope with headwinds up to 85 KT if the service is to be maintained at least 95% of the time, noting that adverse headwinds are more common in December than at any other month. This method can also provide a convenient comparison between alternative tracks to aid selection of the optimum route for regularity or fuel efficiency.

Estimates for eastbound flights differ slightly from those for westbound flights because the effect of the wind component at right angles to the track is always adverse. This adverse effect due to drift depends on the airspeed but is a relatively small component, hence the airspeed used in calculations is not critical and results are valid for an approximate range of air speed of -25% to $+50\%$. The curve on the left of Fig. 37 represents the tailwinds for eastbound flights that are least advantageous on 95% of occasions. Using a computer archive of climatolological mean winds it is possible to calculate the mean equivalent headwind for any specified route at a selection of altitudes for each month. It should be noted that for an aircraft with low airspeed, say less than 200 KT, the equivalent headwind for a complete route can be a significant proportion of the airspeed and can therefore be a

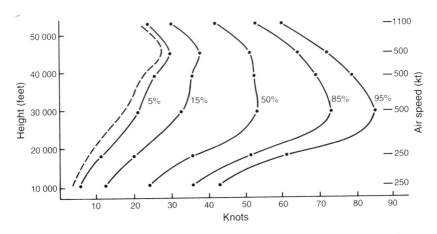

Figure 37. Mean equivalent headwinds — London to New York in December. Continuous lines represent headwinds for westbound flights less than the indicated value on nominated percentage of occasions. The dashed line represents tailwinds for eastbound flights greater than the indicated value on 95% of occasions.

critical factor in determining whether such a flight is feasible, either as routine or on a particular occasion.

Computation of flight plan

Given forecast values of the wind and temperature along an intended flight track, it is possible to calculate the expected time of transit and the amount of fuel required for the flight. These calculations can be performed manually but increasingly, operators are using computers for this purpose, using meteorological data in digital form from an appropriate meteorological centre. With the high cost of fuel, more attention is being paid to producing accurate flight plans. If excess fuel is carried on a flight, more fuel is used during the flight because of the additional weight and this leads to a financial penalty. However, for safety reasons sufficient fuel must always be carried to allow for diversions for bad weather and other contingencies.

The time of flight of a given aircraft between two terminals varies to a considerable extent with the winds encountered. On long flights especially it becomes desirable to avoid strong headwinds; a route can usually be found which, although geographically longer than the direct route, can be flown in less time. While there are many factors other than wind which together determine track selection on any occasion (notably air traffic control restrictions) it is usually practicable to effect an appreciable saving of time by careful choice of track. Once the winds over an extensive area covering the route have been forecast, the computation of the quickest track is a navigational matter and beyond the scope of this handbook. Computations of minimum-time tracks for the route London to New York show that they often vary widely from the great circle and change from day to day according to the winds. Such variations are very inconvenient operationally. An alternative procedure is to lay down several fixed tracks for a given route and to select the most appropriate one for any particular occasion, having regard not only to time of flight but also to other factors such as avoidance of bad weather. The most suitable track of the set will usually be apparent from inspection of the current and forecast weather charts; it will avoid adverse headwinds as far as possible and will take account of the variation of wind in the vertical as well as horizontally. In cases of doubt the times of flight of two or more routes can be computed or, if a flight planning computer is being used, the optimum track may be selected.

It must be reiterated that an aircraft's performance and its most economical cruising speed both vary considerably with the altitude at which the flight is made. On this account the quickest route and operating height do not necessarily coincide with that method of flying the route which will effect the greatest economy in fuel consumption. Indeed, the final flight plan has to be a compromise between the aims of achieving minimum time, minimum cost as regards fuel, avoidance of bad weather and satisfying the constraints of aircraft performance and air traffic control.

CHAPTER 6

FORMATION OF CLOUD AND PRECIPITATION

6.1 WATER IN THE ATMOSPHERE

The water vapour of the atmosphere must be transformed into water drops or ice crystals before cloud can appear, and the cloud particles must increase still further in size before they are able to fall out as precipitation. Before going on to describe the methods by which cloud and precipitation are formed from the vapour, it is necessary to define more fully than has been done hitherto the terms used to specify the state of the atmosphere in respect of its water vapour content, and to consider the changes of state between vapour, water and ice.

The dry air and water vapour composing the atmosphere may each be considered as separately satisfying the laws of gases. The total pressure is the sum of the partial pressures of these two constituents (Section 4.2). The partial pressure of the vapour, or more briefly the vapour pressure, is denoted by e and the total pressure as usual by p, so that the partial pressure of the dry air is given by $(p - e)$.

When dry air is confined in contact with a surface of water or ice, evaporation takes place and the vapour pressure increases. At any one temperature there is a limit to the amount of vapour that can be taken up in this way. When this limit is reached the air is said to be saturated and the vapour pressure has reached its maximum value, the saturation vapour pressure e_s, for that particular temperature. If the vapour pressure is less than the saturation vapour pressure then the air is unsaturated.

Apart from vapour pressure there are several other ways of specifying the state of the atmosphere in regard to its vapour content: the more important of these are:

Humidity mixing ratio (r) (see Appendix I) is the mass of vapour contained in unit mass of dry air. In meteorology it is usually expressed as the number of grams of vapour per kilogram of dry air (g kg^{-1}). Isopleths of humidity mixing ratio for saturated air are shown as pecked lines on the tephigram.

Relative humidity is the percentage degree of saturation. It may be defined as 100 times the ratio of the actual vapour pressure to the saturation vapour pressure at the same temperature, or $100 e/e_s$.

Vapour concentration or *absolute humidity* is the mass of vapour contained in unit volume. It is usually expressed as the number of grams of vapour per cubic metre (g m^{-3}).

Dew-point is the temperature to which moist air must be cooled in order to just reach the condition of saturation with respect to a plane water surface. Further cooling results in condensation on solid surfaces. Even slight cooling beyond the dew-point will ensure condensation on dust particles in the air, forming fog or cloud. Fog may form even in unsaturated air, as will be explained later, and its presence should not be taken as indicative that the temperature is at or below the dew-point.

Frost-point is the temperature to which moist air must be cooled in order to just reach the condition of saturation with respect to a plane ice surface. Further cooling induces deposition of ice in the form of hoar-frost on solid surfaces, including other ice surfaces.

Wet-bulb temperature is the lowest temperature to which air may be cooled by evaporation of water. It is measured with a wet-bulb thermometer (Section 11.4); in conjunction with the dry-bulb temperature it forms the standard method of measuring humidity at the earth's surface. As heat is absorbed in the process of evaporation, the wet-bulb becomes cooled below the air temperature unless the air is saturated.

Water vapour can change directly into ice, a process known as sublimation, and conversely, ice evaporates directly into vapour. Moreover, water droplets in suspension readily remain liquid or supercooled at temperatures below 0 °C. Consequently at such temperatures it is necessary to consider the saturation vapour pressure not only with respect to ice but also with respect to supercooled water. It is found that the saturation vapour pressure over ice is slightly less than that over supercooled water at the same temperature (see Table 5); hence if unsaturated air is cooled progressively below 0 °C, the frost point is reached while the air is still unsaturated with respect to water.

TABLE 5. *Saturation vapour pressure (SVP) (hPa) over water and ice*

Temperature (°C)	−60	−50	−40	−30	−20	−10	0	10	20	30	40
SVP over water	—	0.06	0.19	0.51	1.25	2.86	6.11	12.3	23.4	42.4	73.8
SVP over ice	0.01	0.04	0.13	0.38	1.03	2.60	6.11	—	—	—	—

From Table 5 it is seen that the saturation vapour pressure increases rapidly with temperature so that warm air, when saturated, holds more water vapour than cold air.

The amount of vapour present in a given mass of air can be varied only by means of evaporation or condensation and (at a given pressure) does not depend on the temperature unless this is reduced below the dew-point, when the excess vapour is condensed. In contrast, the relative humidity varies widely with temperature. A rise of temperature implies a rise in the saturation vapour pressure and consequently a fall in relative humidity, although this may be partly offset by evaporation from the surface or from vegetation; conversely a fall of temperature increases the relative humidity unless the air is already saturated.

The diurnal variation of temperature over land is accordingly reflected in a diurnal variation of relative humidity, the lowest values occurring at the warmest time of the day and the highest at night when, if 100% is approached, fog may readily form. Even in desert regions the relative humidity at the surface may reach 100% at night due to intense radiative cooling, so giving heavy dew or even fog. The lowest values of relative humidity occur in air subjected to prolonged heating such as might result from insolation over dry land, from advection over a warm, dry surface or from adiabatic subsidence; the highest values occur during prolonged evaporation from the surface, as when air is in contact with the sea or wet ground, or as a result of cooling by radiation, advection or adiabatic ascent. On account of the prevalence of convection, air in the upper troposphere is frequently near saturation. In the lower stratosphere extremely low relative humidities are the rule; in temperate latitudes the average is about 2% and it rarely exceeds 10%.

Condensation, sublimation and freezing

When the air temperature is reduced below the dew-point, water droplets condense on minute particles suspended in the air which act as condensation nuclei. Without such particles the vapour pressure would surpass the saturation value without condensation, i.e. the vapour would become supersaturated, but in practice suitable nuclei are invariably present in large numbers so that supersaturation with respect to water is not likely to be great. As the condensation nuclei are often hygroscopic, that is, having a special affinity for water, they may bring about condensation even before saturation is reached; this explains the occurrence of mist and fog with relative humidity below 100%. The main origin of the nuclei is probably the combustion products of domestic, industrial and other fires. Sea salt particles probably contribute about a tenth of the nuclei involved in droplet formation.

When the vapour is cooled below the frost-point, it may be that ice crystals are formed on sublimation nuclei. Laboratory evidence indicates that condensation does not take place until after the vapour has become saturated with respect to water and the first product is then a supercooled droplet; subsequently the droplet may freeze spontaneously if it contains a solid nucleus which is active as a 'freezing nucleus', presumably because its shape is similar to that of an ice crystal. In any case, the rarity, if not the complete absence, of sublimation nuclei in natural conditions means that on cooling, water vapour readily becomes supersaturated with respect to ice while still unsaturated with respect to water, a condition which is of common occurrence. If on the other hand ice crystals are already present, having perhaps fallen from higher levels, and if the vapour pressure exceeds the saturation value with respect to ice, then direct sublimation takes place on to these ice crystals.

Supercooled drops are in an unstable state and usually start to freeze when brought into contact with ice particles or other objects; this aspect will be considered further in relation to the formation of ice on aircraft (Chapter 8). When freezing of supercooled droplets takes place spontaneously, the larger droplets tend to freeze more readily than the smaller ones. Generally, the freezing of droplets becomes increasingly probable as the temperature continues to fall. In cloud a few frozen particles may be present at a temperature of $-10\ °C$. At still lower temperatures the number of ice particles increases and at $-32\ °C$ there is a further marked increase, but it is not until the temperature falls to about $-40\ °C$ that freezing is likely to become general. Thus cloud at temperatures between $0\ °C$ and $-10\ °C$ may be considered as consisting almost entirely of supercooled drops; between $-10\ °C$ and $-40\ °C$ there are both supercooled drops and ice particles, the latter being more numerous the lower the temperature; while cloud at temperatures below $-40\ °C$ consists mainly or entirely of ice crystals, giving the cirrus types, although there are exceptional cases of water-droplet clouds existing even below $-40\ °C$.

Clouds with strong upcurrents often contain a relatively high proportion of water drops which are carried up before they have an opportunity to freeze, but the ice crystals grow more rapidly than the water drops because adiabatic cooling of the ascending air maintains a state of saturation with respect to water and therefore supersaturation with respect to ice.

6.2 GENERAL CAUSES OF CLOUD AND PRECIPITATION

A cloud is formed by the condensation of water vapour into droplets, or occasionally into ice crystals. The immediate cause of condensation to water drops is the reduction of air temperature below the dew-point. In nature this may be effected in any of the following ways:

(i)   loss of heat by conduction to a cold surface,
(ii) loss of heat by radiation from the air, or
(iii) adiabatic cooling due to ascent.

The first process may result only in a deposition of dew on the cold surface (or of hoar-frost if the temperature is below freezing point) but if the air near the surface is subject to slight turbulent mixing the cooling may spread upwards and temperature may then fall below the dew-point through an appreciable depth. Condensation takes place within the air itself and a cloud is formed resting on the surface: this cloud is known as either mist or fog according to its opacity and will be dealt with in Chapter 9 together with other causes of reduced visibility.

Direct cooling by radiation from the air itself, or rather from the water vapour contained in the air (process (ii)), may modify the formation of fog and cloud, but its precise importance is not easy to estimate. When a fog or cloud has formed, radiation from its upper surface may affect its further development but it is doubtful whether radiation from the air is ever the sole cause of condensation.

Apart, therefore, from fog due to surface cooling, the methods of cloud formation reduce to only one — adiabatic cooling by reduction of pressure — which is almost entirely associated with vertical motion. The different types of cloud are then to be accounted for by various modes of upward motion which, in accordance with the discussion in Section 5.5, may be classified as follows:

(i)   turbulence,
(ii) orographic ascent,
(iii) convection, and
(iv) slow widespread ascent.

Two or more of these effects may occur simultaneously, giving a wide variety of cloud types which do not necessarily fall neatly into any simple class.

Condensation level
When cloud is formed by adiabatic cooling, the process can be followed on the tephigram as illustrated in Fig. 38. Air with a temperature of 14 °C is represented by the point T, and the dew-point temperature, 8 °C is marked as D on the same isobar. The pecked line through D indicates the humidity mixing ratio of the air represented by T. If a sample of air from T ascends adiabatically, its temperature follows the dry adiabatic through T; meanwhile its vapour content, as given by the humidity mixing ratio, is unchanged, so that the dew-point moves along the isopleth of humidity mixing ratio through D; the lines of constant humidity mixing ratio are for this reason also known as dew-point lines. Thus, when the temperature of the ascending air is represented by T', the corresponding dew-point is given by D' on the same

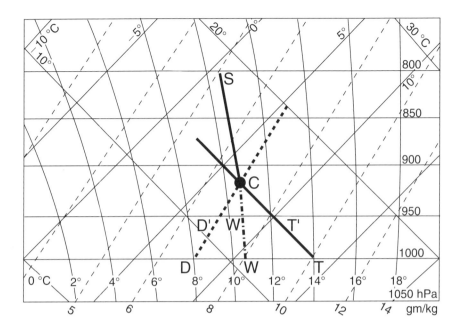

Figure 38.   The condensation level of ascending air.

isobar. Where the dry adiabatic and dew-point lines intersect, the temperature and dew-point coincide, so that the air becomes saturated at the point C. This point determines the base of cloud formed in the ascending air and its height (or pressure) is termed the 'condensation level'. Beyond this point, any further ascent follows the saturated adiabatic CS.

If the wet-bulb temperature is marked as the point W, then the condensation level is also determined by the intersection of the saturated adiabatic through W with the dry adiabatic through T. This result follows from Normand's theorem which may be stated as follows:

> On the tephigram, the dry adiabatic through the dry-bulb temperature, the saturated adiabatic through the wet-bulb temperature, and the dew-point line through the dew-point, all meet at a point.

It follows from Normand's theorem that the ascent path which is followed above the condensation level by a sample of air of given temperature and humidity is determined solely by the wet-bulb temperature. Moreover, even in the unsaturated stage of the ascent, the wet-bulb temperature follows the same saturated adiabatic. The temperature at which the pressure on the saturated adiabatic becomes 1000 hPa is called the wet-bulb potential temperature by analogy with the potential temperature which was defined in relation to dry adiabatics. It is seen that the wet-bulb temperature remains constant during any change which follows a saturated adiabatic. On the tephigram, the saturated adiabatics are labelled with values of wet-bulb potential temperature at 2 degC intervals.

Size and terminal velocity of drops

Cloud particles, as distinct from raindrops, have an average diameter of about 0.02 mm and their rate of fall in still air is about 0.012 m s^{-1}. This rate of settlement is trivial and the particles float in the air or are carried upwards in the vertical currents which give rise to the cloud. Before precipitation can occur, some of the particles must increase in size until they become heavy enough to fall out of the cloud. A falling drop quickly attains a limiting velocity relative to the air, when the air resistance just balances its weight. This is known as the terminal velocity; some values are given in Table 6 for drops of various sizes.

TABLE 6. *Terminal velocity of water drops in stagnant air at pressure of 1013.2 hPa and temperature 20 °C*

Type of drop	Diameter of typical drop *mm*	Terminal velocity *m s^{-1}*
Cloud droplets	0.0	0.003
	0.02	0.012
	0.1	0.27
Drizzle drops	0.2	0.72
	0.4	1.62
	1.0	4.03
Raindrops	2.0	6.49
	4.0	8.83
	5.0	9.09
	5.8	9.17

The terminal velocity increases at first with the size of the drops but reaches a limit of about 9 m s^{-1} for drops of about 5.5 mm diameter. Larger drops are deformed by the resistance of the air and if greater than 5.5 mm they break up into smaller drops. Hence there is an upper limit to both the size and the terminal velocity of raindrops.

There is no sharp demarcation between cloud particles and raindrops. Since vertical velocities due to convection not uncommonly exceed 9 m s^{-1}, drops up to the largest size may be found in the body of a convective cloud. Generally the average size of drops in a cloud increases with the intensity of the upward motion.

Precipitation

The mechanism by which some of the particles in a cloud attain a size and terminal velocity great enough to enable them to fall out as rain or snow must now be considered. In many clouds no such process is effective, and since convective clouds often develop to great heights without giving precipitation, it is clear that continued cooling by adiabatic ascent, although essential, is not itself sufficient to give rain in all cases. Drizzle drops have a diameter of about 0.2 mm; although they form readily from cloud particles, they can fall to the ground only when the upcurrents are very slight. The reason for the growth of cloud particles to the size of raindrops has presented much difficulty. The problem is still not fully understood but it is realized that adequate growth can be achieved only by collisions between cloud particles; an essential factor for this purpose is the difference in fall velocity of droplets of differing size, so that the faster falling particle sweeps up the smaller particles in its path. Present theories suggest two main methods for the release of rain from a cloud.

Ice-particle theory of precipitation. The theory that release of precipitation requires the presence of ice crystals in the upper part of the cloud was advanced by Bergeron in 1935. From what has already been said about the freezing of droplets, it is seen that when the adiabatic reduction of temperature in the vertical currents is carried beyond 0 °C the cloud particles become supercooled. If the cloud is of sufficient development, the region consisting wholly or mainly of supercooled drops extends over a height range of many thousands of feet above the level of the 0 °C isotherm. It was seen that as lower temperatures are reached, an increased proportion of droplets is likely to become frozen, giving a mixture of supercooled drops and ice crystals. For reasons already explained, ice crystals in this part of the cloud grow by sublimation and so acquire a fall velocity relative to the supercooled drops. They increase in size by collision with these droplets and subsequently by the overtaking of drops at temperatures above 0 °C in the lower part of the cloud; eventually they fall out from the base of the cloud as snowflakes or raindrops according to the temperature.

If the ice-particle theory was true universally, it would imply that every raindrop originates as an ice crystal and that no precipitation, other than drizzle, can be released except from clouds extending above the level of the 0 °C isotherm. This in turn implies a considerable vertical development on most occasions, especially in summer and in low latitudes. It explains the observation that precipitation in temperate latitudes in winter sometimes occurs from comparatively shallow clouds, whereas clouds of similar depth in summer would probably fail to give precipitation. There is little doubt that this theory correctly explains many, perhaps most, cases of precipitation, but observations have nevertheless shown that precipitation (not only drizzle) can occur from clouds with temperatures entirely above 0 °C.

Coalescence theory of precipitation. This theory aims primarily to explain the observed occurrence of precipitation in warm clouds, where temperatures are entirely above 0 °C. It is generally thought that gravitational coalescence of droplets is the responsible mechanism. For gravitational coalescence, that is the capture of smaller droplets by a larger, faster-falling drop, to produce rain on a realistic time-scale, current theories require the initial existence of a broad spectrum of droplet sizes. The process by which such a broad spectrum can become established is still subject to debate, but once it is established, it can be shown that the larger drops will grow by gravitational coalescence and eventually reach raindrop size.

6.3 CLOUD FORMED BY TURBULENCE

Formation of layer cloud by turbulent mixing
The prevalence of frictional turbulence in the first few thousand feet above the earth's surface and the effect of turbulent mixing on the lapse rate were discussed in

Section 5.3. It is now necessary to consider the distribution of humidity. The mixing process tends to even out the water vapour content and to produce a condition in which the mass of vapour in each unit mass of dry air, in other words the humidity mixing ratio, becomes equalized throughout the friction layer. Now suppose the lapse rate from the surface upwards to be represented by the line ABC on the tephigram at Fig. 39, whilst the dew-point curve is shown by A'B'C'. The effect of vigorous mixing of this air between 1000 and 900 hPa will be to make the lapse rate change towards the dry adiabatic represented by the line JL placed so that the mean temperature of the layer is unaltered. Another effect will be the tendency to produce a constant humidity mixing ratio throughout the layer; thus the original dew-point curve A'B' will tend towards J'L' located so that the average mixing ratio for the layer is unaltered. If this line intersects the dry adiabatic at a point K within the mixing layer, then saturation occurs at this point and a cloud layer extends from this level to the top of the mixing layer, the lapse rate in the cloud approximating to the saturated adiabatic KM.

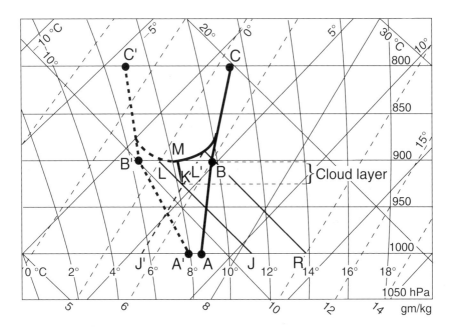

Figure 39.   Effect of turbulence on lapse rate and humidity. After mixing, the temperature curve ABC becomes JKMC, and the dew-point curve A'B'C' becomes J'KMC'.

The lowest point K at which condensation occurs is known as the mixing condensation level. It is, in general, different from the condensation level of the original undisturbed air, as was defined earlier, although after mixing has taken place, the two condensation levels become identical. Reference to Fig. 39 shows that the tendency towards an adiabatic lapse rate is accompanied by a rise of temperature in the lower part and a fall in the upper part of the mixing layer. The top of this layer therefore coincides, at least in typical cases, with the base of an inversion which, by its stability, effectively limits any further upward spread of turbulence. Consequently the top of the cloud layer extends only a little above the inversion base. Often, both upper and lower surfaces of the cloud are undulatory and sometimes breaks are seen, owing to cloud being formed in the turbulent upcurrents and evaporated in the downcurrents. The cloud type is then stratocumulus, some photographs of which are reproduced at Figs 72 and 73. At other times, usually when the wind is quite light, no structure is apparent in the cloud, which is then classified as stratus. Both types of cloud may also be formed by processes other than frictional turbulence, although vertical mixing is never entirely absent. Thus when air is subjected to gentle surface heating, thermal turbulence may be the sole factor, but more often thermal and frictional turbulence act together, reinforcing each other. With rather more active heating and an inversion aloft, stratocumulus may be formed by the spreading out of cumulus, a development which is considered in the next section.

The formation of turbulence cloud, stratocumulus and stratus, is further illustrated at Fig. 40. It is clear that certain conditions are required for cloud formation by turbulent mixing:

(i)   Turbulence must be sufficiently active to steepen the lapse rate in the friction layer so that it tends towards the dry adiabatic.
(ii) Humidity must be great enough for the mixing condensation level to be reached within the friction layer.
(iii) The lapse rate of temperature above the friction layer must be stable.

If condition (i) is not fulfilled and if there is cooling by radiation or by advection over colder ground, then the lowest temperatures are likely to be found near the ground and fog rather than low cloud will result. If condition (ii) is not satisfied, then no cloud is formed. With regard to condition (iii), it has been said that mixing results in an inversion or stable layer immediately above the friction layer. On the other hand, a pre-existing stable lapse rate is favourable to the formation of layer

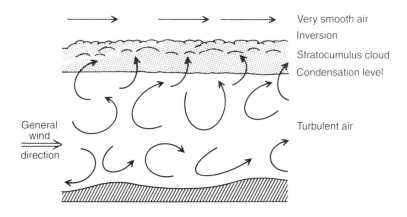

Figure 40.   Formation of a layer of turbulence cloud.

cloud for reasons which will be given presently. In contrast, an unstable lapse rate aloft would permit convective developments which are usually incompatible with the formation of layer cloud.

General characteristics of cloud formed by turbulence
Forming within the turbulent surface layers, such cloud is necessarily low. Fog is really only an extreme example of turbulence cloud, so the cloud base may vary from near the surface to possibly 3000 or 4000 ft, beyond which height turbulence from the ground rarely penetrates. The vertical thickness may be as much as 3000 ft but is usually less; there is no lower limit to the thickness and thin wispy patches of cloud may occur, forming or dissipating locally according to variations in temperature, humidity and turbulence. The cloud type varies from fractostratus to a continuous layer of stratus or stratocumulus. The base is generally at a fairly uniform height but often undulating; at the greater heights the cloud may assume a semblance of structure with denser and thinner patches occurring with some regularity; the lower bases are often associated with the lighter winds. The presence of an inversion above the cloud has been attributed to an effect of mixing in the friction layer but there may be other processes at work tending to produce or to intensify an inversion. Thus a pre-existing subsidence inversion at a suitable height confines the upward diffusion of water vapour to within the friction layer, so raising the humidity there and favouring cloud formation. Cooling of the upper surface of the cloud at night by emission of long-wave radiation also helps to maintain not only the inversion above, but the steep lapse rate within the cloud. Being cut off from the supply of surface moisture, the air above the cloud often has a much lower relative humidity than that below; this effect too is intensified if the air above is subsiding.

For adequate frictional turbulence, the surface wind speed must exceed about 10 KT, but once formed the cloud may persist with less wind. Bumpiness is generally noticeable below and within the cloud, but except in strong winds it is not usually more than moderate; above the cloud layer flying conditions are invariably smooth.

As the clouds are continually undergoing formation in ascending currents and dissolving during descent and have little vertical extent they rarely reach the precipitation stage — they provide the phenomenon of dull overcast skies without rain. Only when the cloud is dense, drizzle, slight rain or light snow may fall, but if precipitation is considerable it may be assumed with fair confidence to be falling through the turbulence cloud, having originated at a higher level.

The effect of a cloud canopy in reducing loss or gain of heat by the surface has already been mentioned. With low thick clouds there may be little diurnal variation of temperature at the ground.

Some situations giving rise to turbulence cloud
One necessary condition for cloud to form is that the relative humidity of the surface layers should be sufficiently high. This is favoured by prolonged surface cooling; turbulence cloud is therefore very common when air originating over subtropical oceans arrives in temperate latitudes. In the neighbourhood of the British Isles moist south-westerly winds frequently bring a continuous layer of very low cloud; over the western approaches this may occur at any season of the year,

but in summer over the land it usually clears during the day as a consequence of surface heating. If the wind is very light, fog is more probable. In this type surface cooling and the origin of the air are the important factors.

Prolonged surface cooling is also characteristic of the air in anticyclonic regions over the continents in winter; a cloud layer may be formed if turbulence is set up by an increase of wind or by surface heating as the air drifts over a warmer region, such as the sea. Such a layer may be persistent and extensive, maintaining itself partly by the cooling of the upper surface of the cloud by radiation to the clear sky, while in industrial areas the accumulation of smoke particles in the cloud produces the well-known anticyclonic gloom of quiet winter weather. Similar conditions may occur in other seasons if the air is sufficiently humid.

While certain occurrences of these clouds may be anticipated with confidence, there are numerous occasions when their formation demands a precise adjustment of humidity and turbulence and when a slight variation in one or the other may make all the difference between clear and overcast skies. A particularly difficult factor to allow for is the effect of the diurnal variation in turbulence, caused by the heating of the ground by day and cooling by night, combined with the associated variations in relative humidity. The variations in turbulence and in relative humidity are greatest in the evening and again in the early morning and it is at these times that turbulence clouds are most likely to form or to disperse — but the nature of the change is not always the same. The heating after dawn leads to an increase in turbulence and a decrease in relative humidity; the former tends to the production of cloud, the latter to its clearance, and which effect is the more important is a question of circumstances. Often following a clear night, a sudden formation of low cloud just after dawn appears to be attributable to an increase in turbulence; the cloud may clear later in the day, slowly or rapidly, as a result of further heating. If the cloud is dense the sun's heat may be unable to penetrate to the ground and the cloud may persist, a common occurrence in winter over the British Isles and neighbouring continental areas. Even in summer many a potentially brilliant day is spoiled by an unexpectedly thick morning formation of low cloud which fails to clear.

On the other hand turbulence cloud may form at night after a clear day, as a result of cooling and the associated rise in relative humidity. This is particularly so with air coming from the sea; the relative humidity is then often high so that only slight cooling is required to produce cloud, while the increased turbulence over the land due to its greater roughness is another favourable factor. If dense, the cloud may persist through the night, but if thin and if the wind is light, further surface cooling may stabilize the lapse rate so much that the formation either ceases or the cloud lowers to the surface as fog. Also, turbulence cloud already existing over the sea may spread more or less rapidly inland some time in the evening, retreating to the coast again as the land warms up during the following morning. In all circumstances the forecasting of the formation and dispersal of this type of cloud becomes difficult and on occasions when the humidity is high, it may not be possible to go further than to warn of the possibility of sudden changes in cloud amount during the dawn period and again towards sunset or later.

As a further type of turbulence cloud one may mention the very low ragged cloud, fractostratus, which forms below a rain-bearing cloud such as nimbostratus, altostratus or cumulonimbus. The lower air is rendered almost saturated by falling rain, and turbulence easily causes low-cloud formation within it.

In circumstances where the wind changes rapidly with height through a humid layer in the atmosphere above the friction layer, cloud sheets maintained by turbulence may be expected. Some cases of altocumulus or high stratocumulus may perhaps be explained in this way, although there is usually some other contributory factor giving rise to the humid layer.

Dissipation of turbulence cloud
Cloud formed by turbulence often dissipates over the land under the influence of insolation. If sufficient solar radiation penetrates to the ground and so raises the temperature of the air at the surface, then the condensation level rises so that the cloud thins out by a lifting of its base. For example, with conditions as in Fig. 39, the cloud would be expected to disperse completely if the surface temperature were to increase beyond the point R. Sometimes, absorption of solar radiation at the upper surface may cause evaporation and consequent reduction in the height of the cloud top. Cloud which is present on a summer night often disperses entirely within a few hours of sunrise; at other times it may persist all day, especially in winter, but even then a lifting of the cloud base during the day by perhaps 500 or even 1000 ft is usually noticeable. If the general conditions are unchanged, the cloud may be expected to re-form or to lower during the evening as already described.

6.4 FAIR WEATHER CUMULUS

When air at the surface is heated, the thermal currents produced combine with any frictional turbulence to mix the surface layers and the lapse rate tends towards the dry adiabatic; if the dew-point is reached in the cooler levels then cloud is formed, but the amount of cloud and the extent to which it develops upwards are matters of circumstances. If the lapse rate of the air through which the currents ascend is greater than the saturated adiabatic, the cloud is unstable and continues to develop upwards spontaneously until eventually halted at a stable layer; if the prevailing lapse rate is stable, development of the cloud is restricted from the outset. The processes governing the formation and development of convective cloud are advantageously followed with the aid of the tephigram.

The adiabatic ascent of air of given temperature and humidity was considered in section 6.2; it is now necessary to consider such ascent in relation to the prevailing lapse rate. Suppose for example an early morning upper-air ascent shows the temperatures and humidities indicated in Fig. 41. The lapse rate is stable, the air is unsaturated and no convection is present. During the day the surface temperature T increases while the dew-point D may be assumed to remain unchanged. When the surface temperature has increased to say T_1, a parcel of air ascending adiabatically from the surface has its temperature reduced to that of the environment at the point P where the dry adiabatic through T_1 meets the observed temperature curve, and because the environmental lapse rate is stable the ascent comes to a stop at that level. As the condensation level C_1 (the intersection of the dry adiabatic through T_1 with the dew-point line through D) is not reached, no cloud is formed. Evidently the lowest surface temperature at which convective cloud can form is obtained by taking the lowest intersection C_2 of the dew-point line through D with the environment curve, and then drawing the dry adiabatic through C_2 to meet the surface pressure in T_2. Surface air heated to T_2 is then just able to rise to its

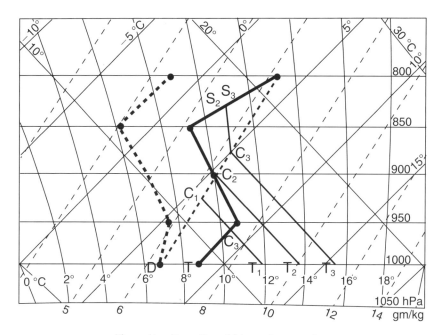

Figure 41. Formation of fair weather cumulus.

condensation level. If the environmental lapse rate at this level is less than the saturated adiabatic, the ascent will be quickly arrested as it loses momentum and any cloud formed will be shallow, no more than a few hundred feet thick. If, on the other hand, the lapse rate is steeper than the saturated adiabatic, as in the case illustrated, then further spontaneous ascent takes place along the saturated adiabatic through C_2 until the environment curve is again encountered at S_2. Thus the cloud base is formed at the level of the condensation point C_2 (900 hPa, approximately 2860 ft above the 1000 hPa level), and it extends upwards as far as S_2 (845 hPa, approximately 4500 ft) or, possibly, individual clouds will be carried up somewhat above this level by momentum of the ascending currents. With a further rise of surface temperature from T_2 to T_3, both the base and top of the cloud are raised.

In discussing the formation of cloud by turbulence it was seen how mixing of the surface layers by friction tends to set up an adiabatic lapse rate and to spread the water vapour so that the upper part of the friction layer is cooled below the dew-point with the formation of cloud. If there is also thermal turbulence, the general character of the situation may be little altered except that any increase of surface temperature raises the condensation level and so increases the height of the cloud base. So long as the condensation level lies within the friction layer, a more or less continuous cloud layer is to be expected, but in other cases cloud can be formed only in currents penetrating above the friction layer, that is, in larger-scale thermal currents; these produce isolated clouds, giving the familiar partly cloudy sky with cumulus clouds drifting with the wind. The cloud bases are flat and clear-cut at the uniform condensation level, which is usually above about 1500 ft, while the domed upper surfaces indicate the limit of penetration of the vertical currents. Sometimes when these currents are terminated by a marked inversion above the condensation level, conditions may resemble those for the formation of turbulence cloud; the cloud then spreads out beneath the inversion into a layer of stratocumulus, usually with lighter or clear patches in it.

Isolated convective clouds of limited vertical extent are referred to as 'fair weather cumulus', since the vertical development is inadequate for precipitation. The thermal currents originate by surface heating due to insolation or advection, or a combination of the two. Air warmed by the ground beneath does not rise as a continuous stream but rather as a series of bubbles; successive bubbles breaking away from the heat source at the ground combine with others to form larger bubbles. A series of bubbles starting in this way make up the convection currents (Fig. 42).

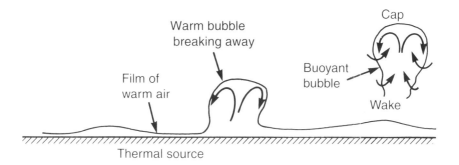

Figure 42.   Development of thermal bubbles.

The upper and outer skin of a rising bubble mixes with the environment and part of this mixed air flows, relative to the bubble, down its sides. When condensation takes place the cloud droplets at the top and sides of the bubble mix with the drier environment and evaporate. The latent heat of evaporation is supplied by the air which therefore becomes cooler and denser and so sinks to form the outer edge to the wake of the bubble.

The convective bubble then consists of a rising dome of cloudy air and a wake, the outer part of which is sinking while the inner part is rising. The inner regions of the bubble continue to rise until the thermal is completely eroded or the buoyancy is counteracted by the increasing stability of the environment. Because of mixing with the comparatively cooler and drier environment, the rising bubble, or thermal, cools at a rate greater than the saturated adiabatic lapse rate and this leads to loss of buoyancy and imposes a brake on development.

As the cloud grows, a number of thermals develop in it and the vertical motion becomes more complex (Fig. 43). Cloudy thermals rising through, and entraining air from, the residue of previous thermals, cool at a rate greater than the saturated adiabatic but the loss of buoyancy is less than when the dry, cool, environmental air is entrained.

When formed over the land by diurnal heating alone, fair weather cumulus is a phenomenon of the day hours only. It usually develops during the morning, reaches a maximum development in the afternoon and clears rapidly when the ground cools in the evening, but if the individual clouds have combined to form a more or less

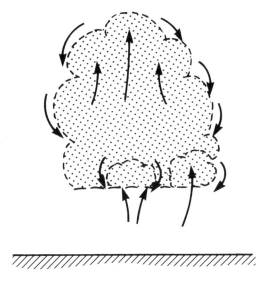

Figure 43.   Cumulus cloud developing from thermals.

unbroken layer, the cloud may then persist into the night, especially if aided by frictional turbulence. When produced by advective heating, the cloud may also be present at night although the added effect of insolation enhances its overland development by day. Over the open sea only the advection type occurs, but because evaporation from and warming by the surface is continuous, the cloud often develops into stratocumulus when the lapse rate is stable, or into intense convective cloud with showers when the lapse rate is deeply unstable.

In general, anticyclonic conditions are most favourable for fair weather cumulus, particularly in summer. In winter anticyclones, thermal currents are less intense and are usually limited by a marked inversion; if cloud forms at all, it is commonly a flat layer at a low elevation, more properly regarded as turbulence cloud than as a convective cloud.

6.5 INSTABILITY CLOUDS AND SHOWERS

Convective cloud with intense vertical development, and therefore liable to produce precipitation in the form of showers may be termed 'instability cloud'. Small cumulus clouds of the type considered in the previous section are prevented from developing further by the stability of the lapse rate aloft, but if the lapse rate above the condensation level exceeds the saturated adiabatic throughout a deep layer, the cloud becomes correspondingly extensive. Cooling less rapidly with height than its environment, it becomes ever more buoyant and accelerates upwards until finally checked by stable conditions.

Entrainment of drier air around the edges of cumulus clouds restricts their development and as a result not all cloud tops reach the height anticipated from the tephigram but as the clouds increase in size the entrainment of environmental air has a proportionately decreasing effect and a stage is reached when the centre of the rising current cools more nearly at the saturated adiabatic lapse rate.

When instability is great enough some clouds will develop sufficiently to produce precipitation. Once precipitation has started cloud turrets may be seen to grow rapidly and, in favourable circumstances, form towering masses of cumulonimbus which frequently reach the tropopause; occasionally severe storms extend some distance above the tropopause. In temperate latitudes convective cloud does not usually precipitate until the tops have penetrated some thousands of feet above the level of the 0 °C isotherm. The base of the cloud may be at, say, 2000 ft and the vertical thickness may be as much as 30 000 ft or more. In rain the base of the cloud may lower with ragged turbulence cloud almost to the surface.

When well developed, instability conditions present violent manifestations of energy. The speed of ascent often exceeds 30 ft s^{-1} and is sufficient to prevent even the largest raindrops from falling to the ground; in vigorous development of cumulonimbus cloud updraughts exceeding 150 ft s^{-1} are possible. The cloud, cooling with height at approximately the saturated adiabatic lapse rate, often extends sufficiently far above the 0 °C level for the top-most region to consist entirely of ice crystals; this part is therefore of cirrus type. Such extensive vertical development promotes the precipitation of rain (and often hail) in accordance with the ice particle theory, but in other cases, more frequent in low latitudes where the 0 °C level is high, the clouds may precipitate, as we have seen, without reaching the ice stage.

On reaching a stable layer aloft, the cloud spreads out horizontally and forms the well-known anvil shape typical of thunder and shower clouds. In the process of spreading out, and in the subsequent decay of the whole cloud system when the energy has been expended, patches or layers of cloud may form at several levels presenting a chaotic appearance to the sky.

The extreme development of instability cloud is the thunder cloud, which is described at length in the next chapter. The stages by which cumulus develops into cumulonimbus are still not fully understood, but some distinction needs to be made between cumulonimbus which develops in a succession of massive towers giving isolated thunderstorms of short duration and the well-organized cumulonimbus of severe thunderstorms which may be accompanied by large hail and possibly tornadoes, and which persists for several hours. Tops of cumulonimbus in some of these severe storms are known to exceed 60 000 ft.

In the formation of instability cloud and showers it is necessary to recognize two more or less independent conditions, both of which are essential: first, the lapse rate must be greater than the saturated adiabatic through a deep layer; secondly, the air must become saturated, i.e. cloud-laden, for if the air is not saturated it does not become unstable until the much steeper lapse rate, the dry adiabatic, is reached. It has been explained (section 3.7) that any lapse rate between the saturated and the dry adiabatics is conditionally unstable and that instability cannot be realized unless the air is saturated. Such a condition is of common occurrence; the more important means by which the instability may become effective are described in the remainder of this section.

Instability cloud and showers in low latitudes
Cumulonimbus often attains a greater height and intensity in the tropics than in temperate regions. The greater height is permitted by the high tropopause of low latitudes, while the greater intensity depends essentially on the higher temperature

103

at the condensation level, the consequently higher water vapour content and the greater amount of energy released by the subsequent condensation. Cloud development up to 50 000 ft or more is not uncommon and tops have been known to exceed 60 000 ft. Often the cirrus plume takes the form of an extensive anvil, and this or other associated cirrus formations may persist in the upper troposphere and even up to the tropopause itself long after the rest of the cloud has disappeared.

The height to which a convective cloud develops before giving precipitation is sometimes considerably less in the tropics than it is in temperate latitudes; showers may be produced when the cloud depth is less than 10 000 ft and so are well beneath the 0 °C level. Precipitation must then be attributed to the coalescence mechanism; this process is more likely in the tropics than elsewhere, since temperatures and dew-points are high and relatively large amounts of water are condensed in the rising air.

Instability due to surface heating
Given a sufficiently high humidity in the surface layers we have seen that heating may result in fair weather cumulus. If however, a cloud turret penetrates into a region which is conditionally unstable it continues to rise and a larger convective system develops. This process may be followed on a tephigram in a manner similar to that explained for small cumulus cloud. The development is illustrated in Fig. 44 which shows the plot of a morning upper-air sounding. It is seen that if the surface dew-point D remains unchanged, then no convective cloud can form until the temperature increases from T to at least T_1; the condensation level is reached at C (875 hPa) and further ascent follows at the saturated adiabatic rate through C to S (580 hPa). In this example the cloud has its base at about 4000 ft and its top a little above 14 000 ft.

This construction, whereby the path of a small parcel of air is followed adiabatically on a tephigram, is commonly referred to as the 'parcel method': this simple theory takes no account of the possibility that momentum acquired by rising air may cause it to continue rising somewhat beyond the level given by S. Neither is account taken of the compensating downcurrents which must be interspersed with the upcurrents, nor of the mixing which takes place between the parcel and its environment. The presence of the downcurrents implies that the cloud forms in isolated masses, more or less extensive and numerous according to circumstances. Probably the most important of these parcel method limitations is the mixing of the parcel with its environment; this frequently limits the cloud tops to levels below those suggested by the tephigram construction in Fig. 44.

Instability is common in air which has undergone prolonged surface heating by travelling from a cold to a warmer part of the earth, the lapse rate tending to become steep throughout a great depth. If the humidity is moderately high, as when the air has been for a considerable time over the sea, the cumulus clouds are easily formed and develop readily to the shower stage. Surface heating may take place by insolation or by advection. Over the British Isles, both processes operate to give the frequent passing showers and bright intervals associated with north-westerly winds. Any precipitation leaves the air progressively drier downwind and showers develop less frequently over the south-east; north-westerly winds in summer often bring brilliant weather, but the lapse rate aloft remains steep and if cloud does form it is likely to develop to a great height, perhaps giving a thunderstorm. Over the land,

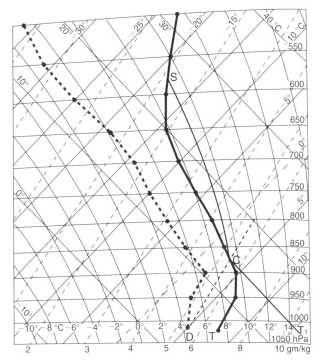

Figure 44. Development of instability cloud.

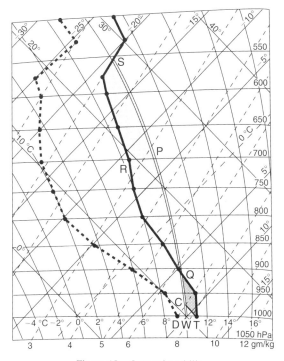

Figure 45. Latent instability.

105

instability showers caused by diurnal heating occur mostly in the daytime, being most frequent in the afternoon and clearing completely at night; when initiated by advective heating they may also occur at night.

Latent instability

The lapse rate shown in Fig. 45 is seen to be conditionally unstable from 950 to 800 hPa but since the air is unsaturated at all heights, the situation is actually stable. If now a sample of air is by some means made to ascend from the surface, its temperature will follow first the dry adiabatic TC, and then the saturated adiabatic CQS, but not until the level of Q is passed does the rising air become warmer than its environment and so unstable. Any such lapse rate in which a parcel of air eventually becomes unstable after forced ascent is said to possess 'latent' instability. Whether this property exists or not in any particular case clearly depends both on the humidity of the lifted parcel and on the observed lapse rate, and it is seen that for latent instability to exist, the saturated part of the ascent curve must at some stage lie to the right of the environment curve. From what has been said in section 6.2, we derive the condition for latent instability: the saturated adiabatic through the wet-bulb temperature W must intersect the environment curve at some higher level.

It is a property of the tephigram that the area enclosed between the parcel path curve and the observed temperature curve is proportional to the energy liberated or absorbed by an ascending parcel of air. In the case illustrated, energy must be supplied to move the parcel up through the stable region TQ, so that the area TCQT counts as negative. Above Q the air rises spontaneously to S and the energy released in this stage accounts for the kinetic energy of the upcurrent and also any electrical energy that may be developed; the area QRSPQ accordingly counts as positive. In this way, the difference between the positive and negative areas between the two curves gives an indication of the intensity of the instability which could be realized; the larger the net positive area, the more vigorous is any development likely to be.

Convective, or potential, instability

Hitherto, attention has been restricted to ascent of isolated parcels of air. We have now to consider the lifting of a whole layer of air. Fig. 46 shows a stable lapse rate AA′ with the associated dew-point curve DD′ for a layer 100 hPa thick. The result of adiabatic lifting of this layer through a further 100 hPa is found by considering what happens at individual levels. Thus air at A (1000 hPa) ascends along the dry adiabatic to C and then along the saturated adiabatic to B where the pressure is 900 hPa. Similarly air at A′ reaches its condensation level at C′ and the 800 hPa level at B′. The resulting lapse rate BB′ is evidently greater than the saturated adiabatic and as the lifted air is everywhere saturated, instability is present. The effect of lifting the layer of air has been to develop instability from what was originally a stable lapse rate. Such instability is termed convective or potential instability; its realization depends upon the existence of some mechanism to bring about the lifting in the first place.

Since for instability the saturated adiabatic through B′ must lie to the left of that through B, it follows that the wet-bulb potential temperature (Section 6.2) of the air at A′ is less than that of the air at A; i.e. the condition for convective (or potential) instability is that the wet-bulb potential temperature should decrease with height.

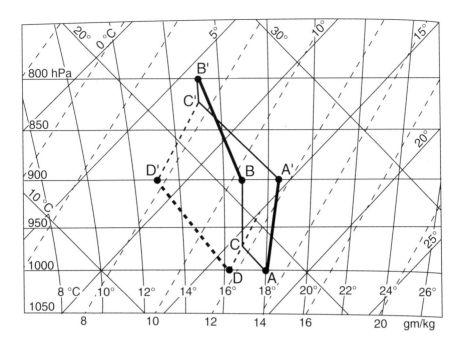

Figure 46. Development of convective instability.

Instability due to colder air flowing over warmer air

When wind direction changes with height the air at upper levels may have a very different origin from that lower down. For example, over north-west Europe southerly or south-easterly winds often have south-westerlies above them. In certain situations, while the lower stream of air comes from warm latitudes the upper stream of essentially cooler air originates in higher latitudes, although at the time it is moving north-eastwards. As the temperature contrast increases, the lapse rate passes the saturated adiabatic and a high degree of instability may become latent; this can be released by any process which produces cloud at an appropriate level and severe thunderstorms may result. The initiating process may be surface heating and development then occurs in much the same way as in simple convection systems during the heat of the day, but frequently the warm surface air is too stable for convection currents from the ground to penetrate to the conditionally unstable layer above. Then the ascent necessary to produce condensation must be initiated by some other mechanism, possibly orographically or by a general ascent associated with a fall in pressure. This effect, which may be only slight, has been referred to in Section 5.5; it is however worth recording here that locally falling pressure is to be regarded as very significant when the upper levels are known to be potentially unstable. Many severe summer thunderstorms over the British Isles originate in this way; the first indication is often the appearance of cumulus type cloud in the altocumulus level. Altocumulus is usually flat, but if it begins to develop a turreted structure (castellanus) it is a certain sign of high-level instability which may develop to the thunderstorm stage. Being independent of surface heating, such storms may break out during the night.

107

Movement of showers
Instability systems generally drift along in the air current in which they are formed. When they result from surface heating, the geostrophic wind is a fair measure of their speed and direction of travel although the change of wind with height should be considered and the wind at say, 10 000 ft may often be a better guide. On the other hand, high-level systems travel with the upper winds and often move at variance with, even contrary to, the wind near the surface when this is light.

Instability at a cold front
An important case of instability is that associated with the displacement of warm air by colder air at a cold front. The study of fronts is undertaken later; it is sufficient to note here that a showery or even thundery type of rain often, though by no means invariably, accompanies the cold front.

6.6 OROGRAPHIC CLOUD AND PRECIPITATION

The effect of a barrier of hills in the path of the wind is to force the air to rise, as has been mentioned already in the theory of the föhn wind and in connection with vertical motion generally. The rate of cooling by ascent of unsaturated air is 3 degC per 1000 ft, and with adequate lifting the condensation point must ultimately be reached, giving cloud on the hills, possibly with drizzle, or even rain or snow, according to the temperature. If there is no precipitation, the condensation level is the same on the lee side of the hill as on the windward side; with precipitation there is less water to be re-evaporated in the downcurrent and a higher cloud base would be expected on the lee side. This is illustrated in Fig. 47 where the shallow cloud is presumed to give precipitation in the form of drizzle. It is evident that the amount of ascent required to produce cloud depends on the humidity of the air and if this is near saturation quite a low range of hills will be sufficient to form cloud, as is well known in the British Isles where orographic cloud commonly forms with moist

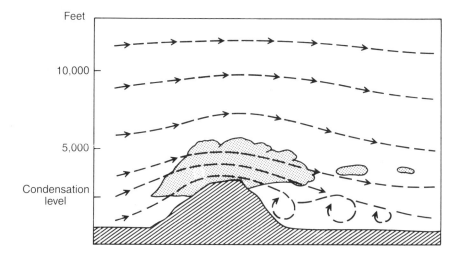

Figure 47.   Formation of orographic cloud with drizzle.

south-westerlies on all the exposed high ground and even at times on hills as low as 200 ft above sea level. Moist winds from the North Sea give the same effect on the low hills of eastern England. On higher ground, condensation often leads to drizzle but whether more intense precipitation occurs depends on the lapse rate and humidity through a deep layer. When there is widespread ascent it is not necessary for an unstable lapse rate to occur to produce continuous rain, but saturation is necessary through a depth of 10 000 ft or more. In other cases the result of lifting may be to develop convective instability. Such effects often produce a local intensification of precipitation in circumstances where rain is already more or less general for other reasons, as in a depression. In certain parts of the world, purely orographic rain occurs in considerable amounts and has a profound effect on the climate of those areas.

The simplest form of orographic cloud is stratus with a flat base and generally of no great vertical thickness; it forms a sheet covering the higher ground with breaks over lower-lying parts. The descent on the lee side causes warming and the cloud dissolves rapidly. Very marked clearances produced in this way are common and often provide clear flying weather when the windward side of the hills is enveloped in low cloud. For example, the better route between London and Scotland, as regards low cloud, is usually along the eastern coasts when the general winds are westerly and along the western coasts when easterlies prevail; similar local variations are well known to pilots operating on air routes abroad. Orographic cloud, it will be noticed, is continually forming on the windward side of the high ground and clearing on the lee, the cloud as a whole remaining stationary while the wind flows through it.

In some conditions, when an extensive cloud sheet is present and the air below is nearly saturated, the slight lifting of the air which occurs in passing over high ground may cause condensation at a lower height above sea level, so that there is a definite dip in the cloud base over even the smaller hills; this should be borne in mind when flying over hilly country in cloudy weather.

When there is a layer of almost saturated air aloft, orographic lifting may cause a persistent cloud cap to form above the high ground (Fig. 48). Like low orographic

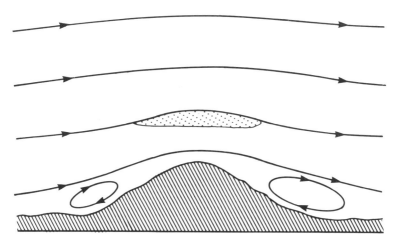

Figure 48.   Lenticular cloud formed over high ground.

109

cloud, this type is stationary with the cloud particles streaming through it, and being little disturbed by turbulence it often presents clear-cut margins; viewed from below it has thin and sometimes pointed ends with a thicker and broader centre, in shape suggesting a lens — it is called 'lenticular' in the international cloud classification. Such cloud may form at great heights in suitable conditions, even at cirrus levels. Its formation in standing lee waves was mentioned in Section 5.5.

Orographic cloud need not necessarily give rise to particular bumpiness, apart from that due to turbulence over the irregular ground, but when circumstances are complicated by vertical instability, the cloud may assume a cumuliform structure and give showers or thunderstorms with the usual attendant turbulence in and adjacent to cloud. Once formed, showers may break away from the hills and travel down wind. The presence of orographic cloud suggests the probability of strong downdraughts on the lee side of the mountain range.

6.7 CLOUD AND PRECIPITATION FORMED BY WIDESPREAD ASCENT

Some characteristics of widespread vertical motion have been considered in Section 5.5. If the relative humidity is high, condensation occurs throughout the whole depth of rising air and gives extensive cloud masses many thousands of feet thick; on other occasions variations of humidity may result in the formation of separate cloud layers. In such cases the lapse rate of temperature may be stable and remain so after lifting. If the lapse rate is such as to favour convective instability, then the cloud masses take on a more convective character and precipitation becomes heavy and of a showery nature, perhaps with thunder, although individual showers may be prolonged or succeed one another with little intermission. Widespread ascent occurs mainly within the area covered by a depression and for that reason the connection between low pressure and bad weather is brought about — but these relationships form the subject matter of later chapters.

6.8 PRECIPITATION IN THE FORM OF ICE

Snow
Snow is precipitation in the form of crystals of white ice, apparently opaque, generally in flakes of light feathery structure. Small flakes, up to 4 or 5 mm diameter, often show a six-rayed star-like structure of great beauty. Larger flakes usually consist of aggregates of such crystals, the basic symmetrical structure being no longer perceptible. Large flakes are usually found only when the temperature is near 0 °C; at low temperatures the snow may fall as a fine powder. For precipitation to reach ground level as snow, the surface temperature must be less than about 4 °C.

Sleet in British usage denotes rain and snow falling together, or snow melting as it falls. In the United States of America the term is used for precipitation of transparent grains or pellets of ice formed when raindrops from warmer air aloft become frozen on falling through a cold layer nearer to the ground. Because of this conflict of definition the term sleet is not used in international meteorological transmissions; where it is necessary to refer to the phenomenon it is described simply as 'rain and snow'.

110

Diamond dust consists of very small ice crystals, so tiny as to appear suspended in the air. They fall from clear skies in calm, arctic conditions, and thus are rarely seen in the United Kingdom.

Snow grains are white opaque ice particles, flat or elongated, generally less than 1 mm in diameter. They fall from thin layer cloud and do not readily rebound or burst when falling on hard ground.

Ice pellets are transparent ice particles, spherical or irregular, rarely conical and generally less than 5 mm in diameter. They fall from thick layer cloud such as nimbostratus.

Hail

Soft hail consists of white opaque pellets, generally rounded, sometimes conical, rarely exceeding a few millimetres in diameter. It falls from shower clouds in cold weather and is small and easily compressed. True hailstones are hard pellets of various sizes and shapes, frequently with a structure of alternate concentric layers of clear and opaque ice. Though usually only a few millimetres in diameter, very much larger stones can occur and some as big as a grapefruit, and weighing a kilogram or more, have been observed.

After the initial formation of ice particles at temperatures well below 0 °C, growth is mainly due to collision and coalescence with supercooled water drops. The opaque layers are caused by air trapped within the ice which forms on the particle when the liquid water content of the cloud is small; the clear layers are the result of slower freezing associated with high liquid water content of the cloud.

Hailstones are supported within the cumulonimbus clouds by strong and possibly increasing updraughts. In conditions favourable for the formation of large hail, those stones which are of such a size that their fall speed is just less than the updraught will remain in the cloud and thus grow larger.

Sometimes the hailstones melt before reaching the ground; this in part accounts for the rarity of hail at low levels in equatorial regions.

CHAPTER 7

THUNDERSTORMS

7.1 CONDITIONS FAVOURABLE FOR THUNDERSTORM DEVELOPMENT

The development of convective clouds was examined in Section 6.5; for a thunderstorm to develop, the conditions required for convective development must be present to a marked degree. Briefly they are:

(i) lapse rate greater than the saturated adiabatic throughout a layer of considerable depth, usually extending several thousand feet above the 0 °C level,

(ii) an adequate supply of moisture from below, and

(iii) a process which produces saturation in the region of high lapse rate.

As a rule, the height reached by the convective cloud will be limited by mixing with, and evaporation into, the air of the drier environment and so will be less than the limit set by buoyancy alone. If the relative humidity of the surrounding air is very low, the evaporation process may be dominant and cloud growth will terminate well below the level expected from consideration of the environmental lapse rate. For deep convection therefore, it is necessary that there is adequate moisture throughout a great depth of the troposphere or that there is some combination of circumstances that insulates a rising parcel from the entrainment of drier air from the environment.

For the conditional instability to be realized, saturation must be reached and this is usually brought about by ascent of air resulting from one or more of the following processes:

(a) insolation over land,

(b) differential advection — warm air undercutting colder air,

(c) orographic uplift,

(d) frontal uplift, and

(e) lifting as a result of convergence, often associated with falling surface pressure.

It will frequently be the case that two or more of the above processes act together; a common synoptic situation favourable for the development of storms over the United Kingdom in summer is illustrated in Fig. 49. Warm moist air resulting from the strong insolation over France and Spain is advected northwards ahead of an advancing cold front and is overlain by a cool and dry mid-tropospheric flow; there is conditional instability and plentiful low-level moisture, satisfying conditions (i) and (ii). In meeting condition (iii) processes (a), (b), (d) and (e) all play a part in contributing to the required ascent.

Once marked convective instability has been released the resulting storms can be classified as either single or multicell storms. The former are common over the British Isles; multicell storms are less common here though common in the tropics,

112

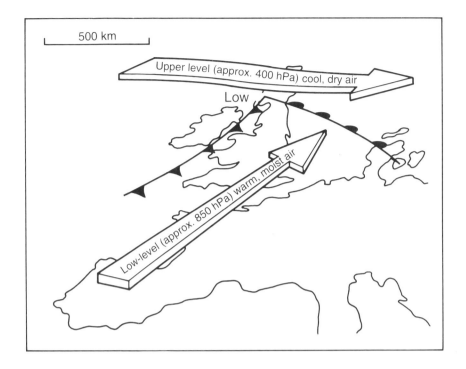

Figure 49.   Differential advection leading to destabilization.

while an extreme development of the multicell storm, the supercell, is rare in the British Isles but not uncommon over some continental areas. Basic to an understanding of these different types is their underlying cell structure.

7.2 THE STRUCTURE OF A SINGLE-CELL STORM IN TEMPERATE LATITUDES

It is convenient to consider the development of a cumulonimbus cell in three stages.

Cumulus or building stage
The building stage begins when one or more cumulus clouds start to grow into a larger cumulus cloud with a base perhaps as much as 10 km across. A general updraught prevails throughout the cell with perhaps extreme velocities of 30 m s^{-1} (100 ft s^{-1}), although more typically 5–10 m s^{-1}. The average life of this stage is short, perhaps 15 to 20 minutes; it does not involve precipitation.

Mature stage
This stage begins when some of the falling particles produce downdraughts within the cloud which ultimately result in rain or hail falling from its base. Cloud tops extend thousands of feet above the 0 °C level and continue to rise. The downdraught associated with the increasing volume of precipitation warms at the saturated adiabatic lapse rate whereas the surrounding cloudy air has a greater lapse rate due to its entrainment of some of the cloud-free air. The downdraught soon acquires a

temperature lower than that of its surroundings; below the cloud base evaporation of the rain results in further cooling and acceleration of the downdraught which on reaching the ground forms a gust front spreading outwards from the storm.

Dissipating stage
This is reached when the storm has used up the local supply of moist air. In the case of a small isolated cumulonimbus the updraught is cut off by the spreading downdraught and the rain dies away. The cloud top begins to spread laterally. If there are large numbers of ice crystals and strong horizontal winds near the cloud top the characteristic anvil is formed. Although the most active period in the life of a cell is about 30 minutes ice crystals in the upper region may persist for 2 to 3 hours. These stages in the life cycle of a single cell storm are depicted schematically in Fig. 50.

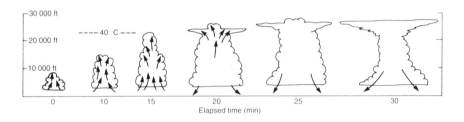

Figure 50. Cross-sections through a developing single-cell storm. Arrows denote major airflows.

7.3 SEVERE LOCAL STORMS

The effects of vertical wind shear
Vertical wind shear is usually detrimental to the early development of cloud cells as it increases the turbulent mixing between updraught and environment; narrow cumulus turrets, rapidly developing through a dry environment, may sometimes be observed to be tilted and ultimately torn apart by strong winds aloft. If, however, the instability is sufficient to overcome this, the cell may become 'locked' into a larger-scale motion in which the updraught will be tilted out of the vertical and, in the mature stage, may actually coexist with the downdraught to produce a totally different kind of organization. This type of development is usually referred to as a 'Severe Local Storm' or as a 'supercell'.

Initial conditions
A particularly propitious condition for Severe Local Storm development, in addition to the necessary strong vertical wind shear and great depth of instability, is the existence of a stable layer which traps warm humid air beneath cold dry air aloft (cf. Fig. 49). The stable layer, in effect, forms a lid which prevents small-scale convection and traps low-level moisture; when insolation or some other process eventually breaks down the stable layer, great buoyancy can develop. In the British

Isles surface wet-bulb potential temperatures of about 20 °C and a wind shear of 30–60 KT between the surface and 500 hPa are considered to be necessary requirements.

Supercell organization

In the mature stage, falling precipitation passes through only a small section of the rising air and the downdraught, enhanced by evaporation into the dry medium-level air, accelerates and reaches the ground as a cold outflow, the leading edge of which is the gust front. The tilted updraught is no longer quenched by the downdraught; its buoyancy is further enhanced by the release of latent heat associated with condensation and the centre of the cloud is insulated from mixing with the environment. The updraught may attain speeds of as much as 50 m s^{-1} and it may extend several kilometres above the tropopause before losing momentum and sinking back into the cumulonimbus anvil. This more or less self-propagating steady state may persist for some hours and the surface weather is characterized by torrential rain, large hail, strong and turbulent winds and tornadoes.

Fig. 51 depicts a cross-section through a storm producing heavy hail. The shaded area is the part of the system detected by weather radars. Droplets entering along the main updraught growing from the main 'pedestal' cloud follow the trajectory marked '0' and are swept up rapidly into the anvil. The trajectory marked 1, 2, 3 corresponds to the stages of growth of large hailstones. As large cloud droplets grow in the updraught they eventually freeze but continue to grow as they collide with their smaller kin overtaking them. Eventually their fall speed exceeds the local updraught and they start to fall through it, growing all the time (2 in the figure). Now, in severe storms the updraught is not vertical, but slanting, and the hail, can be sorted. As the hail descends it encounters the main updraught again. Small hail meeting the strong flow will be flung into frozen cloud (where growth will be very slow) and follow the dotted path. Larger hail will penetrate to nearer the core, lower down where the water concentration is higher, and grow rapidly as they are bombarded with supercooled drops. These follow route 3 in the figure, growing

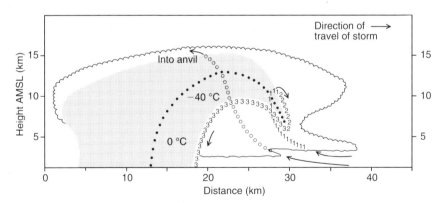

Figure 51. Schematic model of a severe hailstorm. Potential hail entering with the main updraught is rapidly swept into the anvil along path 0. Hail entering the system further out follows path 1, 2 and re-enters the updraught. The majority will follow path ● but some larger hail will enter the main updraught along 3, grow rapidly there and fall out as a cascade at the leading edge of the precipitation, shown shaded. Note that, in general, there is a cyclonic flow around the main updraught.

quickly while riding the updraught, and then falling out in a cascade when too heavy to be held up any longer. It is conceivable that some stones will be the right weight and follow the right trajectory to make several passes through the updraught to fall as giant hail. From the foregoing it should be clear that hail may be found almost anywhere in such a storm up to about 45 000 ft, and for a considerable radius around the main updraught (especially under the overhanging anvil).

A typical vertical sounding through a major thunderstorm is illustrated in Fig. 52. The stippled areas show the positive and negative areas corresponding to the adiabatic ascent of an unmixed parcel of saturated air; positive and negative areas are equal. The positive area is proportional to the energy liberated by the ascending parcel and this could be dissipated by the further ascent of the parcel to the top of the negative area in the stratosphere. The unmixed parcel could, in theory, reach about FL490 but mixing with the environment would act as a brake on the ascent and most cumulus cells would stop far short of the tropopause; in this actual case many tops reached only FL290 (310 hPa) where the lapse rate suddenly diminishes. Air parcels in the centre of a major updraught, and hence insulated from contact with the drier environment, would stand some chance of extending to the tropopause or beyond; in fact the observed highest tops were near FL435 (about 160 hPa), a few thousand feet into the stratosphere.

Supercell motion
Whereas ordinary thunderstorm cells are steered by the mean winds, self-propagating storms tend to travel at an angle to the direction of the mean wind,

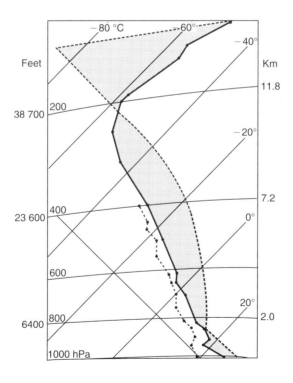

Figure 52.   Typical tephigram for thunderstorm development.

usually about 20° to the right and slower than, or 20° to the left and faster than the mid-tropospheric wind; those travelling to the right are the more common in the northern hemisphere. Observations of storms in the United States Midwest show that the onset of this anomalous direction of travel is closely associated with the appearance of rotational characteristics, the most obvious manifestation being the spawning of tornadoes near the base of the updraught.

Supercell distribution
Supercell thunderstorms are particularly a feature of the continental areas of North America where much damage is caused by the associated tornadoes and giant hail. They are comparatively rare in more maritime climatic regimes, such as western Europe, but they do occur from time to time when conditions are just right. The Wokingham storm of July 1959 is one well-known case whilst the Hampstead storm of August 1975 is an example of a self-maintaining storm that remained essentially stationary for about three hours, affecting an area of only about 100 km²; this latter storm caused severe flood damage and widespread disruption; the maximum recorded rainfall was 177 mm.

7.4 TROPICAL THUNDERSTORMS

The previous discussions relate to the well-researched temperate latitude convective storms. In contrast limited observational data are available for the convective storms of tropical regions. Observational studies indicate that these storms tend to display more signs of organization, often occurring in lines (squall lines). These are very similar in dimensions to the organized bands of thunderstorms that occur ahead of cold fronts in temperate latitudes. There are, however, significant differences in internal structure though strong updraughts and downdraughts are still an important characteristic. In particular the anvil streams off behind the storm rather than in front as it does in temperate-latitude storms.

7.5 FURTHER CHARACTERISTICS OF THUNDERSTORMS

Diurnal and seasonal variation
In so far as insolation over land is a cause of thunderstorms, they are most likely to occur during the afternoon and to die out in the evening. However, a multicell system, once developed, is apt to maintain itself for several hours, so that storms may continue well into the night. Storms started by advective heating can occur at any time, although they are more frequent by day over land since the effects of diurnal heating are then an added ingredient.

In middle latitudes, storms over the land are most frequent in summer. However, the frontal type of thunderstorm is more frequent in winter, because of the greater frequency of active cold fronts in that season. In some tropical regions the effects of high humidity, steep lapse rate, intense insolation and convergence combine to make thunderstorms or showers an almost daily occurrence. Over land in the tropics and subtropics the afternoons are the preferred time for thunderstorm development; over coastal waters though they are often more frequent at night. Convergence of local breezes has an important part to play here; just as convective cloud may develop along the line of a sea-breeze front overland by day, so land-breezes at night may produce enough low-level convergence off-shore to generate showers or thunderstorms. In some cases coastal curvature may be important, a concave coastline favouring land-breeze convergence and a convex coastline (e.g. a circular island) favouring sea-breeze convergence.

The gust front

As the downdraught from a cell nears the ground, it spreads out horizontally and its leading edge has been called the 'gust front'. The downdraught has been cooled in relation to its surroundings so that the outflow above the ground takes on the character of a miniature cold front (see Chapter 16), often giving a severe squall with a marked change of wind speed, probably accompanied by a change in direction; this is the 'microburst' mentioned in Chapter 5. The cold air of the downdraught spreads out all around the cell so that the first gust is usually directed away from the storm.

Pressure fluctuations

Marked fluctuations of pressure often accompany severe thunderstorms and the gust front frequently produces a sudden pressure rise. On these occasions local rises in pressure during the growing stage of the cumulonimbus develop into a region of high pressure which expands as the rain area increases. When a thunderstorm high becomes intense its leading edge is marked by a large pressure gradient and its centre corresponds to the position of the most violent storms.

Turbulence

Turbulence refers to a sequence of local variations of air motion on length scales varying between metres and hundreds of metres which may be regarded as superimposed on the general horizontal flow in the area. In a thunderstorm there are strong updraughts and downdraughts, and gusts occur both inside and outside these main draughts. One area of severe turbulence is indicated in Fig. 51. The strong vertical wind shear associated with the gust front is another favoured region for turbulence.

It may be possible to avoid cumulonimbus cloud by avoiding the radar echoes (see Section 13.1) which are received from them, but severe turbulence has been encountered, even near the level of the cloud tops, as much as 15 km from the radar echo. Until there is some way of distinguishing the most severe storms from the less severe ones, the safest course is to avoid flight through active thunderstorm cloud altogether whenever possible.

Hail

Heavy hail is rare, and when it occurs only a small region of the cloud is affected, so that it is encountered relatively infrequently in flight. Small hailstones cause only superficial damage but there have been reports where large stones have holed and splintered windscreens, shattered canopies, ripped off de-icer boots, and bent radiator fins. Damage by hail usually increases with the speed of the aircraft. There is no reliable method of recognizing in advance those thunderstorms which will produce large hailstones. It is thought that large stones grow because small hailstones, formed on the first ascent, fall into the updraught of the storm and are recycled. As stones grow in size they travel more slowly in the updraught and thus have time to increase into large hail. An example of hail damage to a large aircraft is shown in Fig. 53.

Figure 53. Hail damage to aircraft. Damage to the nose of a jet aircraft sustained over the English Channel in July 1957. The aircraft suddenly encountered severe turbulence, rime icing and hail while flying in cirrus at FL295. Subsequent investigation showed that the cloud was anvil cirrus of such density that the pilot of this and an accompanying aircraft were unaware of the existence of embedded cumulonimbus. The environment temperature at the onset of the icing was -35 °C. Both aircraft received almost identical damage; all leading edges were battered with some of the larger depressions being measured at 6×8 inches. Protective sheathing on some electrical leads in the engine intakes was frayed away.

Clear layers of ice form on the stones in those parts of the cloud where supercooled drops predominate and the stones grow with a wet surface. Higher in the cloud, where ice crystals predominate or supercooled drops are small, opaque layers of ice form (see also Section 6.1).

Lightning
A lightning flash is a large-scale example of an electric spark. A spark or discharge occurs between two points when the difference in electric potential reaches a certain value depending on the conductivity of the air and on the distance between the points. In clear air of normal density this critical 'field strength' is about 3 MV m^{-1}, but in cloud it is reduced to about 1 MV m^{-1}. Such intense fields must be present somewhere in a thunderstorm before lightning can occur, but it appears that they are very localized, the largest field strengths that have been recorded within thunderstorms being of the order of 400 kV m^{-1}. In any case, these differences of

potential imply the existence of electrically charged areas within the cloud. Investigations by sounding balloons and by other means reveal the existence of a positively charged area in the top of the cloud and a negatively charged area lower down, the cloud being said to have positive polarity. Below the area of negative charge there is often a second but more localized area of positive charge. A number of theories have been put forward to account for the separation of positive and negative charges into different parts of the cloud, but as yet there is no completely satisfactory explanation of the known facts; even the relative importance of the many possible processes of charge separation is unknown. Among the suggested processes may be mentioned the movement of water drops in an existing electric field, breaking and coalescence of drops, friction between ice crystals, evaporation and melting of ice particles, freezing of water drops, and sublimation of vapour onto ice particles. All of these processes are found to produce a separation of electric charge in the laboratory.

Once the critical field strength has been built up, a lightning discharge occurs and temporarily neutralizes the field, but if the cell is still active the process is immediately resumed. Discharges may take place from cloud to earth, between two different clouds or two parts of the same cloud, or from a cloud to the surrounding air. An active storm consisting of several cells may produce lightning flashes at an average rate of four per minute; of these, the number entirely within the cloud much exceeds the number passing from the cloud to earth.

The visible lightning stroke is a channel of incandescent air not more than a few centimetres in diameter. Thunder is simply the accompanying explosive report caused by the sudden expansion of the air heated by the lightning flash. Since the flash and the noise originate simultaneously, the distance of the lightning from the observer may be estimated from the interval which elapses between the times when the lightning is seen and the thunder heard. The flash is seen immediately but sound takes about three seconds to travel one kilometre and the thunder is therefore heard an appreciable time after the lightning is seen. As the flash itself may be a kilometre or more in length, the sound which reaches the observer will not all have travelled the same distance so that the noise may continue for several seconds. Echo also prolongs the rumble of thunder.

A lightning strike can be very unpleasant for the occupants of an aircraft; it may occur in or beneath cloud, or between two clouds and even before a thunderstorm has developed. The brilliant flash, the smell of burning and the explosive noise may be alarming and distracting. While many aircraft have been struck by lightning there is little positive evidence of serious damage to metal aircraft by the strike itself, and the occupants are safeguarded by the aircraft bonding requirements which effectively prevent any electrical discharge from penetrating to the interior. Nevertheless there is a danger that in the turbulence of a storm the disconcerting effects may lead to disorientation and loss of control unless pilots are fully prepared.

Static electricity
This refers to the spark discharges which occur when the potential difference between the aircraft and the ambient air exceeds a certain value; it is usually due to a charge accumulated from cloud particles, from precipitation, from contact with dust or sand, or to the aircraft's not immediately taking up the potential of its surroundings after a rapid change of flight level. The phenomenon is usually noticed first as radio noise, particularly on high and medium frequencies; VHF reception is

affected to a lesser extent. Perhaps more noticeable is its effect on precision navigation aids where its effect on the signal to noise ratio may be considerable. As the static electricity increases in severity, the noise increases and in extreme cases a visible discharge — known variously as St. Elmo's fire, brush discharge or corona — observed around some parts of the aircraft. Static electricity is not normally dangerous although there have been rare occasions where a discharge has caused the breakage of windscreens and plastic panels. The onset of static discharge is likely to be delayed in aircraft fitted with discharge wicks, but even then discharges are still likely to be experienced in thundery conditions.

Precipitation static This is static electricity produced when an aircraft encounters precipitation. In this case the charge accumulates from the electricity carried by precipitation elements which strike the aircraft, from the electricity generated by the break up of particles, especially snow crystals, against the aircraft, from friction with solid particles, or in other ways. In particular, charges imparted to the aerial contribute to radio noise.

Noise Noise is caused by electrical effects on the radio. In combination with the effect of hail and heavy rain striking the aircraft the noise may build up to an alarming extent, submerging the normal engine noise and preventing speech on the intercommunication system. The explosive noise of a lightning strike has already been mentioned.

Instrument errors
Both the pressure altimeter and the rate of climb indicator may give faulty readings because of localized turbulence. Partial blocking of the pitot tube by heavy rain may cause the air-speed indicator to read low. If that power has been selected which gives the safest speed before entering the storm, then any fluctuations in air-speed readings should be disregarded provided a reasonably level attitude is maintained. A lightning strike may seriously affect magnetic compasses, which should be checked as soon afterwards as possible. When approaching the storm, the autopilot should be disengaged and the flight instruments checked.

Ice accretion
This is discussed in the next chapter.

7.6 ATMOSPHERIC ELECTRICITY

There are various electrical phenomena which occur naturally in the atmosphere, the thunderstorm being the most spectacular. Investigation shows that the atmosphere carries a net positive charge, even in fine weather, implying a corresponding negative charge on the ground. Measurements of the electric potential show that it increases with height; this rate of change with height is called the potential gradient. Near the ground in fine weather the potential gradient is of the order of 150 V m^{-1} but fluctuations occur continually and there are also regular diurnal and seasonal changes. The potential may reach hundreds of thousands of volts by the middle troposphere, the earth being assumed to be at zero potential.

The potential gradient is increased in haze, fog or cloud. The value at the surface may reach 2000 V m^{-1} in fog, sufficient to cause static discharges from the extremities of metallic conductors connected to earth. When there is precipitation in any form, the electric field becomes more seriously modified. With steady slight rain or drizzle, the electric field may be either increased or decreased compared with the fine-weather value, but no large electrical forces are produced either inside or outside the cloud. With showery rain, especially from detached clouds, strong electrical forces are brought into existence both in and near the clouds. These forces increase with the intensity of the showers and reach their climax in thunderstorms when a spark discharge of lightning occurs.

The occurrence of static discharges from parts of an aircraft has already been noted; they can occur also at the surface of objects attached to the earth. The immediate cause is a sufficient difference in electric potential between a projecting object and the air. It should be appreciated that although thunderstorms provide the most favourable conditions, the phenomenon of static discharge is not confined to those occasions but may occur whenever the electrical field is sufficiently intensified in any way, usually in association with disturbed weather of the types mentioned. An extreme instance concerns cases where aircraft have actually been struck by a lightning-type discharge when no thunderstorms were observed in the vicinity and when radio noise was not enough to suggest the likelihood of a discharge. This comes about through the intensification of an electric field in the vicinity of a conductor, which in this case is the aircraft itself. If the general field strength has increased in convective conditions, even though these have not developed to the thunderstorm stage, then in a critical case the further local intensification in the neighbourhood of an aircraft is sufficient to cause the sparking value to be reached, thereby initiating a lightning strike.

CHAPTER 8

ICE ACCRETION ON AIRCRAFT

8.1 INTRODUCTION

The possibility of ice accretion on the airframe of an aircraft has to be considered whenever flight takes place through cloud or rain at temperatures below 0 °C; engine icing may also occur in clear air and at temperatures above 0 °C. Although various methods are available for the prevention of ice accretion or for removing a deposit of ice after it has formed, there is none that can provide more than partial protection. It is therefore important that a pilot should be aware of the conditions favourable for ice formation so that he can avoid the risk as far as possible and so that he may know what action to take should ice begin to form. In addition to a description of the physics of ice accretion as affecting both airframe and engine and of the meteorological conditions in which it occurs, this chapter includes an account of the effect of ice formation on performance and of the procedures to be followed to reduce the risks. A separate section is devoted to the particular hazards of ice accretion to rotary-wing aircraft. Reference should be made elsewhere for information on methods of prevention and de-icing. It should, however, be noted that the design and application of such methods requires to be properly related to the various types of ice liable to be encountered and to the rate of accumulation. A method which is perhaps effective in one set of icing conditions may be of little use in another.

8.2 FORMS OF AIRFRAME ICING

The formation of a deposit of ice on objects exposed to the atmosphere may occur in two ways: directly from water vapour, i.e. by sublimation, or by the freezing of liquid water drops. On the ground these processes produce the two familiar forms of deposit known as hoar-frost and rime. The same forms of ice may affect aircraft in flight and similar names are used to describe them. However, aircraft encounter a greater variety of icing conditions in flight than on the ground, resulting in a wider variety of forms of ice deposit.

Hoar-frost
This type of icing occurs in clear air on a surface whose temperature is reduced below the frost-point of the air in contact with it (Section 6. 1). The water vapour in excess of that necessary to saturate the air with respect to ice condenses into a white crystalline coating of ice, normally of a feathery nature. It may occur on a parked aircraft in the same circumstances that lead to hoar-frost on the ground, i. e. during a clear night when there is a fall in temperature to a value below 0 °C. The weight of the deposit is unlikely to be serious but it can interfere with the airflow and the attainment of flying speed during take-off, with vision through the windscreen, with the free working of such moving parts as ailerons and with the efficiency of radio reception. Any hoar-frost should therefore be carefully removed from the aircraft before take-off.

Hoar-frost may occur in flight if the aircraft, after flying in a region where the temperature is well below 0 °C, moves rapidly into a warmer and damp layer of air; this may result for example from descent to a lower level, or from ascent into an inversion. If the air passing over the cold aircraft is chilled to a temperature below the frost-point, hoar-frost is deposited but this soon disappears as the aircraft warms up. The effects are similar to those of hoar-frost on the ground. There may be some loss of radio facilities, frost on the windscreen just before landing may cause much inconvenience, and frost on the airframe may increase the stalling speed. In a rapid descent, hoar-frost can also form inside the aircraft, obscuring the instruments and the view through the windscreen unless these parts are fitted with protective heating.

All other types of icing occur in either cloud or rain and are now considered in turn.

Rime ice

Rime occurs when small supercooled water drops freeze on contact with a surface at a temperature below 0 °C to produce tiny ice particles between which air is entrapped to give a rough crystalline deposit. At ground level it forms in freezing fog and the white crystalline deposit grows out on the windward sides of exposed objects.

In flight an aircraft may encounter clouds of low water content composed of small drops comparable with those of freezing fog, and it is then subject to icing which in appearance and method of formation is similar to that formed on ground objects. This type of ice accretion is most liable to occur at low temperatures, where the unfrozen cloud droplets tend to be small and therefore freeze almost instantaneously. Rime ice forms and accumulates on leading edges with no spreading back. The air entrapped between the particles gives the ice a white opaque appearance and it usually breaks away easily. Ice of this type usually has little weight but it alters the aerodynamic characteristics of the wings and it may block air intakes.

Clear ice (glaze ice)

This consists of a transparent or translucent coating of ice with a glassy surface appearance. It results from water flowing over an airframe before freezing. The drops unite while in the liquid state and very little air is enclosed between them. Although the ice surface is smooth it is not always even and bumps and undulations occur. Ice formed in this way is tough, sticks closely to the surface of the aircraft, and cannot be broken away easily. If it breaks away at all it comes away in large pieces which are sometimes of a dangerous size. The danger of clear ice is primarily aerodynamic but it is increased by the weight of the accumulation and by the vibration set up by unequal loading of wings, struts and propeller blades.

Clear ice forms when large water drops at temperatures not far below 0 °C are encountered in flight. The freezing process is comparatively slow. The water spreads back and freezes in contact with the cold surface. It occurs in dense cloud of convective or orographic type where large liquid water drops may be carried up in vigorous vertical currents to levels where the temperature is below 0 °C.

Clear ice may also occur when a rapid descent is made; the aircraft temperature lags behind the ambient air temperature, and if rain is encountered whilst the temperature of the airframe is still below 0 °C the relatively large drops form clear ice over a large part of the aircraft with considerable spreading.

A further example of clear ice formation in rain occurs when there is an inversion of temperature and rain falls from a level where the temperature is above 0 °C to a layer where it is below. In the lower layer impact on an aircraft results in clear glassy ice formation. These conditions are typically found in association with warm fronts where the icing layer occupies a narrow range of altitude below the frontal surface (see Chapter 16); they occur only rarely over the British Isles but are not uncommon over continental Europe where winter warm fronts advance over very cold lower layers overlying snow-covered ground.

Cloudy or mixed ice

Rime ice and clear ice are the extreme forms of ice accretion experienced by aircraft flying in cloud and rain, but as a large range of drop sizes may be encountered, at any temperatures between 0 and −40 °C, a wide range of forms of icing exists between the two extremes. These varieties are usually described as cloudy or mixed ice. The smaller the drops and the lower the temperature the rougher and more cloudy will be the build up on the leading edges, whilst the larger the drops and the nearer the temperature to 0 °C the greater will be the tendency for a smoother and more glassy ice formation with spread-back over the airframe.

In clouds of liquid droplets where temperatures are below 0 °C, ice crystals may be present. These tend to stick if they strike the wet surface of an aircraft and become frozen along with the cloud drops to give a formation of rough cloudy ice. If snowflakes are present they are similarly imprisoned within the ice as it forms, producing an opaque deposit with the appearance of tightly packed snow, and which is called pack snow.

8.3 FACTORS AFFECTING THE FORM OF AIRFRAME ICING

Freezing of supercooled drops

The most important factor for ice accretion on aircraft is the freezing of supercooled drops — either cloud particles or raindrops — following impact with the aircraft. It was seen in Section 6.1 that supercooling of the water droplets in cloud is of common occurrence. The heat used in melting ice is called 'latent' heat because the temperature of an ice/water mixture is held at 0 °C until all the ice has melted. The latent heat absorbed in melting a given mass of ice is considerable, amounting to about 80 times that required to raise the temperature of the same mass of water by 1 degC. When a supercooled drop freezes, it appears at first sight that, unless the temperature of the drop is initially below −80 °C (which never occurs), the latent heat liberated will melt the drop by raising the temperature to above 0 °C. In fact, a fraction of the drop, not exceeding $T/80$ (where $-T$ °C is the initial temperature of the drop) freezes instantaneously. At this stage, the temperature of the partly frozen drop is raised, it begins to lose heat by evaporation and conduction to the air or objects in contact with it, so that the remainder of the drop freezes more gradually while assuming the temperature of its surroundings. The higher the temperature of the supercooled drop, the smaller the fraction which will freeze instantaneously and the greater the amount of liquid which will freeze progressively.

Temperature

Spontaneous freezing of supercooled drops in the free atmosphere is determined partly by the temperature and size of the drop and partly by other factors; experiment shows that the average temperature of spontaneous freezing decreases with the size of the drop. Consequently as the temperature falls the larger drops are likely to freeze first, while at lower temperatures only the smallest drops will remain liquid until freezing becomes general at about -40 °C. Further, we have seen that the higher the temperature of a supercooled drop, the greater the fraction which remains liquid for a time after impact with an aircraft. The liquid portion starts to flow over the airframe and so increases the available area from which the latent heat of fusion can be dissipated to the environment. Thus the higher the (sub-freezing) temperature, the more the formation of clear ice is favoured and the more accretion is allowed to spread back from the leading edge, while lower temperatures tend to favour the formation of rime concentrated near the leading edges. The form of ice accretion cannot however be simply related to temperature, since much depends on other factors, particularly the concentration of liquid water and the size of the drops encountered.

Kinetic heating

This arises in two ways. When an aircraft is in motion, the air follows the streamlines round the component parts of the airframe. The air pressure on the surface of the aircraft varies from place to place, being greatest at stagnation points such as the leading edges where it exceeds the static pressure, and least on the upper surface of the wing where it is less than the static pressure. The local airflow is least where the pressure is greatest, and greatest where the pressure is least. At the stagnation points the airstream is compressed and heated adiabatically, but there is expansion and fall of temperature where the pressure is less than the static pressure. There is another effect due to friction between the airframe and the air which generates heat at all parts of the airframe except the stagnation points. This frictional heating is greatest where the relative motion is greatest and so where the heating due to compression is least. The compressional and frictional heating together constitute what is known as kinetic heating. The amount of the heating varies over the surface of the aircraft; it is a minimum on the upper surface of the wing and a maximum at the stagnation points. Conduction of heat through the airframe, particularly if metal, tends to smooth out the temperature differences. The increase of temperature in clear air is small for slow aircraft — about 1 degC at 100 KT on a leading edge — but increases in proportion to the square of the speed of the aircraft. For a true air speed of 500 KT the heating effect is in the neighbourhood of 25 degC. In icing conditions, relevant surfaces of an aircraft may be wet and any kinetic warming above the ambient temperature may result in evaporation. This in turn will lead to cooling as latent heat of evaporation (600 calories per gram of water evaporated) is taken away, mostly from the wet surfaces. In this way the effects of kinetic heating in icing conditions may be partly or even largely, offset. It may be noted that while a rise of airframe temperature to above 0 °C would prevent ice accretion, a rise to a value near but still below 0 °C would be likely to increase the probability and the severity of icing. In any case, the indicated air temperature, which includes the effects of kinetic heating and latent heat of vaporization at the thermometer element, is probably a better guide to the likelihood of ice accretion than is the true air temperature (see also Section 8. 8).

Concentration of liquid water
The effect of high concentration of liquid water is similar to that of high temperature (but still below 0 °C): there is more latent heat to be dissipated to the air before freezing can take place of all the water impinging on the airframe. In this process the liquid water spreads over a large area with the formation of clear ice.

Air speed
An increase of air speed implies an increased rate of catch of supercooled drops and so has much the same effect as an increased concentration of liquid water in the cloud.

Size of supercooled drops
The smallest supercooled drops tend to freeze immediately on striking the airframe; the latent heat of fusion is quickly removed by the airstream and there is little or no spreading of the drop before freezing is complete. At the same time air is enclosed between the ice particles, so that the accretion takes the form of rime concentrated near the leading edges. On the other hand, large drops are accompanied by a spreading of water over the airframe while the latent heat is being dissipated, so that freezing takes place more slowly and tends to be in the form of clear ice. Drops of moderate size can produce results intermediate between these two, although the effect of drop size is not wholly separable from that of concentration of liquid water.

Severity of ice accretion
The severity of icing is defined as the rate of accumulation of ice by weight per unit area per unit time. Among the meteorological factors determining this rate are the amount of liquid water present and the size of the droplets. These characteristics are not the same throughout a particular cloud, even at one level. A cloud containing both liquid drops and ice crystals may have patches in which water drops predominate and others in which ice particles predominate. Subject to these variations from cloud to cloud and within clouds, icing will tend to be most severe when the temperature is not far below 0 °C, when the cloud droplets are large, and, in convective cloud, when the cloud-base temperature (see next section) is high. Though the likelihood of heavy accretion falls off as temperature decreases this must not be taken to imply that the intensity diminishes with height in any one cloud.

   It should be noted that routine measurements of liquid water content and sizes of droplets in clouds are not available to forecasters and that forecasts of the severity of ice accretion have to be made from the meteorological information which is generally available. An analysis of reports of ice accretion shows a preponderance of occasions at temperatures above about -10 °C and indicates that the frequency diminishes rapidly when temperature falls below about -20 °C; although on occasions icing has been reported at temperatures below -40 °C.

8.4 ICE ACCRETION AND CLOUD TYPE

Convective cloud
Observations show that at temperatures down to about -20 °C cumulus clouds nearly always have water drops. There have been very few observations at lower

temperatures but the occurrence of ice accretion indicates that water droplets must exist in cumulus clouds at lower temperatures. Cumulonimbus clouds have a cellular structure and while some cells are in the growing stage others may be decaying, so the composition of the cloud varies considerably at the same level. As the growing cells mature the liquid water content is continuously diminishing with time because ice crystals grow more rapidly than water droplets in a mixed cloud. Thus there is more liquid water in newly developed parts of the cloud than in mature parts. In general, liquid droplets predominate down to about -15 °C and either liquid drops or ice crystals may predominate between -15 °C and -30 °C.

In convective cloud the following rules may be generally accepted:

(i)   At temperatures below -40 °C the chance of icing is small.
(ii) At heights where temperatures are between about -20 °C and -40 °C the chance of moderate or severe icing is small except in newly developed convective cloud, but light icing is possible.
(iii) At heights where the temperature is between -20 °C and 0 °C the rate of icing may be severe over a substantial depth of cloud for a wide range of cloud-base temperatures.

Effect of temperature of cloud base

The cloud-base temperature has an important effect on the risk and severity of ice accretion in convective cloud because of its influence on the free water content throughout the whole cloud. At the cloud base the air is just saturated, and the higher the temperature, the higher is the vapour content. As the air ascends, vapour condenses and much of the condensed water is carried upwards. It is found that the average level of liquid water content per unit volume shows little variation with height over most of the cloud depth. The increasing condensation is largely offset by mixing with dry air from the cloud boundaries, by accretion on growing ice crystals in the precipitating cloud and, to a minor extent, by the expanding volume through which the drops are distributed. Consequently the free water content at any given level in a convective cloud increases with the temperature of the cloud base. Further, with increased concentration of supercooled water, ice accretion is likely to be more severe and as already seen is more likely to be in the form of glaze ice. The base of convective cloud occurs at much the same height in all latitudes, so that the temperature at the base is much greater in the tropics than it is in temperate latitudes, with the result that the liquid water content in convective clouds in the tropics is often about double that in temperate latitudes. Ice accretion at a given height above the level of the 0 °C isotherm in convective clouds is therefore likely to be noticeably more severe in tropical than in temperate latitudes. Similarly, in temperate latitudes the accretion in such cloud is likely to be more severe in summer than in winter.

Although the average level of water content shows little variation with height, there are local variations at a given level in any convective cloud and there is some evidence that the probability of encounter with local pockets of high water content increases with height above cloud base. Fig. 54 summarizes the dependence of icing intensity upon cloud-base temperature and cloud depth in convective cloud.

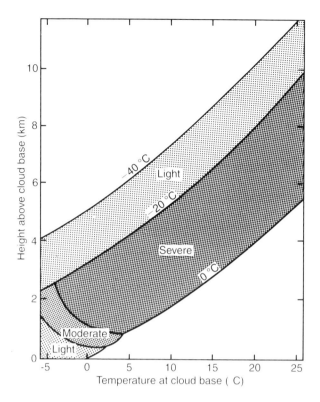

Figure 54. Airframe icing in convection cloud. Approximate thickness of layers within which various degrees of icing may be expected to occur. Base of cloud = 950 hPa, ambient relative humidity = 70%.

Layer cloud

At temperatures down to about −15 °C stratocumulus cloud usually consists entirely or predominantly of liquid drops. Altocumulus cloud usually consists entirely of liquid drops in temperature ranges down to −10 °C; at lower temperatures, down to −30 °C, ice crystals may be present but these are normally outnumbered by liquid water drops. Stratus cloud usually contains only water drops.

In general, the severity of icing in layer clouds of, say, 3000 feet thickness with tops at 850 hPa is moderate when the temperature at the top of the cloud is between 0 °C and −10 °C and light when the temperature at the top is less than −10 °C, but occasional severe icing may be encountered in this type of layer cloud with similar or even lower temperatures. Stratocumulus layers, especially over the sea in winter, are often formed by convection and in this case, and in stratocumulus formed by the spreading out of cumulus, the liquid water content will probably be greater than in stratocumulus formed by turbulent mixing and the severity of icing is also likely to be greater.

Altostratus and nimbostratus are usually formed by slow ascent of a large mass of air over an extensive area. The vertical extent of such clouds may be many thousands of feet. Some part of extensive clouds of this type is likely to contain supercooled water drops, and is thus a potential icing region if within the temperature range 0 °C to −15 °C. If the clouds are associated with active fronts, and particularly if there is an orographic effect due to the proximity of hills or mountains, the chance of severe icing is much increased, and icing may be encountered at temperatures lower than usual. Severe icing in these conditions has been reported at temperatures as low as −20 °C to −25 °C. If severe icing occurs in layer cloud, its horizontal extent can be extensive and the best avoiding action is a change in flight level. This is in distinction to convective cloud where the horizontal extent of any icing risk is limited.

Cirrus cloud
Cirrus clouds are usually composed of ice crystals which do not constitute an icing hazard to aircraft.

Orographic cloud
In clouds formed by the forced ascent of air over hills and mountains, entrainment of dry air is unlikely and the continued forced ascent may lead to further condensation. The continuous upward motion will generally mean a greater retention of water in the cloud, and because of this, icing is likely to be more severe in clouds over hills and mountains than in similar clouds away from high ground.

Stable air may become unstable when lifted or a weak front may easily become more active when passing over high ground. When stable air is lifted orographically the 0 °C isotherm is lowered and icing may be experienced at a lower level than in the same air mass over level ground.

The importance of the increase in the severity of icing in cloud subjected to orographic lift cannot be overemphasized.

Precipitation
On rare occasions, precipitation can become supercooled and lead to the formation of severe clear ice.

(i)   Rain falling into air with temperature below 0 °C. This occurs at low levels and is often associated with a warm front advancing against a cold air mass.

(ii)   Large water contents apparently composed of precipitation-sized drops have sometimes been reported at temperatures far below 0 °C in cumulonimbus clouds.

8.5 EFFECTS OF AIRFRAME ICING ON PERFORMANCE

The various parts of the airframe are affected in different ways by ice formation, both with regard to the types of ice likely to form and with regard to the effect of the accretion. The effects on performance are described below.

Aerodynamic effects
When ice forms on the leading edges of the airframe, the pattern of the airflow becomes modified round the affected part. This leads to an increase in drag, a decrease in lift, an increase in stalling speed and perhaps the buffeting of the tail.

Ice accretion on the leading edges of the fin and rudder and other movable parts may interfere with the airflow to such an extent that control is seriously affected.

As an object moves through air containing water drops, it catches only a fraction of the water which is present in the path swept out; this fraction varies with the shape of the object and is found for example to be greater for a thin wing than for a thick wing, other things being equal. It does not follow that a greater total weight of ice is collected by the thin wing, since the path swept out has a smaller cross-section. On the other hand, a small deposit on a thin wing may cause greater aerodynamic disturbance than a similar deposit on a thick wing. This dependence on shape explains why thin objects such as aerials, struts, leading edges of propellers, etc., are more liable to icing than are the more bluff parts of the airframe such as the nose of the fuselage.

The extremities of the propeller blades have a much higher speed than other parts of the aircraft and for this reason too one would expect this component to be susceptible to icing, but there is some protection from icing by kinetic heating.

The aerodynamic effects of ice accretion are of course not confined to disturbance at the leading edges. Ice forming on other parts of the wing or fuselage may lead to a considerable increase in drag. Ice formation under the wing may be particularly dangerous in that it is normally out of sight and its existence may be inferred only from a change in the performance of the aircraft.

Effect of weight of ice
The effect of the accumulated weight of ice is not generally of primary importance. An unequal distribution of ice may have serious effects however, particularly when it occurs on the propeller, for with this component, the lack of balance when part of the ice breaks away may lead to serious vibration. This type of hazard may also occur in connection with aerial masts, exposed balance weights and the arms actuating control surfaces; in extreme cases it may lead to fracture.

Effect on instruments
Any small projection from the skin of an aircraft is liable to gather ice; the pitot–static system and aerial masts are particularly susceptible. Apart from the risk of vibration and fracture already mentioned, the effect may be to reduce the efficiency of the part affected, leading to serious errors in measurement of air speed and to loss of communication facilities.

Effect on control surfaces
Normally there is a gap between the edge of a control surface and the surface to which it is fixed. In some positions of the controls, the air flows through the gap and ice may accumulate not only on the leading edge of the movable surface but in the gap itself, possibly sufficient to jam the control. The risk is greater on a small aircraft than on a large one, since on the former the gap is smaller and the movable part thinner, leading to a greater rate of accumulation.

Miscellaneous effects
Other common effects include the formation of an ice coating on windscreens and canopies so that vision is obstructed. This may be caused by flight in icing cloud, or may be due to hoar-frost formation in clear air when the very sudden occurrence may be disconcerting.

8.6 ENGINE ICING

Piston engines

Ice formation in the air intake and induction system of a reciprocating engine results in loss of engine power due to the obstruction of the air passages and to disturbance of the fuel metering, while movable parts may become inoperative. Engine icing is not only a low-temperature phenomenon; it may occur at air temperatures well above 0 °C and in clear air as well as in cloud and precipitation. There are three main types of induction system icing.

Impact ice   Impact ice may occur in much the same circumstances and manner as other airframe icing; ice builds up on air intakes and filters during flight through cloud or precipitation when either the ambient temperature or the temperature of the aircraft itself is below 0 °C. This is likely to be the only engine icing hazard for turbocharged engines.

Fuel icing   This occurs when water, held in suspension in the fuel, precipitates out and freezes at elbows in the induction piping; it is not a common occurrence.

Carburettor icing   This is the most common and most serious form. Carburettor icing is caused by the sudden temperature drop due to fuel vaporization and due to adiabatic cooling following the pressure reduction as air is accelerated through the carburettor venturi. The combined effect can reduce the temperature of the air within the carburettor by as much as 30 degC; the build up of ice gradually blocks the venturi, upsetting the fuel/air ratio and causing a progressive, smooth loss of power. The effect varies with the throttle settings; with reduced power settings engine temperatures are lower and the partially closed butterfly can be more easily restricted by an ice accumulation. Conventional float-type carburettors are more vulnerable to this form than pressure-jet types.

Carburettor icing can occur when the ambient temperature is well above 0 °C, indeed it is likely to present a greater hazard on humid summer days than on cold winter days when the vapour content of the air will be much reduced. It can occur in cloud or in clear air; because of the increased humidity the greater risk will be in cloud but the clear air occurrences are the more dangerous because of the lack of visual warning. Because of the dependence upon engine characteristics and throttle settings, specific forecasts of carburettor icing are never attempted. If temperature and dew-point information is to hand Fig. 55 may be used to assess the icing risk during flight in clear air. In the absence of such information the pilot should be alert to any other clues which might suggest high ambient humidity; some possible situations are:

(i)   when low-level visibility is poor, especially early morning and late evening,
(ii) when close to a large water surface,
(iii) when ground is wet and winds light,
(iv) just below cloud base or between layers, and
(v)   in clear air just after fog or cloud dispersal.

132

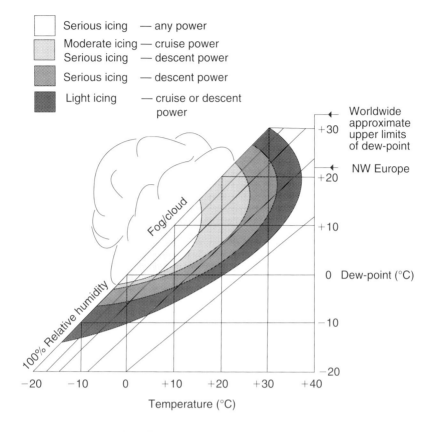

Figure 55.   Carburettor icing risk in clear air.

Turbine and jet engines

The intakes of turbine and jet engines are subject to icing in the same way as the airframe when flight is taking place in supercooled droplet cloud. The susceptible parts are the rim of the intake where the radius of curvature may be small, any struts across the intake, and the vanes in the early stages of the compressor. Thereafter temperatures are usually too high for icing to be a problem, although lumps of ice or lumps of snow breaking away from parts near to the entrance may cause damage or a flame-out in the engine.

Generally speaking, engine icing will be directly proportional to the rate of airflow through the engine and thus to the number of engine revolutions per minute. It is frequently found that the rate of icing may be reduced by decreasing engine revolutions.

When the jet engine is operating at high revolutions during flight at low speeds, as during take-off or landing, or whilst stationary, as in running up, the pressure within the intake is much less than the pressure outside. The consequent adiabatic expansion in the intake causes a drop in temperature of as much as 5 degC. If the clear indrawn air is moist and the temperature is near 0 °C, prolonged operation may result in condensation and ice formation when this would not occur on the airframe. This effect may accentuate the icing which would normally be expected when the flight is in icing cloud, or when the aircraft is taking off or landing in freezing fog. Usually jet engines ice up in flight only under those conditions which might be expected to produce airframe icing.

The intensities of icing on the airframe and in the engine may be different since the airframe icing rate depends upon the air speed, whilst engine icing depends in addition upon the engine speed (r.p.m.). At high air speeds the engine tends to be supplied with more air than it needs and there is a ram effect, whereas at low speeds, below about 250 KT, air is sucked in. Because of the ram effect at the higher speeds some of the air is deflected round the intake, but the inertia of the water drops results in a higher water concentration within the intake and the icing rate increases markedly with increase of air speed above 250 KT. At speeds where the air is being sucked in the water concentration of the air entering the intake remains virtually the same as in the free air, so that the engine icing rate tends to be constant with decreasing airspeed, whereas the airframe is likely to be showing a marked decrease of icing rate with decreasing air speed.

8.7 HELICOPTER ICING

As compared to fixed-wing aircraft, helicopters are particularly sensitive to the effects of ice accretion. The rotor blades are finely balanced to avoid vibration and the rotor head is subject to large centrifugal stresses. Even a comparatively small deposit of ice on the blades may have a serious effect on performance by destroying the aerodynamic lift, by causing vibrations and by increasing the centrifugal stress on the rotor head. Dangerous situations can arise within minutes of entry into icing conditions. Ice accretion on the head itself may interfere with the control of the blades. During running up on the ground, any vibrations set up by ice formation on the blades are liable to be transmitted to the springs of the undercarriage where sympathetic vibrations may become large enough to overturn the helicopter. There is danger also from pieces of ice leaving the blades at high speeds. Other problems include ingestion of snow by engines, and the icing of windows and aerials.

Helicopters are normally operated clear of cloud and therefore occasions of airframe icing are limited to flights at temperatures below 0 °C in rain, drizzle, wet fog or snow, although icing protection systems are being developed to enable helicopter operations in adverse winter conditions. The deposition of ice on a helicopter on the ground may be expected to occur as for a fixed-wing aircraft.

Present research is designed to establish the precise meteorological parameters which are most important for the accretion of ice on helicopters, and to determine the likelihood of these conditions occurring in relation to basic meteorological data. This will lead to an improved basis for the forecasting of the occurrence and severity of icing conditions and to the establishment of criteria to which icing protection systems must be designed.

8.8 PROCEDURES IN RELATION TO ICING RISKS

Pre-flight procedure
If an aircraft is left in the open on cold nights it should be protected from hoar-frost, rime, snow or rain ice. Any frozen deposit which has formed should be carefully and completely removed before take-off.

Route forecasts usually contain information giving the height of the 0 °C isotherm and, when cloud is expected at levels where the temperature is favourable for icing, the estimated icing conditions are indicated by one of the following terms: 'light icing', 'moderate icing' or 'severe icing'; these criteria are defined in Table 12 (Chapter 12). At certain airports the routine flight documentation may include a significant weather chart; this will include the height of the 0 °C isotherm. Where icing is expected this is indicated by a symbol on the chart together with the height range within which the hazard is expected to be confined.

Even if the forecast indicates a negligible risk, the pilot should nevertheless be prepared for icing, particularly if clouds are likely to be encountered at temperatures near or below 0 °C. It has been seen that the likelihood of icing depends in part upon the characteristics of the aircraft, but the forecaster cannot be expected to be aware of such differences. The pilot must therefore consider his own particular aircraft when deciding in the light of the forecast whether or not its performance is likely to be seriously impaired during flight. It must be remembered that a situation which presents no difficulty in normal conditions may become dangerous if the aircraft is handicapped by ice accretion with a possible reduction of lift and engine power and perhaps loss of control.

In-flight procedure

The fullest use should be made of any indication available in flight regarding the likelihood or type of ice accretion. The possible indications are explained below under the relevant headings.

Temperature. The indicated temperature given by the aircraft thermometer includes the effects of kinetic heating at the position of the thermometer element, but we have seen that the temperature is not uniform over the surface of the airframe. In clear air, the free-air temperature is obtained by applying a correction to the indicated temperature (Section 12.3), but in cloud or precipitation the required correction is not known precisely; moreover the reading may be falsified by ice on the thermometer itself. It is clear that implicit reliance should not be placed on either the indicated or the corrected temperature when in the neighbourhood of the 0 °C isotherm. It should be remembered too that engine icing can occur with air temperature well above 0 °C.

Radar echoes. Some aircraft are fitted with radar equipment which can be used to detect liquid or frozen water in the atmosphere. It appears that a radar echo of meteorological origin is likely to indicate a region where ice accretion is probable if the temperature is below 0 °C. With experience it is possible to recognize the kind of cloud associated with the various types of echo which appear on the screen. A clear-cut echo of high intensity frequently indicates a cloud of the convective type. A line of such echoes on the screen may indicate a line of cumulus or cumulonimbus clouds which may be embedded in other cloud which is not producing an echo. Warm front clouds (Chapter 16) usually give echoes which are less well defined and less intense. It must be emphasized that absence of an echo does not imply freedom from icing. The intensity of the echo is dependent upon the concentration and drop size of the liquid or frozen water in the cloud and if these are inadequate there will be no echo although ice accretion may still occur if the temperature is suitable. If it is possible to avoid the sub-freezing regions giving radar echoes then the worst icing conditions will probably be avoided also.

Optical phenomena. It is sometimes doubtful whether a particular cloud consists of ice particles or water drops. In this connection it is useful to remember that a halo of 22° radius (Section 10.9) is an indication of ice crystals, though absence of a halo does not necessarily indicate that the cloud is of water droplets. Also, a water cloud may be recognized from above by a 'glory', a system of coloured rings surrounding the shadow of the aircraft.

It might be thought that the visibility in a cloud should give a guide to the amount of water per unit volume and hence the risk of icing at appropriate temperatures. Unfortunately this is not a sound criterion and should not be used as the visibility depends on both the droplet size and the number of droplets and these are not proportional to the amount of water per unit volume.

Type of ice. If ice is seen to start forming on the airframe, some information can be obtained from its type. If the deposit is opaque, appears light in texture and grows out into the airstream, the conditions are probably not severe. If clear ice is observed to be forming, the rate of growth is likely to be rapid and immediate action is desirable.

Melting and evaporation of ice. Any ice formed might be expected to melt if the aircraft is flown to a region or level where the ambient temperature is above 0 °C. The critical temperature however is not necessarily 0 °C, because the ice evaporates slowly and acts as a wet-bulb (or ice-bulb), so that before melting can occur it is necessary that the wet-bulb temperature of the air should be above 0 °C. The effective wet-bulb temperature is that given by the uncorrected reading of a suitably placed wet-bulb thermometer which thus takes the kinetic heating into account. (For a similar reason, snow or hail falling through unsaturated air does not start to melt immediately on passing through the 0 °C isotherm but continues to fall unchanged in form until the corrected wet-bulb temperature is above 0 °C.) Although direct evaporation of airframe ice also takes place at temperatures below 0 °C, this is a very slow process. Successive traverses of cloud may therefore lead to a progressive accumulation of ice, and flight through clear air at only a few degrees above 0 °C provides no guarantee that the ice will disperse. Some possible procedures in relation to various conditions of airframe icing are discussed in the following paragraphs.

Procedure in relation to clouds

Altocumulus and altostratus. While altostratus cloud usually consists of ice crystals, the possibility of supercooled drops must not be ignored. Altocumulus usually has water droplets predominating, at least down to −30 °C. In both types the water content and the rate of ice accretion are likely to be low. Prolonged flight in such clouds may cause appreciable accretion but there should seldom be difficulty in getting out of the clouds, which are generally shallow, by change of flight level.

Stratocumulus. This is essentially a layer cloud in the lower part of the atmosphere. The vertical extent seldom exceeds 3000 feet so that it will usually be easy to climb above it. It is a water cloud of comparatively low water content so that the ice accretion is usually light or moderate and only very occasionally severe. It is unlikely to be serious unless flight in the cloud is prolonged. If it is known that a stratocumulus cloud has been either convectively or orographically formed, then a higher water content and a higher rate of icing should be expected than in stratocumulus formed by turbulence. There is also a possibility that cumulus clouds may penetrate the layer of stratocumulus; icing would then be intensified during flight through any embedded cumulus.

Convective clouds. Ice accretion is liable to be severe in large cumulus and cumulonimbus. A reduction in the intensity of icing cannot be expected as a result of increasing height unless the temperature eventually reached is less than about -20 °C and even then it is by no means certain that serious icing would be avoided; it is not until the temperature falls to about -40 °C that the risk becomes negligible. Hence if icing occurs during flight through large convective clouds, height should be reduced, subject to maintaining adequate ground clearance, to a level where the temperature is above 0 °C, or flight should be continued without deliberate change of height or heading until emergence from the cloud. Since the lateral dimensions of such clouds seldom exceed a few kilometres, the time occupied in a traverse is brief. Alternatively the clouds can often be avoided altogether, which is undoubtedly the safest course, not only with respect to ice accretion but also in regard to other risks inherent in flight through this cloud type (Chapter 7).

A proper appreciation of the remainder of this section requires some knowledge of the structure of frontal cloud systems. These are described in Chapter 16 to which cross reference should be made if needed.

Cold fronts. On occasion, large convective clouds amalgamate along fronts to form a belt possibly some hundreds of kilometres long and in extreme cases tens of kilometres wide. An increase in the width of the belt is usually accompanied by a decrease in the intensity of convection, but icing may be moderate or severe over a considerable distance. If flight below such a belt is impracticable, the use of radar, as already described, may be of considerable assistance in avoiding the worst places. A belt of this kind should be crossed at right angles. In this connection the importance of obtaining pre-flight advice about the location and orientation of fronts is emphasized. Extensive areas of convective cloud also occur at times in unstable air over mountainous country. In such cases the practicability of flying high enough to avoid most of the clouds should be considered.

Warm-front cloud. A characteristic of warm fronts is the extensive and almost horizontal layer of cloud. The base of the cloud (nimbostratus) is low near the surface front, where there is frequently steady rain, snow or a mixture of both. Ahead of the front the base of the cloud becomes higher and the whole cloud sheet thins out into a layer of altostratus or cirrostratus. The main cloud sheet near the front extends from a few hundred feet above the surface to at least 5000 ft and frequently above 10 000 ft, while some part of the frontal cloud system certainly contains supercooled drops and is thus a potential icing region.

If it is known that the air temperature is well above 0 °C in the lower layers, it is probably best for the low-flying aircraft to cross the front at a level where the temperature is above 0 °C, if terrain permits. If there is a large area of uniform frontal precipitation, serious icing should be anticipated within cloud in the temperature range 0 °C to -15 °C, i.e. in a layer perhaps 10 000 feet in depth. Moreover, supercooled rain may exist beneath the cloud (see below). At temperatures less than $-15\ °C$ there may be snow and the cloud will consist largely of ice crystals. The proper action then is to fly at a level where the temperature is either above $0\ °C$ or below $-15\ °C$, whichever is the more practicable in the prevailing circumstances. On the warm side of the front uniform precipitation is unlikely and the cloud may consist of water drops for a considerable height above the $0\ °C$ level. Flight should then be made, if possible, at a height below the $0\ °C$ level unless it is certain that flight can be made above the cloud layer.

If ice formation starts during flight in a cloud layer, descent may well prove better than ascent since the performance of the aircraft will already be affected to some extent by the ice and putting the aircraft into a climbing attitude will increase the risk of icing under the wing where it cannot be seen. It should be realized too that cumulonimbus clouds are occasionally embedded in warm front systems.

High ground near a warm front is particularly dangerous. Not only does the cloud obscure the hill tops but there is an increase in the free-water content of the air when forced to rise over the hills (Section 8.4). Furthermore, this lifting of air over hills may reduce the stability of the air mass with the possible formation of cumulus and cumulonimbus clouds.

Cold-front cloud.   At cold fronts the clouds are not usually extensive or unbroken and accordingly there is a better chance of avoiding the worst icing regions. Such clouds are, however, of the convective type with strong ascending currents so that the free-water content and rate of icing are liable to be higher than in warm-front clouds; embedded cumulonimbus clouds are a fairly common occurrence at the more active cold fronts.

The activity of a front is increased on passage over high ground and the possibility of large convective clouds and serious icing is increased.

Occlusions.   As the characteristics of an occlusion cover a range of conditions intermediate between those appropriate to warm and cold fronts, the icing characteristics of an occlusion may tend towards those of either type of front.

Procedure in relation to supercooled rain
Supercooled rain occurs under cloud ahead of warm fronts and warm occlusions and sometimes to the rear of cold fronts. When present, there is necessarily a warmer layer above, in which temperatures may exceed $0\ °C$. In low flight the best procedure for avoiding icing is to climb into the warm layer which will usually be found at no great height, although this should not be attempted unless the pilot is reasonably sure of the details of the meteorological situation. Descent to a layer where temperature is above $0\ °C$, if one exists, may be dangerous because of the low cloud base in the vicinity of the front. As with frontal cases discussed above, the belt of frontal cloud and rain should be crossed at right angles so as to give the shortest traverse through the icing region. A particularly dangerous procedure would be to fly parallel with the front in freezing rain, since this might result in a heavy accumulation of clear ice.

CHAPTER 9

VISIBILITY

9.1 INTRODUCTION

Modern developments in radio and radar have made it possible, in principle at least, to fly without ever looking outside the cockpit, but visibility remains a factor of great importance in all ordinary aircraft operations, both civil and military. A pilot's interest in visibility arises because he wants to know how far off he will be able to see various things — landmarks, targets, obstructions, beacons, both in the air and on the ground. Unfortunately a meteorologist cannot usually answer all of the pilot's questions fully and accurately because the range at which an object can be seen depends on many things besides the state of the atmosphere; it depends on the size, shape and colour of the object, on its illumination and background, on the pilot's keenness of vision, on the speed with which he is moving and on the transparency of his windscreen. Even if all these things could be known and allowed for there remains the fact that the state of the atmosphere often changes rapidly with height — a dense layer of fog at ground level may be associated with clear air at heights of a few hundred feet — and from place to place on the ground. It must therefore be emphasized that the meteorologist's reports and forecasts of visibility normally apply to horizontal visibility near the surface for particular localities, and in this form they often give little guidance about the visibility to be expected from aircraft in flight.

9.2 SOME DEFINITIONS

Meteorological observations are the subject of a later chapter, but it is probably worthwhile to consider some aspects of visibility observations at this point, for in conditions of visibility impairment the aviator will often be confronted by a METAR which contains two different visibility measurements, one which has come to be referred to as 'met vis' and the other the RVR. To avoid confusion it is important to know exactly what these two measurements mean.

To the atmospheric physicist the term 'visibility' will probably be interpreted as a measurement of the clarity of the atmosphere; in both meteorology and within the field of aviation the word is used rather differently to describe a distance, specifically, the furthest distance that could be seen if there was an unobstructed view; both 'met vis' and RVR are such distances, i.e. they are both 'visual ranges'.

'Met vis '
The meteorological visibility, or 'met vis' as we have called it above, is more properly known as the Meteorological Optical Range (MOR) and has been very precisely defined by the World Meteorological Organization in order to standardize observations worldwide. In all that follows we shall simply refer to the MOR as the 'visibility'; a down-to-earth definition of visibility is as follows:

Visibility is the greatest horizontal distance at which suitable objects can be recognized for what they are in daylight, or at which lights of specified candlepower can be seen at night, by a person of normal sight. In meteorological reports, when the visibility varies with direction of view, the usual procedure is to report the lowest visibility. (A few countries, notably USA, follow a different procedure.)

RVR

The runway visual range (RVR) may be defined as follows:

RVR is the maximum distance in the direction of take-off or landing at which the runway or the specified lights delineating the runway can be seen from a position on the centreline at a height corresponding to the average eye-level of the pilot at touchdown.

RVR versus visibility

From the above definitions it will be obvious that there are two major differences between the concepts of RVR and visibility measurements:

(i)   whereas RVR is concerned with the visual range in a single direction, the visibility is the lowest visual range within the whole 360° range of vision. If there is a patch of denser fog away from the runway, this may affect the visibility but not the RVR,

(ii)   visibility aims to measure only the transparency of the atmosphere and achieves this end at night by employing lights of known (low) candle-power whereas RVR systems may use high intensity lighting to maximize the visual range.

Other differences may arise from differing observation heights (the visibility refers to eye-level but RVR lights may be at a different height, even flush with the ground) and from the short baseline of instrumented RVR systems (the instrument may sample an unrepresentative patch).

Because of its great variability both in space and in time and its dependence upon the variable intensity of runway lighting, no attempt is made to forecast RVR and it is left to the pilot to infer landing conditions from the forecast visibility in the terminal aerodrome forecast (TAF). Inevitably, pilots look for some simple rule that will allow visibility to be converted into RVR but there are manifest dangers in the slavish adoption of any such 'rule', as may be seen from Fig. 56 which compares simultaneous observations of visibility and instrumented RVR (IRVR) at Heathrow. It will be recognized that there is a statistical relationship between the two observations, especially by day, but more striking is the wide observational scatter. The threshold of runway 28R (now re-designated 27R) is the nearest touchdown area to the meteorological observation site; an even greater disparity is found at the more distant runway thresholds.

9.2 IN-FLIGHT VISIBILITY

Air-to-ground visibility

It has already been pointed out that normal meteorological measurements of visibility are made horizontally at ground level and thus give little information

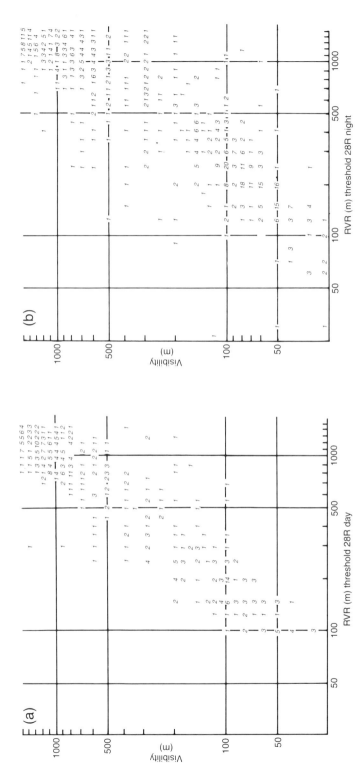

Figure 56. RVR versus Met. vis. at London (Heathrow), October 1972 to December 1979. Figures indicate the number of observations of simultaneous occurrences of RVR and visibility during (a) daylight hours, and (b) at night. Hours of twilight are not included.

141

about the visibility from points above the ground. Even from heights as low as 100 ft the 'slant visibility' may be much greater (when above a shallow layer of fog) or much less (when in a low cloud layer) than the horizontal visibility at ground level. The slant visibility may depend on the angle of slant; a common case is illustrated in Fig. 57 which represents a layer of fog covering an aerodrome with clear air above. From positions well above the fog, objects on the aerodrome can often be seen relatively clearly through a fairly small thickness of fog, but on descending to the level of the fog it may be impossible to see the aerodrome at all since a greater thickness of fog has to be penetrated. Moreover, glare caused by diffuse reflection of sunlight from the top of a layer of fog or haze, capped by a low-level inversion, can seriously reduce the air-to-ground visibility. For various reasons, then, there will on occasions be little relation between air-to-ground visibility and the normal visibility; in particular, it is important not to be deceived into thinking a landing easy because the aerodrome is clearly visible from above.

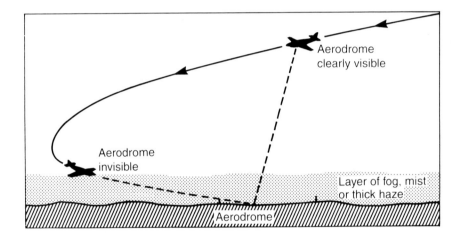

Figure 57.   Slant visibility through shallow fog.

Fig. 58 shows that in clear air above a layer of mist or haze the greatest horizontal distance at which the ground is visible from an aircraft increases steadily as the height of the aircraft increases. However, at higher altitudes objects on the ground are less easily seen because of diminished size, and in practice on any particular occasion there is an optimum altitude which gives the greatest horizontal ground range concurrent with the identification of ground objects. Sometimes it is possible to estimate the depth and opacity of the layer of mist or fog from ground observations and hence to deduce the ground range from any height, but the estimates can seldom be precise or reliable.

Air-to-air visibility
As with objects at ground level, the ability to see an object at higher levels (whether in a horizontal direction or not) depends not only on the state of the atmosphere but also on the state of the object being observed and on the observer himself. Thus the

142

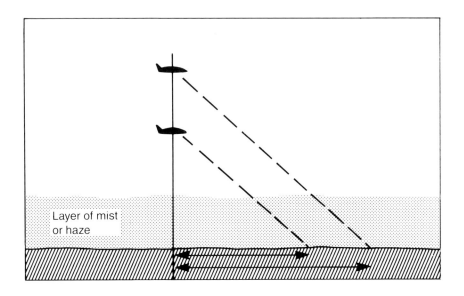

Figure 58.   Dependence of forward visual range upon altitude.

ability to see one aircraft from another depends among other things on the size, colour, illumination, background and speed of the remote aircraft, on the sight of the observer, the bearing of his line of sight relative to that of the sun or moon and on the transparency of the cockpit windows. The transparency of the atmosphere depends chiefly on the presence or absence of clouds. In cloud, visibility is almost always very low (though at great heights more tenuous clouds, equivalent to a thin mist, may be encountered); outside cloud and precipitation, visibility is normally good though layers of dust or haze may reduce it to one or two kilometres. In general, however, factors such as the size and speed of the object and the position of the sun in relation to object and observer play the chief part in deciding the range at which an object can be located visually.

At great heights, as in the stratosphere, cloud is rare and dust and haze are almost unknown but it does not follow that conditions for seeing an object are always good. The fact that the apparent brightness of the sun increases with the height of the observer while that of the sky decreases leads to greater dazzle than that which occurs at lower heights. Moreover, in the absence of objects on which to focus, the eye adjusts itself to a focus midway between distant and near vision and the location of an object at great heights is less easy than at small heights.

9.3 CAUSES OF ATMOSPHERIC OBSCURITY

The previous sections have shown how the distance at which an object can be seen depends on the position and characteristics of the observer and the object, as well as on the obscurity of the atmosphere between the two. In the remaining sections of this chapter we shall deal with the strictly meteorological aspects of visibility — the conditions determining the obscurity of the atmosphere at a given place and time.

The main causes of atmospheric obscurity may be classified as follows:

(i) fog and mist ....water droplets or ice particles,
(ii) cloud and precipitation .....water droplets or ice particles,
(iii) wind-blown sea spray ......water droplets,
(iv) smoke ....solid impurities,
(v) dust and sand ....solid impurities.

The invisible water vapour does not contribute to atmospheric obscurity, nor do the microscopic condensation nuclei referred to in Section 6.1.

9.4 FOG AND MIST

By definition, fog is composed of a suspension in the air of very small water droplets (or ice crystals in ice fog) reducing the horizontal visibility at the earth's surface to less than 1000 m. In mist, which is otherwise similarly defined, the visibility does not fall below 1000 m; the 1993 TAF and METAR codes impose an upper limit of 3000 m to mist which is there represented by the contraction 'BR'. Relative humidity is generally near 100% in fog and is at least 95% but generally less than 100% in mist.

Fog composed of water droplets (or possibly of ice crystals) may be looked upon as a cloud on the surface. Over high ground fog may indeed be merely one or other of the usual cloud types, requiring adiabatic ascent for its formation; the hills may protrude into a sheet of cloud or may themselves be the cause of local orographic cloud. Apart from such cases, condensation in the great majority of fogs is produced as a result of a relatively cold underlying surface. Two distinct types come within this category:

(i) radiation fog caused primarily by radiational loss of heat from the ground at night, and
(ii) advection fog caused by the transport of moist air over a relatively colder surface.

There is no essential difference between these types of fog except in the mode of cooling — in (i) the air remains stationary or slow moving while the ground cools, in (ii) the air is transported to a place of lower surface temperature. In addition to fog formed by condensation over a cold surface, there are two other types of water-drop fog:

(i) steaming fog caused by evaporation into cold air lying over warmer water, and
(ii) frontal fog caused by precipitation or low cloud.

While fog particles are usually water drops, they can be ice crystals. Such ice fogs are liable to occur in polar regions when the temperature is less than about −20 °C, the wind is light and other conditions are favourable.

9.5 RADIATION FOG

The development of radiation fog depends upon the cooling of the ground at night (Section 3.3). It is therefore a fog which forms only over land, although having once formed it may drift over coastal waters. There are occasions when radiation fog occurs before saturation is reached, even with relative humidity as low as 80%. These cases are explained in part by the presence of hygroscopic nuclei and in part by smoke pollution. Generally the air needs to cool at least to the dew-point before fog will form. The immediate cause of the cooling is the colder ground; the air in contact with it is cooled by conduction and the cooling is spread upwards mainly by turbulent mixing and to some extent perhaps by radiation. As the initial cooling takes place at the ground, an inversion tends to develop with the lowest temperatures on the ground and, if the dew-point is reached first on the surface itself, moisture extracted from the air is deposited as dew. In quiet conditions with little turbulence the cooling extends slowly upwards and the ground becomes much colder than the air at the height of a few feet. Just as condensation of water takes place on the cold walls of a room when the air is humid without there being any visible moisture in the air, so a copious deposit of dew may be formed without fog. In such cases the air above the surface is progressively dried so that its dew-point remains below the air temperature.

Take now the other extreme, strong winds with well-developed turbulence; the loss of heat from the ground by radiation may be equally rapid but the cooling is spread through a deep layer of air and air temperature falls but slowly. Since turbulence ensures a lapse rate approaching the dry adiabatic, the lowest temperatures are not near the ground but towards the top of the friction layer. If therefore the dew-point is reached at all it is likely to be at a height well above the surface, giving stratus or stratocumulus cloud but not fog.

If then, the air contains ample moisture, a rather delicate adjustment between the rate of cooling and the degree of turbulence is required to ensure that condensation shall take place in the air near the surface and not only at the ground as dew or above the surface as low cloud. It is therefore not surprising that radiation fog is erratic in its development, affecting one locality while leaving another clear when the differences in general conditions are otherwise hardly noticeable.

The conditions favourable for radiation fog are therefore:

(i)   a high relative humidity so that little cooling is required to reach saturation,
(ii) little or no cloud so that heat is lost by radiation from the surface, and
(iii) little wind so that cooling is confined to the surface layers, but sufficient to give some turbulence. A wind of 2–8 KT near the surface is considered to be the most favourable, although in practice fog should be expected even if the wind is calm.

An inversion of temperature is sometimes stated to be a further favourable factor; this is true of smoke fog but as regards water fog it is rather an accompanying condition than a cause, both condensation and inversion being caused by the surface cooling. The inversion usually appears near the ground before condensation begins, but as the fog forms the lapse becomes roughly isothermal from the ground upwards until the displaced inversion is found at the top of the fog. Loss of heat by radiation from the ground is almost completely prevented by a layer of fog, but further cooling by radiation takes place mainly from the top of the fog itself.

Dispersal of radiation fog
Generally, radiation fog clears during the day as a result of incoming radiation. Morning insolation heats the fog layer, turbulent mixing assists the process, and a point is reached where the visibility improves above the fog limit. Further heating may lead to a breakdown of the inversion, and mixing with the drier air above results in a further improvement in visibility.

Dispersal of the fog is complicated by changes in cloud cover. A layer of cloud spreading over early in the day may prevent fog clearance by reducing insolation, but on the other hand the fog may clear even more quickly if the loss of insolation is accompanied by a sufficient gain in downward long-wave radiation from the cloud base (see Section 3.3). The arrival of a cloud sheet during the night also modifies the radiation balance. Radiation from the top of the fog is reduced and the flux of heat upwards in the soil may raise the temperature of the air in contact with ground enough to clear the fog.

An increase in wind speed aids fog dispersal either by lifting the fog into low stratus, or by mixing the surface layers with drier layers above.

Diurnal and seasonal variation
The minimum night temperature occurs on average about dawn; the highest frequency of radiation fogs might naturally be expected at the same time, but experience shows that the maximum appears about an hour after sunrise. The slight increase in turbulence is considered to be the factor which causes existing fog to thicken or a sudden formation to occur when only dew had formed before. Whatever the cause, the fact is important, and consideration should be given to the possibility of a sudden formation of fog just after sunrise following a clear quiet night. The fog formed either during the night or in the early morning requires further heating before it will clear. In winter when the sun has little strength the clearance may be long delayed and a thick fog, which shuts out the heat of the sun, is particularly likely to persist; in summer, radiation fog is infrequent and unlikely to persist much after sunrise. Because of the long nights and the generally low land-temperatures, the winter half of the year is very liable to radiation fog, although in most districts there is a greater incidence in autumn, with its greater diurnal range of temperature, than in winter. The seasonal and diurnal variation of fog at Heathrow is shown at Fig. 59; such a distribution is typical of many inland British Isles sites although one would expect differences in some coastal areas and in different climatic regimes. The principles are everywhere the same, but climatic differences are all-important; in some very dry climates fog is almost or entirely unknown.

Local influences
The topography and the condition of the ground are factors responsible for the local nature of many radiation fogs. When conditions are very favourable the fog becomes widespread and may cover a large area in an unbroken sheet, but usually its incidence is more localized. Aggravation by smoke pollution will be considered later; it is the pure water fog with which we are now concerned. The most noticeable feature is its tendency to develop first in valleys, due partly to the

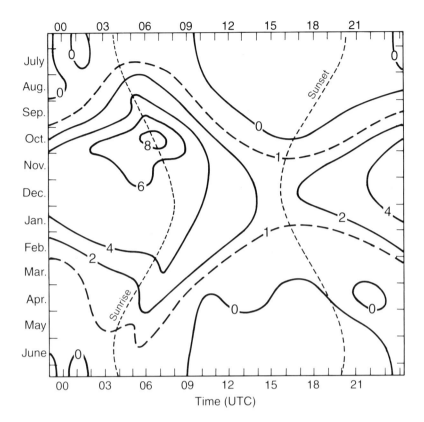

Figure 59.   Diurnal and seasonal variation of fog. Percentage frequency of visibility less than 1000 m at London (Heathrow) Airport, 1965–1991.

katabatic drainage of cold air into the lower-lying places, and partly to the marked nocturnal fall in surface temperature in sheltered localities; the higher humidity when a stream or river flows along the valley is a further factor — although if the river is wide its higher temperature may keep the air immediately above free from fog when the surrounding banks are enveloped. Although waterlogged or moist ground is less easily cooled at night than the dry ground, the effect on humidity is generally the more important, so that fen country is notoriously foggy; similarly, fog is particularly likely when the sky clears at night after rain. Apart from moisture content there are other properties of the ground, particularly the conductivity, which account for local peculiarities.

Not infrequently, observations show that fog forms first on high ground, and this is especially true of some sudden developments in the early morning. We should, however, always remember that the conditions favourable for fog and for low stratus cloud are much the same, the difference being a matter of turbulence; the fog which forms on higher ground may generally be better regarded as low cloud. When fog clears it often passes through the stage of stratus which is sometimes then described as lifted fog; fog lifting from valleys may envelop nearby previously clear hill sites before it finally disperses.

Vertical thickness

There is no precise lower limit to the vertical extent of a fog; it may be a few feet in depth forming a ground fog, while many valley fogs are also quite shallow. In general, however, fog develops to occupy the whole of the friction layer; although, in average circumstances, the depth of the friction layer is usually taken as 1500 ft or more, it is much less in the light winds and stable lapse rate of foggy conditions. Most radiation fogs have a depth of only a few hundred feet. The upper surface is usually sharp with clear air above; seen from above, there is little or nothing in the appearance to distinguish between a thick fog and low stratus cloud.

In meteorological reports, distinction is made between fogs through which the sky is discernible and those through which it is not. The depth of fog necessary to prevent the sky being observed in daylight is roughly 300 feet.

Pressure types associated with radiation fog

Several types of pressure distribution may be associated with radiation fog but all have one feature in common, a slack pressure gradient, i.e. with the isobars widely separated, so giving little wind. This condition eliminates most depressions, which are also unfavourable because of their cloudy skies, but on occasions in a weak or decaying depression the slack pressure gradient and scarcity of cloud do allow fog to form readily. In general, however, one associates radiation fog with quiet anticyclonic conditions, an indefinite pressure distribution, or a col. Long foggy periods in winter are invariably associated with a persistent anticyclone.

9.6 ADVECTION FOG

Advection fog occurs when air moves over a cooler surface of land or sea, the surface temperature being below the dew-point of the moving air. Over the land, advection fog is particularly likely in winter after a cold spell when a supply of milder air arrives from the sea. The humidity is often already high, for the air may have become almost saturated over the sea, and further cooling by contact with the land readily produces fog and perhaps even drizzle. The conditions for fog are especially favourable during a thaw produced in this way, since melting snow maintains the temperature of the ground at 0 °C, while evaporation ensures an ample supply of water vapour. In other cases the ground itself becomes gradually warmer until after a few hours its temperature rises above the dew-point and the formation of fog then ceases; thus a broad belt of fog advances across country in the forward position of the mild air. If the wind is more than moderate, turbulence lifts the condensation level above the surface and low cloud is formed rather than fog, although if drizzle is present it may keep the surface visibility below 1000 m, the defining limit of fog. Even if there should be no fog at low levels, the moist air very readily becomes saturated by orographic lifting forming 'fog' over quite low hills, as discussed above; the frequent winter fogs over southern and south-western England with south-westerly winds are a combination of both effects, except when caused by fog drifting from the sea.

Over the sea, advection fog may form in three different ways. In the first place, the transport of relatively warm air from the land to a colder sea produces fog, mostly in spring and summer, since the temperature contrast is then most favourable. Even if the air from the land is not particularly moist, evaporation will accompany the surface cooling and sooner or later the dew-point will be reached. Secondly air may flow from a warmer part of the sea over a much cooler current, a well-known example being the fog of the Newfoundland Grand Banks caused by the cold waters of the Labrador current. Thirdly, advection fog may develop in an extensive mass of air as it becomes cooled on moving into higher latitudes. For example, if air from the subtropical oceans moves polewards it easily becomes saturated on arrival over the sea in temperate regions, for the cooling may amount to some 10 or 15 degC. Sea fog, in contrast with fog over land, can form and persist with moderate or even strong wind; often the drizzle stage is reached, reducing visibility below the fog limit even if the fog itself should be lifted off the surface. Fog formed in this way is often widespread and occurs in any season but it is much more frequent in summer than in winter. Coastal regions with an onshore wind may be similarly affected by sea fog at any time of the year, but on a warm day the fog dissipates on passing inland. An example of advection fog drifting over the coast is the 'haar' of eastern Scotland.

There is little or no diurnal variation in advection fog over the sea. Clearance occurs with a change of air mass, or less commonly, with an increase of surface wind.

Advection fog is not confined to any particular pressure distribution, since the only general requirement is that the air should move towards a cooler surface and this is as likely to happen in a cyclonic as in an anticyclonic circulation. Some further remarks about advection fog will be found in Chapters 15 and 16.

The above paragraphs have treated advection and radiation as quite separate fog-forming processes; in most cases this will be so but in others radiation and advection (and also upslope) may all contribute to fog formation. The example of Stansted may be mentioned: a light south-easterly advection of moist air from the Thames estuary over gently rising ground under good radiation conditions will often cause fog to form when it fails to occur at other places where one or other of the three ingredients is lacking.

9.7 STEAMING FOG

This is named by analogy with the condensed vapour or steam appearing above water which is heated; invisible vapour is given off from the water but is almost immediately recondensed on coming into contact with the colder air. The process requires that the air should be much cooler than the water; in these circumstances convection currents rapidly develop and fog cannot form unless certain other conditions are also present. These are:

(i)   a marked surface inversion in the air before it moves over the sea or inland water, otherwise the lapse rate would quickly be rendered unstable through a deep layer.

(ii) a low temperature, usually about 0 °C or below, so that a comparatively small amount of moisture will produce supersaturation. If this condition is not satisfied, the heating process will outweigh the tendency towards saturation.

Fogs of this type are in consequence confined to water surfaces near a source of cold air, such as frozen land, or ice-floes in polar regions; the sudden break-up of

149

sea ice to expose relatively warm water is a classic situation for this phenomenon; the steaming of roads and bitumen-covered roofs in sunshine after rain is another example of the same process. In Icelandic and Norwegian fjords and similar regions elsewhere, the fog may attain a depth of 500 ft or more and drift inland so that nearby airfields may be rendered unserviceable. Other names for this type of fog are 'Arctic sea smoke' and 'frost smoke'.

9.8 FRONTAL FOG

Both radiation and advection fog may be described as 'air mass' fogs since they depend on cooling taking place within an extensive and more or less uniform mass of air (see Chapter 15). In contrast, 'frontal' fog is associated with the interaction between adjacent air masses. It occurs in one of two ways, either as cloud coming down to the surface with the passage of a front, a type which is more common over hills than over low ground; or it may develop because of saturation occurring in continuous rain preceding the warm front or warm occlusion of a depression, when it forms a belt some hundreds of kilometres in length and perhaps 300 km in breadth which advances with the front (see Chapter 16).

9.9 VISIBILITY IN CLOUD AND PRECIPITATION

Visibility in cloud
Horizontal visibility in cloud varies from less than about 10 m to over 1000 m according to cloud type. In cirrus, visibility usually exceeds 1000 m, in medium cloud it ranges from about 1000 m down to 20 m, while in all types of low cloud the range is generally below 30 m and may fall below 10 m in cumulus and cumulonimbus; see Table 7.

Visibility in precipitation
Visibility through rain may be shown to be inversely proportional to both the total water content and the number of raindrops. Thus visibility deteriorations are greatest in heavy rain (large mass of water) and in drizzle (small droplet size). For rain (as distinct from drizzle) statistical studies in various countries have consistently revealed logarithmic relationships between visibility and rainfall rate of the form shown in Fig. 60. The relationship shown assumes, of course, that the visibility reduction is entirely due to the rainfall and there is no pre-existing atmospheric obscuration such as fog or smoke. Even so, there will be some divergence in individual cases due to varying rainfall drop-size distributions. It is seen that slight rain has little effect, moderate rain usually gives a visibility of 5–10 km, while heavy showers may reduce visibility to about 1000 m. The heavy rain of tropical regions is associated with a visibility of 50–500 m.

Snow has a much greater impact on visibility than rain, the visibility commonly falling below 1000 m even in moderate snow, while in heavy snow it may vary from about 200 m to less than 50 m. Again, individual cases may deviate from the precise relationship implied by Fig. 60 and in particular, it should be noted that with dry snowflakes visibilities will commonly be only about half those given in the figure; as snowflakes become wetter at temperatures near to 0 °C they collapse to

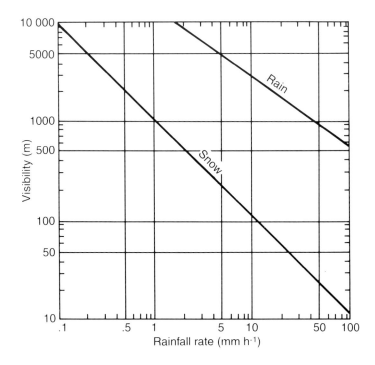

Figure 60.   Visibility in rain and snow.

occupy a smaller volume and become translucent, thereby allowing the passage of some light.

In drizzle the visibility ranges according to intensity from about 3000 m down to 500 m but on some occasions the simultaneous presence of fog droplets reduces the visibility to less than 500 m.

Visibility can also be reduced, at times seriously, by snow raised from the ground by the wind; this is described as drifting snow (DRSN in TAF and METAR codes) if the raised snow remains within two metres of the ground or as blowing snow (BLSN in TAF/METAR) if it extends above two metres. This is most likely to occur when the snow is dry and powdery, that is to say when temperatures are low, hence it is particularly a phenomenon of higher latitudes.

9.10 WIND-BLOWN SPRAY

When the surface wind speed over the sea reaches Beaufort force 5, many 'white horses' are formed and spray begins to form from the breaking waves. With stronger winds, foam is blown in streaks along the wind but it is not until the strength reaches force 9 (severe gale) that spray begins to reduce surface visibility. The effect intensifies with further increase of wind and in hurricane-force winds (force 12) the visibility is said to be 'very seriously affected'. The deterioration is confined to levels within the friction layer. Coasts with onshore winds may similarly be affected by spray.

151

9.11 REDUCTION OF VISIBILITY BY SMOKE

In quiet weather the air is often polluted with haze caused by the smoke from industrial and domestic fires. The larger particles settle easily under gravity and do not drift far from the source areas, but much of the pollution is in the form of finely divided particles, comparable in size with the water droplets in a cloud, which may remain suspended in the air until eventually washed out by rain or snow.

The obscurity produced by smoke depends on:

   (i)   the rate at which smoke is being produced,
   (ii) the rate at which it is dispersed by wind and turbulence, both horizontally and vertically, and
   (iii) the distance from the smoke source.

In light winds and calms, the smoke remains near the source and local visibility may be seriously reduced. The smoke may be dissipated upwards by convection during the day but at night, and by day also if there is an inversion of temperature, it is generally confined near the surface and horizontal visibility remains low. The stronger the wind, the more rapidly is the smoke carried away and dissipated through the atmosphere. Not only does the plume of smoke broaden as distance from the source increases, but it also tends to spread vertically unless confined by an inversion.

For the reasons given above, the reduction of visibility by smoke occurs mainly near large industrial areas in the winter season. Although visibility in the vicinity of a particularly troublesome source may fall below 1000 m, it is unusual in regions where smoke emissions are controlled for industrial haze to reduce horizontal visibility below 3000 m.

Smoke emissions are a plentiful source of hygroscopic nuclei, i.e. particles which accelerate the condensation of water vapour; for this reason radiation fogs tend to form more readily in smoky conditions, often some time before the relative humidity reaches 100%. The name 'smog' was coined to describe these smoke-augmented radiation fogs but the term is now more often used to describe the reduced visibilities and poor air quality of large cities where strong sunlight reacts with the hydrocarbon emissions from motor vehicles to produce elevated levels of ozone and other photochemical pollutants.

9.12 REDUCTION OF VISIBILITY BY SOLID MATTER

Volcanic ash
One source of atmospheric dust is the solid matter thrown out from active volcanoes; it is carried as haze to great distances and is indeed regarded as an important climatic factor since it reduces the intensity of the solar radiation reaching the ground; as an element in aviation meteorology it is normally of little significance. However, there have been reports of jet engines being damaged and even extinguished as a result of their ingestion of excessive quantities of volcanic dust and clearly, active volcanic regions should be avoided where possible; volcanic ash is now included in the list of hazards for which SIGMET warnings are issued.

Dust or sand?

The sources of solid matter which are of more general concern to aviation are the sandy deserts and, in the dry season, the semi-desert regions of the world. Dust and sand from these regions can constitute a serious visibility hazard.

Meteorological codes have not as a rule distinguished between dust and sand, but the 1993 TAF and METAR codes do now allow a distinction to be made, dust being represented by DU and sand by SA. In fact, there are important differences between the behaviour of the two forms. Desert sand grains usually have a mean diameter of between 0.15 and 0.3 mm and a lower limit of 0.08 mm. Any particle of smaller diameter than 0.08 mm is defined as dust. The distinction is meteorologically important since vertical currents near the surface are not usually sufficient to raise sand grains more than a metre or so above the ground whereas dust particles are readily raised and may be held in suspension in the atmosphere to very great heights.

Sand

Sand moves across the surface by the process of 'saltation'. When a flying grain falls to the ground, if it should strike the hard surface of a pebble, it bounces off to be driven by the wind in a low curving trajectory before falling once again to the ground; at the moment of impact it disturbs other grains, setting these in motion too. The bounding process continues until eventually the grain reaches a non-resilient surface into which it sinks or it is trapped between pebbles or it arrives at a hard surface where there are no other grains to be disturbed. It follows that movement of the type described will never be found to occur far from locations where there is not a plentiful source of sand; such an observation may seem too obvious but it is all too easy to assume that any site in an arid zone is sandy when in fact many desert areas consist of rock or pebble plains and are therefore not susceptible to driving sand.

The wind speed at which sand movement commences depends upon the grain size as well as the stability but in most situations movement should be expected when the wind speed (at standard anemometer height of 10 m) reaches about 20 KT. The height to which sand is raised will increase with increasing wind speed and ultimately horizontal visibility at eye-level will be impaired; often however, the driving sand will form a low-flying cloud below eye-level; low objects on the ground may be obscured while taller objects stand proud above the sand cloud. The incidence of sandstorms is closely related to the diurnal cycle of wind changes and hence these storms are primarily a daytime phenomenon but intense desert depressions may on occasion produce deteriorations at other times of day.

Remote airstrips, where there is little disturbance of the surface by traffic, may experience pure sandstorms of this type but most major desert airfields will be located near to inhabited areas where human, animal and especially vehicular activity play an important part in breaking down the sandy surface to produce the finer dust or soil; here any increase in wind speed is likely to produce the very different duststorm or a mixed storm of sand and dust together.

Dust

Disturbance of the finer dust particles is likely to begin when the wind speed at 10 metres reaches about 15 KT, although here again much depends upon the condition of the surface and the degree of instability. Once raised into the air the saltation process will take place as described above and some of the larger particles will fall back to earth to disturb further small particles, but because of their much lower terminal velocities the smallest particles will be retained in suspension by the turbulent flow and may be carried to great heights and far beyond the source region. As the wind speed increases visibility reduction soon extends above eye-level and with winds of 30 KT or more the horizontal visibility may fall to a few hundred metres. As with sandstorms, duststorms are principally a feature of the daylight hours, beginning as the wind picks up after dawn and easing once cooling commences after mid-afternoon, but they may occur at other times due to the passage of frontal systems or depressions or as a result of local wind circulations. Moreover, because so much material is held in suspension, the improvement of visibility after the wind has dropped out is likely to be slow and visibility impairment may continue for a day or so after the more severe duststorms.

The terms 'duststorm' and 'sandstorm' are usually reserved for those occasions when the horizontal visibility is reduced below 1000 m ('fog' limits) but there is no international uniformity and pilots flying to areas known to be subject to these phenomena would be well advised to check on national practices in this respect.

Dust and sand in Britain
We typically think of North Africa and other desert areas when considering the effects of dust and sand but it should not be overlooked that visibility deteriorations from these phenomena do sometimes occur in Britain. Airfields bordering the south side of the Moray Firth are particularly subject to blowing sand from coastal dunes whilst stations in East Anglia are occasionally affected by fenland 'blows' in which finely cultivated top-soil is raised by stronger-than-usual winds at times of drought, typically by the dry continental easterlies of early spring before growth has started.

Haboobs
Among the more severe types of duststorm are the haboobs of the Sudan. The term has been loosely used in the past in connection with any duststorm but is better restricted to the duststorms of summer which are associated with cumulonimbus clouds. Because of the gusty wind and the strong convection in and below the clouds, the dust is carried high into the air, sometimes even to above 10 000 ft, especially when the cloud base is this high. The storms can be seen approaching at distances of 80 km or more as an apparently solid wall of dust and their arrival is characterized by a sudden increase of wind and a rapid deterioration of visibility. It may not always be practicable to fly over them, but in most cases they can be avoided. In local flying a careful watch should be kept; if a landing is contemplated it should be made in good time and the aircraft placed if possible under cover as a protection from the penetrating dust and the possibly violent squalls. Although the storms form initially during the day, the time of occurrence at any one place depends on the locality, as they frequently form in association with a line-squall and travel along with it.

Dust devils or sand pillars
During the heat of the day over any hot and dusty region, small whirlwinds develop by convection; these are known as dust devils or sand pillars. Their diameter is quite

small, perhaps a few metres, but the wind may easily exceed gale force in the whirl and surface dust is picked up and carried in a dense column to 1000 or 2000 ft. Minor structural damage is not uncommon but as a factor in visibility they are of no particular consequence owing to the small area covered. They should of course be avoided in flight, particularly at take-off and landing.

Dust haze
The fine dust carried upwards in duststorms of various sorts is gradually dissipated through the atmosphere and gives a general haziness to all air of desert origin. Polluted air may remain hazy for days or even indefinitely because the particles are too small to fall at any measurable speed by gravity. Haze commonly extends to 10 000 ft; it seldom reduces visibility to less than 1000 m but the air-to-ground visibility is invariably less than that at the ground. The final clearance may not occur until the particles are washed out by rain or snow, perhaps thousands of miles from the place of origin. This process gives rise to the 'coloured rain' or 'blood rain' which sometimes reaches the British Isles.

Haze layers
Sharply defined layers of haze may occur at any level in the troposphere and give a haze horizon when viewed from above. The most common occurrence is when the surface air, polluted with smoke or dust, is carried upwards by turbulence and convection until it meets a reduced lapse rate or inversion which the upcurrents cannot penetrate. Largely on account of the diffuse reflection of light from the upper surface, the layer may completely obscure the ground in any direction far from the vertical; on some occasions the ground may be entirely invisible although the aircraft may be seen clearly by an observer on the ground. Occasionally a haze layer is found in a position which would be occupied by cloud if the air were sufficiently humid, or it indicates a layer previously occupied by cloud which has been evaporated by descent and adiabatic warming. Anticyclonic regions, in which subsidence is characteristic, have usually one or more haze layers in the higher levels. Dust would not be expected to penetrate to any observable degree into the stratosphere, but when free from cloud, the tropopause may be revealed as a well-marked haze layer when viewed from above.

9.13 ARTIFICIAL DISPERSAL OF FOG

The problem of the artificial dispersal of fog on an airfield is one of some importance in aviation. It became a practical proposition during World War II but since then its use has been severely limited because of the expense.

The method used then was to produce heat by petrol burners arranged in lines forming a rectangle enclosing the runway but at a distance of at least 50 m from its boundaries. When air containing fog droplets is heated, some of the heat is absorbed in evaporating the drops and the rest in raising the temperature of the air. After the fog has been dispersed by heat, small convective clouds form and these tend to merge into a stratocumulus layer. This layer can delay re-formation of the fog. For radiation fogs it was found that the amount of heat required to disperse a dense fog was equal to that required to produce a rise of 4 degC in clear conditions; smaller amounts of heat were found sufficient to disperse thick and moderate fogs.

Experiments also showed that the larger fog droplets take an appreciable time to evaporate, even though ample heat is available. The amount of heat required depends among other factors on the speed of the wind and on its direction relative to the runway. The artificial dispersal of advection fog is more difficult because of the greater wind speeds which are usually present.

In more recent years a number of different methods have been tried operationally to clear, or to effect a thinning of, radiation fog. These include strategically placed jet engines placed alongside the runway and spraying with propane. Any process which involves the combustion of fossil fuels not only produces heat but adds more water vapour to the air, hence any improvement is usually short-lived. Fogs in sub-zero temperatures have been dispersed in the USA and in the former USSR by seeding with dry ice (solid carbon dioxide). As the dry ice falls it produces many tiny ice crystals which grow into snow at the expense of the supercooled drops. The visibility usually improves within about 30 minutes and the improvement is maintained for about an hour.

CHAPTER 10

SPECIAL TOPICS

10.1 CONDENSATION TRAILS

Condensation trails (contrails for short) are elongated streaks of cloud formed by the passage of an aircraft. Although commonly associated with the upper troposphere, they can form at any level, even at the ground, depending upon temperature, humidity and characteristics of the aircraft. They are formed in various ways, the more important of which are described below.

Exhaust trails
One of the combustion products of petrol and other aviation fuels is water; this is ejected through the exhaust and tends to raise the relative humidity of the air in the wake of the engines. On the other hand, the heat generated by the engines tends to lower the relative humidity by raising the temperature in the wake. In certain conditions the net result is to increase the humidity to saturation so that a cloud is formed which trails behind the aircraft. This type of trail can ordinarily occur only if the air temperature is below a critical value which varies almost linearly from about -24 °C at sea level to about -45 °C at 50 000 ft. The critical temperatures, which are only slightly affected by the type of aircraft, are indicated on the tephigram by a line marked MINTRA and apply to an aircraft flying at cruising speed in an atmosphere just saturated with respect to ice; the corresponding temperatures for saturation with respect to water are lower by about 2 or 3 degC. It should be mentioned that trails can occur exceptionally at temperatures above the MINTRA value, for example when the free air is supersaturated with respect to ice, or when fuel consumption is greater than it is under normal cruising conditions, as when operating with throttle fully open. Conversely, trail formation may at times be lessened or even avoided by reducing the throttle setting.

Once a trail is formed, it broadens by diffusion. If the surrounding air is at or near saturation, the trail evaporates only slowly or not at all and is then long and persistent; if the relative humidity is low, the trail appears only as a short plume behind the aircraft. It was remarked earlier that supersaturation with respect to ice is not uncommon. Since the exhaust gases contain sublimation nuclei, any trail formed in these conditions is persistent and may thicken until the ice particles fall out as snow. In the stratosphere, because of the extremely low relative humidity normally found in this region, exhaust trails are usually short-lived. If, however, the temperature is very low, then only a small increase in vapour content is required for saturation so that persistent trails may then be formed; these conditions are most likely to occur in the tropical stratosphere where the lowest temperatures are to be found.

The MINTRA temperature at any level is such that condensation trails cannot ordinarily form at any higher ambient temperature. The converse that trails should form when the air temperature is less than MINTRA is not true. The attainment of saturation is not sufficient for the trail to become visible; condensed water or ice particles must be present in a sufficient concentration to be seen, and this depends upon illumination, background contrast, distance, and other viewing conditions.

The MINTRA is that temperature above which a trail will not ordinarily form even if the ambient air is already saturated. A DRYTRA would be a line joining temperatures at which trails must occur even if the ambient air is completely dry. Between these two limits, corresponding with saturation and complete dryness, trail formation may be expected to depend on the relative humidity of the environment. It is generally accepted that at temperatures less than 11 degC below MINTRA, visible trails are not expected; at temperatures 11 to 14 degC below MINTRA, non-persistent short trails are probable; at temperatures more than 14 degC below MINTRA, persistent long trails are expected.

Trails may form at any height attained by an aircraft provided that the temperature is suitable. Over southern England the height at which exhaust trails would be expected to form in the winter ranges from about 26 000 to 70 000 ft; in summer, when the stratosphere is warmer, the range is from about 30 000 to 45 000 ft. At high latitudes, trails can occur at low levels or even at ground level.

Wing-tip trails
These very thin transient trails are formed aerodynamically by the reduction of pressure at the extremities of the wings of an aircraft, the adiabatic expansion causing a reduction of temperature to below the dew-point. These trails are most frequently seen in association with aircraft in tight turns as the maximum reduction in pressure at the wing tips occurs at these times. If the temperature is already low, insufficient water may be condensed to produce a visible trail; furthermore, if the air is very dry the condensation point may not be reached. Accordingly these trails are usually seen in mild, damp weather at low altitudes. Similar effects may occur at the tips of the propeller blades and over the upper surface of the wings.

Formation of condensation trails
From what has been already stated, it can be seen that the formation of condensation trails depends on the ambient temperature and humidity at the flight level of the aircraft. If it is desired to avoid the formation of trails, it is necessary to fly at an altitude where the air is either sufficiently warm, with a temperature above the MINTRA value, or is very dry. If the throttle setting is reduced as far as is practicable, it will reduce the amount of water injected into the atmosphere and will therefore decrease the likelihood of trails forming.

10.2 MACH NUMBER

At high air speeds compressibility of the air as it impinges on the airframe assumes great importance but the significant factor is not the actual speed of the aircraft but the ratio of its speed to the local velocity of sound; this ratio is known as the Mach number. During flight, the disturbance caused by the aircraft sets up pressure waves which spread out in all directions with the speed of sound. At air speeds much less than the speed of sound, the pressure waves move ahead of the aircraft so that when the aircraft reaches any point the air is already modified and flow over the airframe is reasonably smooth. When, on the other hand, the air speed is greater than that of sound, the pressure waves set up by the motion cannot reach the air ahead; the aircraft is then flying into undisturbed air; there is intense compression on the leading edges and the flow pattern is much less smooth than the one which prevails at low speeds. These changes have an adverse effect on lift and drag, on the stability of the aircraft and on its reaction to the controls, and begin to become noticeable at about two-thirds the speed of sound. Knowledge of the Mach number is therefore vital for pilots and is given directly by a meter on the instrument panel.

The speed of sound in dry air is proportional to the square root of the absolute temperature. At sea level (temperature 15 °C) in the International Standard Atmosphere the speed of sound is 663 KT; in the stratosphere (-56.5 °C) it is 574 KT. Thus the machmeter has to be designed to take account of the dependence of the speed of sound on temperature. The meter however makes use only of pressures, as the following argument shows. If p' is the dynamic pressure on a leading edge as measured by a pitot head, and p the static pressure, then $p' - p$ is proportional to ρA^2 where ρ is the air density and A the air speed. Thus A is proportional to $\sqrt{\{(p' - p)/\rho\}}$ or to $\sqrt{\{(p' - p)T/p\}}$, where T is the temperature in kelvin. Also the speed of sound a is proportional to $\sqrt{T}$, therefore the Mach number A/a is proportional to $\sqrt{\{(p' - p)/p\}}$ and so depends only on the dynamic and static pressures.

10.3 WINDS AND TEMPERATURES IN THE STRATOSPHERE

With the advent of satellites stratospheric observations are now readily available; observations show that conditions in the stratosphere vary considerably between summer and winter.

In the northern hemisphere during the summer months winds and temperatures usually change little with time. Average values of July temperature and wind at 50 hPa (approximately 67 000 ft) are shown at Figs 61 and 62. These will be fairly representative of conditions at any time during summer months. The main feature of the temperature field at 50 hPa is a warm area near the pole, which is in continuous daylight, and a gradual decrease in temperature towards the equator. As would be expected with this temperature distribution, Fig. 62 shows there is a mean easterly flow over the whole hemisphere.

The 50 hPa temperatures and winds for winter in the northern hemisphere are represented by January maps, shown in Figs 63 and 64. There is a cold vortex near the pole, a warm region over the Aleutians, a warm belt around the hemisphere near latitudes 45° to 55° N and a cold region over the tropics. Fig. 64 shows a well defined belt of westerly winds, with speeds in excess of 50 KT, near the pole. In general the zonal westerly component increases with height up to the stratopause. In lower latitudes and in accord with the reversed thermal gradient from 45° N to the equator the average 50 hPa wind is a light easterly. In the tropics the winds are more complex than the mean picture suggests and in places there is a pronounced fluctuation between easterlies and westerlies with a period of between 22 and 35 months — the so-called quasi-biennial oscillation (QBO).

Late winter and early spring marks the time of change from winter to summer regime when the thermal gradient towards the pole reverses. There is considerable variation from one year to the next in the timing and manner of this change; the change may be abrupt, being completed in a matter of days, and it may occur as

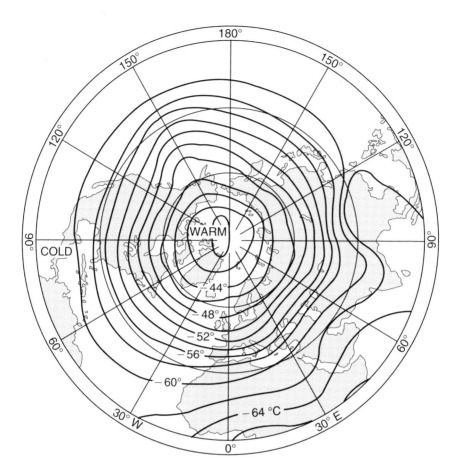

Figure 61.   Average 50 hPa temperature in July.

early as January or as late as April; local changes of 50 degC in a few days have been observed. In other years the temperature might fluctuate between its winter and summer values for a period of weeks before settling down.

Summer conditions in the southern hemisphere are similar to those in the northern hemisphere and are characterized by a warm South Pole and an easterly flow symmetrically placed about the pole and the winds are generally a little stronger because the thermal gradients are greater. The winter southern hemisphere is also subject to sudden warmings. These disturbances appear to be less common than they are in the northern hemisphere winter.

10.4 SUPERSONIC FLIGHT — A SUMMARY OF NATURAL HAZARDS IN THE TROPOSPHERE AND LOWER STRATOSPHERE

Despite the general observation that most of the weather is confined to the troposphere, hazards from meteorological and other phenomena still exist for flight

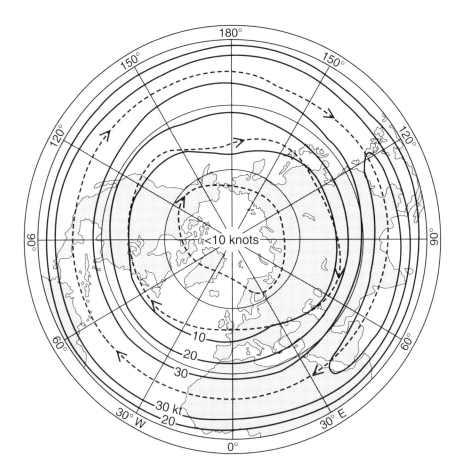

Figure 62. Average 50 hPa wind in July. Solid lines are isotachs and broken lines are streamlines.

above the tropopause. Known hazards and the range of altitude in which they may be encountered are summarized in Fig. 65.

Turbulence in the stratosphere, although much less frequent than in the troposphere, is by no means negligible. It can be experienced near and above cumulonimbus clouds. Mountain lee waves and waves above cumulonimbus tops which protrude into the stratosphere, although normally smooth, can break up into turbulent areas at times.

As aircraft speeds increase, the damage caused by heavy rain and hail increases. Hail can occur in cumulonimbus, and can also fall through clear air through the overhanging cirrus canopy. Airborne weather radar assists in pinpointing heavy precipitation, but a precise knowledge of the precipitation occurring within 100 km of an airfield prior to take-off is only available where weather radar information is received.

The thrust of a jet engine decreases with increasing temperature. Flight planning on the basis of the International Standard Atmosphere will give an optimistic

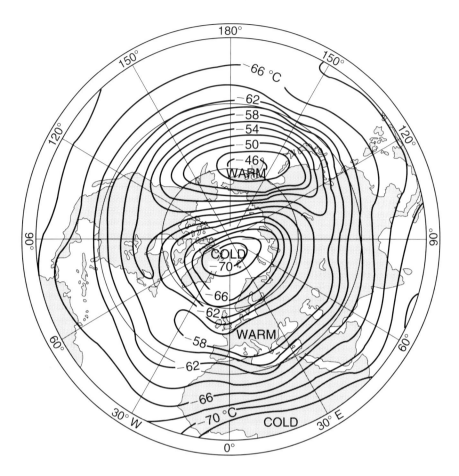

Figure 63. Average 50 hPa temperature in January.

estimate of the available thrust on days when the atmosphere is warmer. Large changes of temperature occur in clear air around and above cumulonimbus clouds and in the large-scale stratospheric warmings in winter and spring.

Intensity and location of a sonic boom, although dependent on aircraft characteristics, are affected by wind and temperature structure between the aircraft and the ground. The speed of sound is proportional to the square root of the kelvin temperature but the track of the sound from any point is influenced by the local wind. Changes in wind and temperature as the aircraft climbs can cause a focusing of sound rays from different parts of the track, leading to a local increase in the noise.

Concentrations of ozone above the tolerable limit are normal in the atmosphere from about 50 000 to 100 000 ft. Air fed to cabins may need to be filtered in some way to free it from excess ozone, but the high temperature in the compressor from which the cabin air is taken will assist by causing thermal decomposition of the gas.

Cosmic radiation of normal intensity is not a hazard, but at times of solar flares, outbreaks of radiation may be unacceptably high and flight at lower levels may be advisable to give the necessary screening.

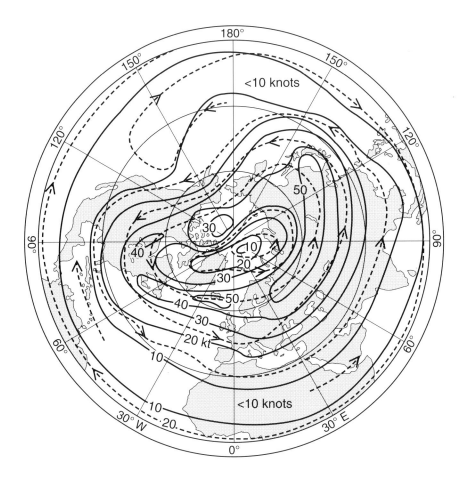

Figure 64. Average 50 hPa wind in January. Solid lines are isotachs and broken lines are streamlines.

Knowledge of meteorological processes is increasing steadily but much remains to be discovered, particularly about the lower stratosphere and the details of cumulonimbus clouds. It is clearly important that a pilot should have as full a knowledge as possible of when and where hazardous conditions are likely to occur. Such knowledge will be obtained partly from his own experience and from observations made during flight, and partly from forecasts and reports supplied before take-off and in flight. To some extent adverse conditions may be avoided by flight planning or by action taken during flight, but often risks have to be accepted and then foreknowledge is important so that necessary precautions can be taken in good time.

10.5 FLYING CONDITIONS IN CLOUD — A SUMMARY

The flying conditions in clouds have been considered under a number of different subject headings in the preceding chapters. Many of the conclusions have been

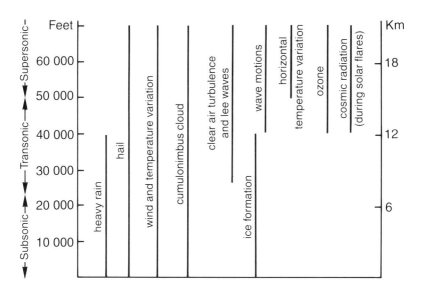

Figure 65.   The extent of natural hazards likely to be encountered during subsonic, transonic and supersonic flight (after R.F. Jones).

gathered together here in Table 7 as a brief summary of the likely conditions to be expected in each of the main cloud types. Circumstances may dictate that flight has to be conducted above, within or below cloud; it is important that the pilot should be able to recognize the type of cloud and hence to be able to form an idea of what conditions are to be expected in carrying out his mission.

10.6 DESIGN OF AERODROMES

Many factors come into the siting of an aerodrome which are independent of meteorology and are likely to be of paramount importance. As regards the meteorological aspects, the main factors which need to be considered are as follows: visibility, particularly for the frequency of fog; cloud, particularly for the frequency of low cloud; and finally wind, especially for the occurrence of strong or gusty winds which could be caused by local topographical features.

Layout of runways in relation to wind
An aerodrome runway is considered to be unsafe for use by an aircraft when the wind component at right angles to it exceeds a certain critical value which depends upon the type of aircraft. The 'usability' of a runway in relation to wind is the percentage of time during which the cross-wind component is equal to or less than the critical value. From climatological tables of the frequency of occurrence of various wind speeds and directions, this 'usability' factor can be determined for any particular critical value of the cross-wind component.

Siting of blind-approach systems
The radio installations which provide aids for blind approach to an aerodrome need to be sited to be of use on as many occasions as possible. The placing is therefore

TABLE 7. Summary of flying conditions in cloud

Cloud type	Constitution	Continuity	Height of base	Vertical thickness	Horizontal visibility	Airframe icing	Turbulence	Remarks
Cirrus (Ci)	detached			usually thin, but may reach 5000–10 000 ft in low latitudes; may extend to tropopause	over 1000 m	rare, light	nil or slight except when merging into Cb	may merge into Cs or Cb
Cirrostratus (Cs)	ice crystals; rarely mixed*	continuous	usually above 20 000 ft					may merge into As
Cirrocumulus (Cc)	ice crystals, or water drops, or mixed*	layer clouds composed of detached globular masses		usually thin				may merge into Cs
Altocumulus (Ac)	usually water drops to −10 °C, some crystals at lower temperatures		6500–20 000 ft		20–1000 m	rime, light to moderate		
Altostratus (As)	usually ice crystals, occasionally mixed*	continuous, often 8 oktas cover	6500–20 000 ft but occasionally less than 6500 ft	up to 15 000 ft				often merges below into Ns
Nimbostratus (Ns)	water drops	continuous	surface to 8000 ft	merges into As	10–20 m	rime or moderate clear ice; possibly rain ice below cloud	severe near base, moderate elsewhere	envelops hills
Cumulus (Cu)	water drops	isolated, but may cover 6 oktas	usually 1500–15 000 ft	up to about 15 000 ft	generally less than 20 m, and at times less than 10 m	rime or clear ice, possibly heavy; no safe lower limit to temperatures	severe	large Cu may develop into Cb
Cumulonimbus (Cb)	mainly water drops to −15 °C, mixed* at lower temperature	usually isolated clouds 5–10 km diameter; occasionally form a continuous line; may be embedded in layer cloud	usually 1500–5000 ft but may be down to surface over water	15 000–30 000 ft or more, especially in low latitudes; may reach tropopause			severe or very severe within 15 km horizontally and 5000–10 000 ft vertically	risk of lightning, severe 'static' and hail
Stratocumulus (Sc)	mainly water drops	layer of globular masses or rolls, often continuous	usually 1500–4000 ft	500–3000 ft	10–30 m	rime, moderate	moderate	sometimes penetrated by large Cu or Cb
Stratus (St)	water drops	continuous	surface to 2000 ft	200–1000 ft		rime, light to moderate	nil or slight	envelops low hills

*i.e. containing both water drops and ice

165

influenced by the most frequent direction of the wind on occasions when poor visibility or low cloud produces blind-approach conditions. This direction is not usually the same as the direction of the prevailing wind. A meteorologist with experience of conditions at the aerodrome in question may be able to give an opinion as to which end of the runway should be chosen, but generally it is essential to make a statistical examination of the association of bad visibility and low cloud with wind speed and direction. Such an examination will show also whether more than one blind-approach installation would be required to provide adequate coverage.

10.7 METEOROLOGY FOR HELICOPTER OPERATIONS

Meteorological factors of importance in the operation of fixed-wing aircraft have been emphasized from time to time in preceding chapters. The somewhat different considerations which apply to the operation of helicopters are brought together here and described briefly under the various parameter headings.

Surface wind
Ground operations. In conditions of wind speeds over 25 KT or of gusty winds, caution in handling the helicopter on the ground is necessary. Under these conditions rotor blades are liable to undergo marked vertical oscillations (blade sailing) when rotating slowly during starting up and stopping, and to flap up and down when at rest. Both blade sailing and flapping constitute a serious hazard to personnel and equipment within the rotor diameter as well as to the aircraft fuselage. Conditions conducive to both of these phenomena are often found to lee of hills, large buildings (hangars etc.), large trees and other similar structures. Certain types of helicopter are fitted with stops to confine these oscillations within safe limits in wind speeds up to about 40 KT. As wind speed increases, taxiing the helicopter across wind becomes progressively more difficult.

During take-off and landing. The speed and direction of the surface winds are of great importance for take-off and landing in very restricted areas. Particular care must be taken at night when marked cooling at the surface may result in the surface wind being much lighter and markedly backed in direction from the wind at a few hundred feet above the surface; the resultant shearing often gives turbulent conditions on the last stage of the descent. Before a landing is made in a valley, the wind direction should be checked carefully, as valley winds can vary in direction to a considerable extent from the general wind.

The phenomenon of 'running snow' is encountered when a strong wind blows over frozen or partly frozen snow and 'grains' of snow are set in motion across the surface; a layer of moving snow is formed and the pilot receives the impression that he is moving forward, particularly if he is touching down in a large flat snowfield. Snow may acquire a frozen surface layer as a result of melting in the sun followed by re-freezing; several landings will break up this surface and in strong winds the snow may 'run' on the landing area.

Turbulence
Turbulence has a serious effect on helicopter operations particularly when these are in mountainous regions, or at low levels in poor visibility, and when instrument or

night flying is undertaken. Turbulence often dictates what flight path the helicopter pilot must choose to ensure the safety of his aircraft, particularly when approaching landing zones in mountainous terrain. It is possible that even entry into autorotation will not arrest a climb induced by a strong updraught, or conversely, the application of full power may not prevent a helicopter from descending in a marked downdraught. Further, one of the most serious effects of turbulence is the effect on retreating-blade stall speed. An up-gust increases the blade's angle of attack and can cause a blade already operating at a high angle of attack to stall. It is on record that a helicopter with a computed stall speed of 80 KT actually stalled at 40 KT because of turbulence.

During operations in mountainous regions particular attention needs to be paid to the possibility of standing waves (Section 5.5) or rotor-streaming turbulence which may make operations dangerous or even prohibitive. The probability of sharp changes in wind speed and direction in rotor zones close to cliff edges makes them particularly dangerous landing sites in strong winds.

Temperature

Increased air-intake temperatures will decrease the power output of a piston engine at a given throttle setting and for a gas turbine engine the same applies for a given compressor speed. This can limit the power available and affect the performance of the helicopter. As most helicopters on operations normally fly to maximum all-up weight, the effects of high temperatures, possibly accompanied by high moisture content, on the air density (Chapter 4) and hence on the performance of the helicopter, may have to be considered during the planning of an operation. Low air-intake temperatures may be conducive to the formation of engine icing.

Visibility

If the horizontal visibility is less than 1500 m, it may be necessary to reduce the cruising speed, for reasons of safety, to below the economic speed with a consequent increase in fuel consumption and loss of endurance. It should be remembered that when there is smoke or haze beneath an inversion the haze is often thicker near the inversion than at the surface. Thus a pilot flying at, say, 500–1000 ft above ground and just below the inversion may experience a horizontal visibility appreciably less than that which prevails at ground level.

Cloud

As long as the ground can be seen, very low cloud bases are not in themselves a problem to the helicopter pilot, although they may force him to fly so close to the ground that turbulence may become a problem. Flying in cloud is generally avoided although there may be limited flying in stable stratified cloud. Flying should not be planned in very turbulent cloud, nor in any type of cloud at temperatures below 0 °C.

Diffused light conditions are very dangerous when flight is near snow-covered mountains. The light, broken up by a layer of cloud or haze, forms no shadows and this makes it difficult for the pilot to gain an impression of relief, or to judge distances to a point on the ground, which appears as a uniform layer.

Precipitation
If precipitation reduces the horizontal visibility below 1500 m there may be loss of endurance as already explained.

When a flight is made at low speed in moderate or heavy snow or when the helicopter is hovering, snow may collect in appreciable amounts on the nose of the aircraft and may cover air-intake grills; this causes air starvation, loss of power and possibly engine failure. If this snow becomes compacted, possibly turning to ice, and breaks off and enters the engine, turbine damage may result. When the ground is covered with dry powdery snow, helicopters taking off, landing, or flying very near to the ground often experience extremely poor visibility ('white-out') because of the recirculation of the snow.

Ice formation
This very important topic has been fully discussed in Sections 8.5–8.7.

10.8 RADIO METEOROLOGY

The term 'radio meteorology' concerns the relationship between meteorological conditions and the transmission and reception of radio signals. As such it includes the production of radio echoes by clouds and precipitation, a subject which is dealt with in Section 13.1. We now consider the effect of weather on radio communications, whether these are for ground-to-ground or ground-to-air links. In the United Kingdom, the radio communications used by Air Traffic Control have been designed to be independent of any weather phenomenon. This aim has been achieved by use of an adequate number of transmitters with sufficient power to overcome any atmospheric effects. The discussion in the remainder of this section is confined to the phenomenon of 'anomalous propagation' of radio waves and its effect on radio communications.

In normal atmospheric conditions, when the temperature decreases from the surface upwards roughly according to the normal lapse rate and when there is no marked variation of humidity with height, the horizontal range of radio transmissions of wavelength less than about 10 metres is limited to the distance of the 'radio horizon'. Since even in these conditions the radio waves undergo a small amount of downward refraction, the radio horizon is somewhat beyond the optical horizon. The distance of the optical horizon from a point at height h above the earth's surface is $(2 h R)^{0.5}$ where R is the earth's radius; the distance of the radio horizon is greater than this by about one-third. When anomalous propagation occurs, the range may be many times the normal and for this to be possible the rays must be bent or refracted so that they remain near the earth's surface. Adequate bending of the rays occurs when the conditions near the surface are such that with increase of height either the temperature increases or the humidity decreases at rates greater than certain critical values. For temperature this value is almost 4 degC per 100 ft, the exact figure on any occasion depending on the actual temperature, pressure and humidity. If the humidity is expressed in terms of mixing ratio, then at a temperature of 15 °C the critical value of the humidity lapse is 0.5 g kg^{-1} per 100 feet while at other temperatures the value is somewhat modified. Thus for super-refraction to occur there must be marked inversion of temperature or a decrease of absolute humidity with increase of height. In practice, the variations of temperature and humidity need to be considered together and the conditions to be satisfied then reduce to a single criterion, namely the condition that the algebraic sum:

$$\frac{\text{temperature gradient}}{\text{critical temperature gradient}} + \frac{\text{humidity lapse}}{\text{critical humidity lapse}}$$

should exceed unity.

Special investigations show that either or both of the critical gradients are in fact exceeded in the surface layers on a small percentage of occasions in the neighbourhood of the British Isles, while in subtropical and tropical latitudes the conditions are satisfied much more frequently, especially over the sea.

Radio ducts
In most cases of anomalous propagation, the ray has a path of the type illustrated in Fig. 66. After leaving the transmitter at a small angle to the horizontal, the ray is gradually bent downwards in the super-refracting layer until it meets the earth's surface; here it is reflected and the process repeated. It is found that the direction of emission must be limited to within about half a degree of the horizontal, for otherwise the refraction is insufficient to keep the ray near the surface and it escapes into the upper atmosphere. The layer within which the state of super-refraction exists is called a 'radio duct'. It will be appreciated that the energy of the waves is effectively trapped within the duct, so that the signal strength is maintained over great distances with little attenuation. Naturally, for anomalous propagation it is necessary for a duct to exist not only at the site of the transmitter but also over the whole range of propagation.

A radio duct does not necessarily rest on the earth's surface as in the illustration but may occur raised above the surface. Super-refraction is, by definition, limited to the actual duct, but rays emerging from its lower surface eventually re-enter the duct after reflection at the earth's surface. Below the duct, rays are usually refracted upwards. This does not interfere with propagation provided the duct is near enough to the surface, but if not the ray re-enters the duct at too great an angle to the horizontal and so escapes through the top of the duct. In practice the height of the upper boundary of a surface or elevated duct is often within 1000 feet of the earth's surface, although this figure may well be exceeded in certain regions. The depth of duct required for abnormal propagation increases with the wavelength, being about 50 ft for a wavelength of 3 cm and about 600 ft for a wavelength of 1 m. Since a

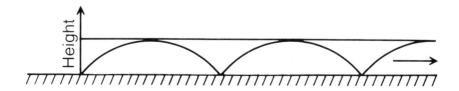

Figure 66.   Radio propagation through a surface duct. The ray is alternately refracted in the duct and reflected at the earth's surface.

surface duct is usually less than 1000 ft deep, the frequency of occurrence of the phenomenon is greater at the shorter wavelengths.

Some practical results
Anomalous propagation has been reported from many places but the most striking results occur in tropical and subtropical areas and may be illustrated by observations made in the vicinity of the Indian subcontinent. There the meteorological conditions at certain times of the year are such as to give super-refraction almost continuously and days on which the range is 'normal' are unusual. Observations from Bombay with a 1.5 m radar transmitter with a normal range of about 50 km showed that echoes were received from the Arabian coast 1300 km distant (as well as from ships in the Arabian Sea) on 67 days out of 105 during a period in the early part of the year; the extreme range exceeded 2400 km. Similarly, in Bengal, super-refraction over land was reported at a similar installation on 232 nights in a single year.

Effect of wavelength
Anomalous propagation is observed only with wavelengths from about 10 m to less than 1 cm (30 to more than 30 000 MHz) and the shorter the wavelength the more effective is the super-refraction. Waves longer than 10 m (frequency less than 30 MHz) depend on ionospheric reflection for propagation beyond the radio horizon (Section 1.3). On the other hand, short waves used for radar, even when not super-refracted, are not reflected by the ionosphere.

Meteorological conditions in relation to anomalous propagation
Since the conditions of temperature and humidity in which a radio duct forms are concerned only with a shallow layer near the surface, detailed observations are rarely available to indicate the existence of a duct at the position of the transmitter, still less over the extensive range for which anomalous propagation might be expected. The meteorological processes favouring the formation of ducts are, however, known and the first step is to be able to recognize when such processes are present. Some notes on these will now be given, but whether a useful duct is actually formed on any occasion is, apart from actual trial, a matter requiring quantitative investigation and is not considered any further here.

Subsidence. When this takes place over the sea, the descending air is warmed while the sea surface temperature remains practically unchanged; hence a surface inversion is set up provided the subsiding air reaches a low enough level. Also, the water vapour content is high in the air in contact with the sea and lower in the subsided air, so that both temperature and humidity profiles are favourable to duct formation. These conditions are commonly associated with anticyclonic areas and also with certain other types of flow, including the trade winds and the north-east monsoon of Asia.

Advection. When relatively warm dry air moves over the sea, evaporation takes place and the resulting humidity lapse is usually sufficient to form a duct; in addition there may be a temperature inversion. This type is found in the vicinity of India and Iran, over the Mediterranean and off the coasts of most continents. When the air which has been heated over land during the day passes over coastal waters, both the temperature inversion and the humidity lapse may be adequate for a duct, but the effects diminish as the air drifts further out to sea.

If cold dry air is passing over a relatively warm sea, the temperature decreases with height and so is unfavourable for a duct, but this disadvantage may be outweighed by the strong humidity lapse. Whether or not a duct forms can be decided only by further investigation.

Over land, the advection of relatively dry air can be effective in producing a duct when the surface is wet, for example, after rain, for a humidity lapse is then established. Naturally these conditions no longer remain favourable after the ground has become dry.

Sea-breeze. An effect of the sea-breeze is to bring moisture inland in the lower layers for a short distance, so setting up a strong humidity lapse; in addition the humidity lapse over the sea surface is increased somewhat. Thus the humidity conditions become favourable for the formation of a duct which, although limited to an area of a few kilometres either side of the coastline, may be useful for coastwise transmission.

Nocturnal radiation. This is effective in setting up the necessary temperature inversion over land at night. It is most pronounced in anticyclonic and other conditions associated with clear skies and light winds or calms, and a surface duct forms unless fog develops.

Fog. No surface duct forms in fog, since in this condition the temperature and humidity show little change with height. There may, however, be an elevated duct near the top of the fog, owing to the rapid reduction of humidity in this region. This is most likely to occur when the top of the fog is sharply defined, as with radiation fog; with advection fog the top is often diffuse and possibly merges into cloud, and no duct would then be formed. A duct elevated in this way can be effective only if the fog is shallow, for it has been seen that a duct which is raised too far above the ground is unable to give super-refraction.

Strong winds and turbulence may be mentioned as factors particularly unfavourable to the formation of ducts, since the tendency with them is towards a fall of temperature with height and a constant humidity mixing ratio. Surface heating is also unfavourable since it produces a temperature lapse, but on occasions this effect is overcome by that of a strong humidity lapse.

Nature of the surface. In addition to the meteorological conditions, the terrain should be considered. The sea presents an essentially flat surface, as the waves are too small to interfere with radio propagation; consequently the determining factors in the formation of a duct over the sea are solely meteorological. Similarly over desert areas the conditions may be almost uniform, but elsewhere over land the undulations of the surface and the variations in type of soil and vegetation make it impossible to assert the existence of a duct over an extensive area except in extreme conditions which should be easily recognized. Over rugged country the problem of duct formation becomes even more difficult and, moreover, the method by which anomalous propagation takes place in these circumstances is not fully understood. In such situations the practical results obtained by radio operators are of the utmost value to the forecaster.

10.9 OPTICAL EFFECTS

Atmospheric optical phenomena provide a field of investigation of great scientific interest, but they have little practical significance in aviation although they occasionally provide some useful clues as to the constitution of the cloud particles concerned, information which may be relevant to the risk of ice accretion (Section 8.8). A brief account follows of some of some of the more frequent optical manifestations.

Rainbow

The common or primary rainbow is a circle, or an arc of a circle, of coloured light, the centre of which is always in line with the observer's eye and the sun, while the radius of the circle subtends an angle of about 42° at the eye. The bow results from refraction of the sun's rays both on entering and on leaving a raindrop, together with one internal reflection. In the conventional bow, the colours are those of the visible spectrum from red on the outside to violet on the inside, but the coloration is not the same in all rainbows, being dependent on the size of the drops. A secondary rainbow concentric with the primary is occasionally seen but with a radius of about 52° and with the colours in the reverse order.

Halo

The term halo is used by the meteorologist only for the luminous effects produced by the refraction and reflection of light by prismatic ice crystals and hence in most cases by some form of cirrus cloud. The commonest case is a circle of light of angular radius 22° centred at the sun or moon. When well developed the halo round the sun shows a pure clear red on the inner side but other colours are usually difficult to recognize and the outside of the ring appears white. A halo may be seen in whole or in part on the average on one day in three at any one place in the British Isles. There is a large variety of other halo phenomena of less frequent occurrence, such as the halo of 46° radius, 'mock suns' or patches of light at the same elevation as the sun and close to the 22° halo, vertical pillars and curved arcs of various radii.

Corona

Coloured luminous rings of various angular radii may often be seen surrounding the sun or moon. They are formed by diffraction of light from water drops and the colours are usually dull, red appears on the outside and blue on the inside, similar to the succession in the primary rainbow and opposite to that in the halo. They are most frequently seen when the watery sun or moon shines through a thin layer of altostratus cloud. The radius of the corona is inversely proportional to the size of the cloud droplets and the colours are purest when the droplets are of uniform size.

Glory

Another manifestation often observed from the air is a ring of colours surrounding the shadow of the aircraft on a cloud layer. This is called the 'Brocken spectre' or the 'glory'. It may be seen from an elevated position on the ground if the sun casts the shadow of the observer onto a layer of low-lying mist or fog.

Mirage

Rays of light passing through the atmosphere are subject to a certain amount of bending on account of the varying refractive power of air of varying density. For this reason objects below the geometric horizon sometimes become visible and curious distortions of the sun near the horizon are common. Even in ordinary conditions, the sun is already below the geometric horizon before the disc begins to disappear at sunset. In abnormal conditions, refraction accounts for the phenomena of mirage.

Inferior mirage. Mirages are of two kinds. Inferior mirage occurs when air near the ground is much hotter and thus less dense than that immediately above, a common condition by day over a heated desert. Rays coming down from the sky at a gentle inclination may be bent up again to the observer to whom they appear to come from a bright water surface, while the images of objects near the ground are inverted. Mirages of this type may often be seen over smooth road surfaces on calm sunny days.

Superior mirage. The opposite effect, known as superior mirage, occurs in conditions of a marked inversion of temperature, the light rays in this case being bent downwards. This is seen more frequently in polar regions. The image, usually inverted but sometimes erect, appears above the objects. As the stratification which produces superior mirage is stable, the image is clear and well defined in contrast to the shimmering image of the inferior mirage; moreover, the distances are much greater so that the details can hardly be observed without telescopic aid. The phenomenon of anomalous propagation of radar signals (Section 10.8) bears an obvious resemblance to that of superior mirage in so far as the temperature effect is concerned.

Iridescence

Iridescence or irisation refers to the appearance of the rainbow-like colours which are occasionally observed on high clouds, generally within about 30° of the sun. Green and pink predominate, the colours often resembling those seen on mother-of-pearl; they are sometimes in the form of bands parallel with the cloud edges. Within about 10° of the sun it is thought that diffraction is the main cause but at greater angular distances, interference is the most likely mechanism.

PART II

METEOROLOGICAL OBSERVATIONS

CHAPTER 11

SURFACE OBSERVATIONS

11.1 OBSERVATIONS IN GENERAL

Meteorological observations are made for various reasons and the particular parameters which are observed and the way in which the observations are conducted at any particular place or time are determined by the purpose for which they are to be applied. Some observations are intended for climatological and statistical research, some for specific research application, and some for aviation and forecasting services. For aviation, detailed observations are required at regular and frequent intervals from a network of stations which includes selected airfields. There is a broad division into 'principal' and 'supplementary' stations. At the former, all the elements listed in Table 8 are observed while supplementary stations may observe only a selection of these elements.

Pilots should have a general acquaintance with the distribution of stations within the observing network and the types of observations made, so that they may be aware of what information is available and how it is obtained. In this book only a brief description of the techniques of making observations can be given but this should be sufficient to enable the reader to form an appreciation of the methods by which the raw material of meteorology is obtained. Detailed information is contained in the *Observer's Handbook* (Meteorological Office 1982a) and *Cloud Types for Observers* (Meteorological Office 1982b), whilst technical descriptions of the instrumental aids are to be found in the *Handbook of Meteorological Instruments* (Meteorological Office 1982c).

11.2 PRESSURE

The fundamental significance of atmospheric pressure as a meteorological variable was considered in an earlier chapter. The barometric or static pressure at any point is equal to the weight of air contained in the column of unit cross-section extending above that point. The traditional instrument for measuring pressure has been the mercury barometer in which the weight of the overlying air is balanced against the weight of a column of mercury, but this has now been replaced as the standard instrument by the precision aneroid barometer; this uses the variation in the shape of an aneroid capsule to give a measure of the pressure.

Aneroid barometer
The elastic properties of a thin metal membrane or diaphragm are used in aneroid barometers. If such a membrane is held at the edges it will be deformed if the pressure on one face is greater than that on the other. In an aneroid barometer, two such membranes form the walls of a capsule; one membrane is usually fixed at its centre while the movement of the other, responding to changes in atmospheric pressure and consequential changes in the thickness of the capsule, is magnified mechanically, optically or electrically so that the pressure may be read off at a

TABLE 8. *Observations made at principal stations in the United Kingdom*

Element	Units	Instrumental equipment or other aids
wind direction	degrees from true north	cup anemometer
		hand anemometer
wind speed	knot	manual estimation
pressure	hectopascals	precision aneroid barometer
pressure tendency and characteristic	tenths of hectopascals per 3 hours	aneroid barograph
temperature and dew-point	degrees Celsius	dry-bulb, wet-bulb, maximum, minimum, grass minimum, concrete minimum thermometers; thermograph, hygrograph
visibility	metres or kilometres	known distance of fixed objects, transmissometers, visibility meter
present and past weather	—	rainfall-rate recorder
cloud type	—	atlas of cloud types
cloud amount	eighths (oktas) of sky covered	—
cloud height	feet	cloud-base recorder, cloud searchlight, balloons
state of ground	—	representative patch of bare ground or representative area
precipitation	millimetres	rain-gauge, rainfall-rate recorder
sunshine	hours	sunshine recorder
snow depth	centimetres	ruler

convenient scale. To avoid errors due to temperature changes, it is necessary to reduce the air pressure inside the capsule to a very low value.

In the United Kingdom, the Meteorological Office has adopted a type of precision aneroid barometer in which the force required to operate the indicating mechanism is provided by the observer, and thus the capsule is allowed to respond freely to pressure changes. The movements of the capsule are measured with a micrometer screw and the pressure in millibars or hectopascals is shown on a digital counter.

Corrections required
    (i)   *Correction for index error.* A certificate is provided with each instrument, setting out the necessary corrections at different points on the scale.
    (ii)   *Correction for temperature of the instrument.* The instruments are almost completely compensated for temperature variations likely to be experienced in normal use; any corrections required if the instrument is used under more extreme conditions are included in the test certificate.
    (iii) *Reduction to standard level.* When the previous corrections have been applied, the reading gives the pressure at the level of the barometer. As explained in Section 2.3, a further adjustment is necessary to obtain the pressure at any other height, for example at aerodrome level or at sea level. In routine practice, a table is specially prepared for each instrument in its given situation, incorporating a correction to sea level (QFF) with the index error and temperature corrections. Separate tables may be prepared to facilitate the determination of the pressure for each of the altimeter settings, QFE and QNH.

The capsule stack of an aneroid barometer is under continuous stress due to its low internal pressure. All metals undergo slow changes in their state of strain when in a stressed condition and this leads to a small calibration drift. It is therefore necessary for routine checks to be carried out to ensure that any change in the calibration of an instrument is within acceptable limits.

Mercury barometer
Mercury barometers are no longer used operationally for pressure measurements by Meteorological Offices within the United Kingdom, but are still in use at some aerodromes where weather reports are undertaken by air traffic services staff. The main advantage of the mercury barometer is that it provides a standard measure of pressure which is not subject to the calibration drift of the aneroid barometer. Its great, and overriding, disadvantage is its weight and lack of portability; in use it is not as quick and convenient to obtain a reading as with an aneroid barometer .

Barograph
The standard barographs used by the Meteorological Office are aneroid instruments; their action depends upon the response to variations of atmospheric pressure of disc-shaped capsules made of thin corrugated metal. The capsules are nearly exhausted of air and their surfaces are held apart by an internal spring. If atmospheric pressure falls, the capsule surfaces move apart. If pressure rises, the capsule surfaces are compressed and move together. The small movements thus produced in a bank of such capsules are magnified by a system of levers and communicated to a pivot arm that carries a recording pen. The pen moves vertically and records on a chart (the barogram) wrapped around a drum which is rotated by clockwork about a vertical axis.

Barographs which employ either mechanical or photographic registration to record the changes of height of a column of mercury have been designed for observatory use: these are generally more accurate than the aneroid type but the latter is more compact, cheaper and quite adequate for routine applications.

Barometric tendency and characteristic
Full synoptic reports from most parts of the world include the amount and type of pressure change over the three hours preceding the time of observation. The barogram is used in choosing the type of change, termed the characteristic, and may also be used to determine the amount of change, or tendency.

11.3 TEMPERATURE

The different scales used in the measurement of temperature were described in Section 3.1 and an account of the physics of surface temperature was given in Section 3.3.

The range of temperature observations
The surface observations required for use in connection with aviation include:

(i)   the air or 'dry-bulb' temperature,
(ii) the 'wet-bulb' temperature, which is used in conjunction with the dry-bulb reading for calculation of the 'dew-point' temperature,
(iii) the maximum and minimum temperatures of the air over a given period,
(iv) the minimum night temperature near the ground, the so-called grass-minimum and concrete-minimum temperatures, and
(v)   at sea, the sea surface temperature.

Exposure of thermometers
In order to obtain representative readings of air temperatures, the thermometers (dry-bulb, wet-bulb, maximum and minimum) must be exposed to the free passage of air and at the same time be protected from direct radiation from the sun, the ground, or neighbouring objects, from the loss of heat by radiation at night, and from precipitation. The Meteorological Office screen, designed to serve this purpose, is a wooden cupboard with double-louvred sides to allow free ventilation, mounted securely so that the thermometer bulbs are approximately 1.25 m above ground level, and painted white to minimize the absorption of radiant heat. The door must be kept closed except for the short periods when observations are being made, and to avoid the penetration of direct sunlight when open, the door should face north in the northern hemisphere and south in the southern.

The screen should be placed in an open position well removed from sheltering buildings and over reasonably level ground of short grass (or natural earth surface in those districts where grass does not grow). The height above the ground is particularly important as there are sometimes considerable variations in temperature within the first metre or so. On ships and offshore structures, further precautions need to be taken to avoid unrepresentative readings caused by the passage of air from vents or heated parts of the ship's structure.

Thermometer types

The usual type of thermometer for measuring dry-bulb, wet-bulb and maximum temperatures is the mercury-in-glass pattern in which the temperature is indicated by the position of the end of the liquid column. Alcohol is used in minimum thermometers where a transparent fluid is called for.

Distant-reading electrical resistance thermometers are also in routine use because of their convenience in operation. The thermometers contain a small coil of platinum wire whose resistance varies with temperature. This resistance element is connected either to an electronic device which senses the resistance and displays the measured temperature directly, or to a manually-balanced resistance bridge which is graduated in degrees Celsius. Electrical resistance thermometers can be connected to an indicator or recorder up to 1 km away, thus enabling temperatures to be displayed from a remote site whose accessibility is limited or where the observer's other duties limit the frequency with which the screen may be visited. However, as this type of thermometer is less stable in its calibration than the mercury-in-glass type, it is necessary to make regular comparisons of readings from the two types of thermometer.

Maximum thermometer. The most common maximum thermometer consists of a mercury-in-glass thermometer mounted approximately horizontally in which the retraction of the mercury into the bulb on cooling is prevented by a constriction in the tube, as in the clinical thermometer. As a result, the position of the far end of the mercury column indicates the highest temperature reached since the instrument was last set. The maximum thermometer is reset by swinging it, bulb outwards, at arm's length until the mercury in the stem becomes continuous with the mercury in the bulb.

Minimum thermometer. The thermometer used for recording the minimum temperature usually consists of alcohol in glass, with a small index inserted into the thread of spirit. The thermometer is mounted at an angle of 2° from the horizontal with the bulb down; movement of the index occurs only when it is dragged towards the bulb by the meniscus (i.e. the curved end of the spirit column) as the temperature falls. On re-expansion with rise of temperature, the spirit flows past the index which remains stationary and so indicates the lowest temperature reached. The minimum thermometer is reset by tilting to allow the index to slide along the tube until it comes into contact with the end of the thread of spirit.

Grass minimum thermometer. This is a minimum thermometer used for measuring the lowest temperature reached at night very near to the ground which, as we have noted, may cool well below the screen temperature as a result of radiation on clear nights. The thermometer is exposed outside the screen, supported on two Y-shaped wooden pegs or special black rubber supports, with its bulb just touching the tips of the blades of short grass. The reading is of most value in connection with the occurrence of ground frost. A *concrete minimum thermometer* measures the temperature just above a concrete surface and has relevance in monitoring the occurrence of frost on runway surfaces. Both thermometers are reset by tilting, as for the screen minimum thermometer; during the day they are returned to the screen to avoid condensation in the bore which might otherwise occur.

Wet-bulb thermometer.　This is described in the humidity section which follows.

Thermograph.　A continuous record of the air temperature is provided by the thermograph. In this instrument a coiled bimetallic strip tightens or slackens with variation in temperature and the movement of the end of the strip is used to control a pen which records on a drum-mounted chart. The drum is operated by clockwork: daily and weekly clocks are available. Distant-reading electrical resistance thermometers may also be connected to a similar recording instrument.

11.4 HUMIDITY

The definitions of several humidity measures have been given in Section 6.1. Numerous instruments, called hygrometers, have been designed for measuring humidity but most are suited only to laboratory work.

Dry- and wet-bulb hygrometer.　In operational meteorology the instrument most commonly used is the dry-bulb and wet-bulb hygrometer, formerly known as the psychrometer. The wet-bulb thermometer is identical with the ordinary dry-bulb which is used for measuring the air temperature, except that its bulb is kept moist by means of a tubular wick dipping into a small vessel of purified water. When evaporation takes place from the wick the latent heat required by the water vapour is taken mostly from the air surrounding the wet-bulb and from the water in the wick. The wet-bulb temperature is therefore lowered by an amount that depends on the rate of evaporation and this in turn depends on the relative humidity of the surrounding air and on the ventilation around the wick. Known relationships exist between dry-bulb and wet-bulb readings and the other measures of humidity (such as the dew-point, relative humidity and vapour pressure) and the values of these can be readily obtained from tables or from a special humidity slide-rule or a programmed personal computer. It is important not to confuse the readings of the wet-bulb thermometer with the dew-point. One drawback of this hygrometer occurs when the wet-bulb temperature falls below 0 °C; special precautions must then be taken to ensure the determination of a realistic 'ice-bulb' temperature.

Aspirated psychrometer.　Ventilation is reasonably standard inside the normal Meteorological Office screen but is fully standardized in another self-contained instrument, the aspirated psychrometer, which requires no screen. In this instrument the dry-bulb and wet bulb thermometers are protected from radiation by polished metal shields and a stream of air is drawn over the bulbs by a fan.

Hygrograph.　The hygrograph is a self-recording instrument arranged to provide a continuous record of relative humidity on a drum-mounted chart, the hygrogram. The principle employed is based upon the variation with humidity of the length of a strand of human hair. The hygrogram shows relative humidity directly but it is used more to show the variations with time rather than to give exact values. The hair hygrograph must be checked and recalibrated frequently to give reliable results.

Automatic hygrometers.　A number of automatic hygrometers have been developed for field use, and in particular, for use at remote unmanned sites.

Electric hygrometers utilize the change in an electrical parameter, usually resistance or capacitance, with changes in relative humidity. Sensors constructed on this principle are usually cheap and compact. However they lack the absolute accuracy of a psychrometer unless the wet-bulb temperature is below 0 °C and an additional complication is that their calibration is normally temperature-dependent.

An alternative type of instrument is the automatic dew-point hygrometer in which the temperature of a polished surface is controlled so that the vapour pressure of a deposit of water or ice on the surface is equal to the vapour pressure in the surrounding air. If the deposit on the surface is pure water or ice, the surface must usually be cooled below the air temperature to obtain the vapour pressure balance. However, some instruments employ a surface coated with a saturated solution of a hygroscopic salt, such as lithium chloride, which has a vapour pressure much lower than that of pure water at the same temperature. In these instruments the surface must normally be heated to obtain the vapour pressure balance. Both types of instrument indicate dew-point directly.

11.5 WIND

Wind is the motion of air over the surface of the earth and its expression requires a statement of both speed and direction. The direction is that from which the wind is blowing, and in meteorological reports and forecasts usually expressed in degrees from true north; thus 315° means that the wind blows from the north-west. For aviation purposes the speed of the wind is usually given in knots (ICAO standard abbreviation KT) but metres per second (MPS) and kilometres per hour (KMH) are used in some countries; conversion factors were given in Section 5.1. Ultimately, it is intended that KMH will be adopted universally.

Instrumental measurement
At aerodromes, wind indicators are expected to give the best practical indication of the wind regime which an aircraft will encounter during take-off and landing, and representative of conditions at a height of 6–10 metres above the runway. Thus, as well as mean direction and speed of the surface wind, significant variations in wind direction, gusts and lulls need to be measured, and where topography and obstructions cause significant differences in surface wind along the runways, several sensors may be required.

As with other meteorological elements, the measured velocity and direction of the wind depend on the exposure of the instrument. Because of the marked variation of wind speed and direction with height near the ground, the 'surface wind' is conventionally defined as the wind at a height of 10 metres above ground in an unobstructed situation.

For take-off, wind reports are to be representative of conditions along the runway, and for landings representative of the touchdown zone; the velocity should be averaged over 2 minutes, but variations will be expressed as the extremes in direction and speed recorded during the previous 10 minutes. However, reports disseminated beyond the aerodrome (METARs) are to be representative of the airfield as a whole, with the velocity averaged over 10 minutes. The above are ICAO recommendations and will require compliance at all United Kingdom aerodromes.

The more important types of measuring equipment are described below.

Cup-generator anemometer and wind vane. The anemometer consists of a small electrical generator maintained in a weatherproof housing and driven by the rotation in the wind of a three-cup rotor carried on a vertical spindle. The voltage generated increases with wind speed and is used to operate remotely situated indicating dials graduated in knots. The wind vane uses electrical transmission to indicate wind direction on dials graduated both in degrees and compass points.

The cup-generator anemometer is used in conjunction with the remote transmitting vane for the observation of surface wind at most aerodromes, and until recently it was sufficient for the dials to give instantaneous readings. However, to conform with the ICAO recommendations, the output from the sensors has to be fed through a processor to a display unit, either digital or dial, or a combination of both, capable of providing both 2- and 10-minute means, together with the extremes in direction and speed about the means, updated every few seconds.

Electrical anemograph. The cup-generator anemometer and remote transmitting wind vane are combined as the transmitting head of the electrical anemograph in which a continuous record of wind direction and speed, showing gusts and lulls, is made by means of two pens recording side by side on a moving duplex chart marked for wind speed and direction. A section of such a record was reproduced in Fig. 19. Estimates of the mean velocity and the extremes in direction and speed can be obtained by examination of the trace.

Hand anemometer. This is a portable hand-held instrument which gives a local *in situ* reading of wind speed. The instrument is a small cup-anemometer; the rotation of the cups, whose spindle carries a rotating permanent magnet, gives rise to eddy currents in a copper or aluminium disc or drum mounted on a spindle, and causes it to rotate in the same direction as the cups; its rotation is controlled by a hairspring. The angular movement of the disc or drum provides a measure of instantaneous wind speed, by means of a pointer moving over a scale. Readings below 5 KT are unreliable. When comparing hand-held anemometer measurements with the conventionally observed wind speeds reported in meteorological messages, it must be remembered that the latter apply to a standard exposure at 10 m above the ground: a hand-held exposure would be expected to yield a lower speed.

Estimating wind force — the Beaufort scale. Before the advent of aviation, those most concerned with wind were seamen. A set of descriptive terms for wind strength, evolved according to the effect of wind upon sailing craft and upon sea disturbance, came to be used with a fair degree of uniformity. In 1806 Captain (later Admiral) Beaufort devised a numerical scale ranging from 0 to 12 in which each number corresponded to one of the descriptive terms and was further related to the effects of the wind on a 'well conditioned man-of-war'. As times changed, the original specifications became of more limited value but the scale was retained and is still known as the Beaufort scale. The same scale has been adapted for use on land according to the effect of wind on smoke, trees and buildings, and further precision has been given by correlating each Beaufort scale number with a definite range of wind speed. The Beaufort scale, its wind speed equivalents and overland definitions are reproduced in Table 9: the equivalent speeds are taken to refer to observations made by an instrument exposed at about 10 metres above level ground in open country. Although most reporting stations are supplied with instruments for measuring wind, observers are encouraged to estimate the wind speed with the aid of the Beaufort scale and to compare the result with an instrumental reading. Skill acquired in this way is invaluable when on occasions no anemometer is available.

11.6 CLOUD

Classification of clouds
The study of clouds is particularly important for the purposes of aviation. In order that the character of the sky on any occasion may be fully appreciated and the weather map understood, familiarity with the names and appearance of the more important types of cloud is essential. The study of the causes of cloud formation and an account of the associated flying conditions has already been touched upon in earlier chapters.

Clouds are continually evolving and present an unlimited variety of forms. In these circumstances it is necessary to confine the formal descriptions to certain frequent and characteristic forms, omitting many intermediate and transitional forms. The selected characteristic forms comprise ten genera; each genus may be subdivided into species and varieties. The definitions of the ten genera are given below; it is most important to be familiar with these as they form the basis not only of the more detailed classification but also of the symbolic representation of cloud forms on synoptic charts.

Cloud genera
The following definitions of cloud genera are based on the *International Cloud Atlas*, vol. I (WMO 1975). The ICAO approved abbreviations are also given, but it should be noted that in meteorological literature outside the aviation context, the second letter of the abbreviation will normally be given in lower-case type. With effect from July 1993 the only cloud types specifically referred to in TAF and METAR messages are cumulonimbus (CB) and towering cumulus (TCU).

Cirrus (CI).   Detached clouds in the form of white delicate filaments, or white, or mostly white, patches or narrow bands. These clouds have a fibrous (hair-like) appearance, or a silky sheen, or both. See Fig. 67.

Cirrostratus (CS).   Transparent, whitish cloud veil of fibrous (hair-like) or smooth appearance, totally or partly covering the sky, and generally producing halo phenomena. See Fig. 68.

Cirrocumulus (CC).   Thin, white patch, sheet or layer of cloud without shading, composed of very small elements in the form of grains, ripples, etc., merged or separate, and more or less regularly arranged; most of the elements have an apparent width of less than one degree*.

---

* Or the apparent width of the little finger at arm's length.

TABLE 9. *The Beaufort scale of wind. Speed equivalents are for a standard height of 10 metres above open flat ground.*

Beaufort force	Descriptive term	Speed equivalent mean speed KT	gusts KT	Specifications
0	calm	<1		Calm; smoke rises vertically
1	light air	1–3		Direction of wind shown by smoke drift but not by wind vanes
2	light breeze	4–6		Wind felt in face; leaves rustle; ordinary vanes moved by wind
3	gentle breeze	7–10		Leaves and small twigs in constant motion; wind extends light flag
4	moderate breeze	11–16		Raises dust and loose paper; small branches are moved
5	fresh breeze	17–21		Small trees in leaf begin to sway; crested wavelets form on inland waters
6	strong breeze	22–27		Large branches in motion; whistling heard in telegraph wires; umbrellas used with difficulty
7	near gale	28–33		Whole trees in motion; inconvenience felt when walking against wind
8	gale	34–40	43–51	Breaks twigs off trees; generally impedes progress
9	severe gale	41–47	52–60	Slight structural damage occurs; (chimney pots and slates removed)
10	storm	48–55	61–68	Seldom experienced inland; trees uprooted; considerable structural damage occurs
11	violent storm	56–63	69–77	Very rarely experienced; accompanied by widespread damage
12	hurricane force	64 and over	78 and over	—

Notes

(i) Beaufort force 9 is described as 'severe gale' in the United Kingdom in preference to the WMO description of 'strong gale'.

(ii) Gust criteria are used by the United Kingdom Meteorological Office but are not included in the WMO scale.

Altocumulus (AC).   White or grey, or both white and grey, patch, sheet or layer of cloud, generally with shading, and composed of laminae, rounded masses, rolls, etc., which are sometimes partly fibrous or diffuse and which may or may not be merged; most of the regularly arranged small elements usually have an apparent width of between one and five degrees†. See Figs 69 and 70.

Altostratus (AS).   Greyish or bluish cloud sheet or layer of striated, fibrous or uniform appearance, totally or partly covering the sky, and having parts thin enough to reveal the sun at least vaguely, as if through ground glass. Altostratus does not show halo phenomena.

Nimbostratus (NS).   Grey cloud layer, often dark, the appearance of which is rendered diffuse by more or less continuously falling rain or snow, which in most cases reaches the ground. It is thick enough throughout to blot out the sun. Low ragged clouds frequently occur below the layer, with which they may or may not merge. See Fig. 71.

Stratocumulus (SC).   Grey or whitish, or both grey and whitish, patch, sheet or layer of cloud which almost always has dark parts, composed of tessellations, rounded masses, rolls, etc., which are non-fibrous (except for virga‡) and which may or may not be merged; most of the regularly arranged small elements have an apparent width of more than five degrees. See Figs 72 and 73.

Stratus (ST).   Generally grey cloud layer with a fairly uniform base, which may give drizzle, ice prisms or snow grains. When the sun is visible through the cloud its outline is clearly discernible. Stratus does not produce halo phenomena except, possibly, at very low temperatures. Sometimes stratus appears in the form of ragged patches. See Fig. 74.

Cumulus (CU).   Detached clouds, generally dense and with sharp outlines, developing vertically in the form of rising mounds, domes or towers, of which the bulging upper part often resembles a cauliflower. The sunlit parts of these clouds are mostly brilliant white; their base is relatively dark and nearly horizontal. Sometimes cumulus is ragged. See Figs 75 and 76.

Cumulonimbus (CB).   Heavy and dense cloud, with a considerable vertical extent, in the form of a mountain or huge towers. At least part of its upper portion is usually smooth, or fibrous or striated, and nearly always flattened; this part often spreads out in the shape of an anvil or vast plume. Under the base of this cloud, which is often very dark, there are frequently low ragged clouds either merged with it or not, and precipitation sometimes in the form of virga‡. See Figs 77 to 80.

Altitude of the cloud genera
The identification of clouds is aided by a knowledge of the approximate altitudes at which each genus normally occurs. By convention, that part of the atmosphere, the troposphere, in which clouds are usually found is divided into three levels: low,

---

† or the apparent width of three fingers at arm's length.
‡ trailing precipitation which evaporates before reaching the ground.

TABLE 10 *Approximate altitudes (ft) of cloud levels*

Level	Polar regions	Temperate regions	Tropical regions
High	10 000–25 000	16 500–45 000	20 000–60 000
Medium (middle)	6500–13 000	6500–23 000	6500–25 000
Low		from earth's surface–6500	

High and medium (or middle) level clouds are sometimes collectively referred to as upper clouds.

medium and high. The approximate altitudes of these levels are given in Table 10. The overlapping between the medium and high categories will be noticed. It should also be remembered that the limits given are not intended to be applied rigidly.

Of the cloud genera listed above, cirrus, cirrocumulus and cirrostratus are always high clouds, and altocumulus is always a medium cloud. Altostratus is a medium cloud which often extends into high levels while nimbostratus is a medium cloud which extends to both high and low levels. Stratocumulus and stratus are invariably low clouds but cumulus and cumulonimbus may extend from low to medium and high levels, especially cumulonimbus which will often reach high levels.

Cloud species
The clouds pertaining to a given genus can be subdivided into species. The determination of the species is based on the form of the clouds, or their structure, and whenever possible on the physical processes involved in their formation. Any particular cloud can belong to only one species. These are described briefly below, and illustrations of some will be found in Figs 67 to 80.

Fractus. Clouds in the form of irregular and ragged shreds — the term applies only to stratus and cumulus.

Nebulosus. Like a nebulous veil or layer, showing no distinct details — applies mainly to stratus and cirrostratus.

Stratiformis. Spread out in an extensive horizontal sheet or layer — applies to stratocumulus, altocumulus and occasionally to cirrocumulus.

Lenticularis. Having the shape of a lens or almond, often very elongated and usually with well defined outlines; occasionally showing irisation (iridescence), appearing most often in cloud formations of orographic origin but may also appear in regions without marked orography — applies mainly to stratocumulus, altocumulus and cirrocumulus.

Castellanus. Presenting, in at least some portion of their upper part, cumuliform protuberances in the form of turrets which generally give the clouds a crenellated appearance; some turrets are taller than they are wide, connected by a common base and seeming to be arranged in lines. The castellanus character is especially evident

J.A. Walton

Figure 67.   Cirrus (with cumulus below).

R.K. Pilsbury

Figure 68.   Cirrostratus.

189

Figure 69.   Altocumulus.

Figure 70.   Altocumulus castellanus.

190

Figure 71. Nimbostratus.

Figure 72. Stratocumulus.

S. Cornford

Figure 73.   Stratocumulus as seen from the air.

J.A. Walton

Figure 74.   Stratus covering a hill.

Figure 75.   Fair weather cumulus.

Figure 76.   Cumulus of moderate or strong vertical development.

J.A. Walton

Figure 77.   Cumulonimbus without anvil.

K.B. Shone

Figure 78.   Cumulonimbus with anvil.

Figure 79.   Cumulonimbus mammatus (from ground).

Figure 80.   Cumulonimbus embedded in cloud (from the air).

195

when the clouds are seen from the side — applies to stratocumulus, altocumulus, cirrus and cirrocumulus. See Fig. 70.

Humilis. Cumulus clouds of only slight vertical extent; they generally appear flattened. See Fig. 75.

Mediocris. Cumulus clouds of moderate vertical extent, the tops of which show fairly small protuberances.

Congestus. Cumulus clouds which are markedly sprouting and are often of great vertical extent; their bulging upper part frequently resembles a cauliflower. See Fig. 76.

Calvus. Cumulonimbus in which at least some of the protuberances of the upper part are beginning to lose their cumuliform outlines but in which no cirriform parts can be distinguished. Protuberances and sproutings tend to form a whitish mass with more or less vertical striations.

Capillatus. Cumulonimbus characterized by the presence, mostly in its upper portion, of distinct cirriform parts of clearly fibrous or striated structure, frequently having the form of an anvil, a plume or a vast, more or less disorderly, mass of hair.Cumulonimbus capillatus is usually accompanied by a shower or by a thunderstorm, often with squalls and sometimes with hail; it frequently produces well defined virga. See Fig. 78.

Floccus. A species in which each cloud unit is a small tuft with a cumuliform appearance, the lower part of which is more or less ragged and often accompanied by virga. The term applies to altocumulus, cirrus and cirrocumulus.

Fibratus. Detached clouds or a thin cloud veil, consisting of nearly straight or more or less irregularly curved filaments which do not terminate in hooks or tufts — applies mainly to cirrus and cirrostratus.

Spissatus. Cirrus of sufficient optical thickness to appear greyish when viewed towards the sun.

Uncinus. Cirrus often shaped like a comma, terminating at the top in a hook, or in a tuft whose upper part is not the form of a rounded protuberance (sometimes referred to as mares' tail cirrus).

Cloud varieties
A cloud of a given genus or species may present certain varieties. The particular aspect of a single one of these characteristics will determine a 'variety' of this cloud. The characteristics most often considered for the determination of varieties are on the one hand the transparency of the cloud and on the other the arrangement of the larger cloud elements. The same cloud may possibly be attributed to more than one variety. Nine varieties have been defined but it is unnecessary to reproduce the definitions here.

Special clouds
The cloud forms described below are additional to those of the preceding classification.

Nacreous clouds. Also known as 'mother-of-pearl' clouds, nacreous clouds are rare clouds of the stratosphere, often resembling cirrus or altocumulus lenticularis in form. They show brilliant iridescence at angular distances up to about 40° from the sun's position. Observations of nacreous clouds have been mainly from Scotland and Scandinavia during winter months. Photometric measurements indicate an altitude of about 21–30 km, i.e. in the ozone layer, but the nature of their constituent particles is not definitely known.

Noctilucent cloud. These clouds are features of the twilight sky around midsummer; they have a superficial resemblance to cirrus and it is believed that they consist of minute ice crystals which have accumulated at the mesopause at a height of between 75 and 90 km. To be perceptible it is necessary that the brightness contrast between the clouds and the twilight sky should be sufficiently great. Sufficient contrast does not occur until the sun is about 6° below the observer's horizon; it reaches a maximum at about 10° after which it diminishes until at about 16° below the horizon the clouds are no longer illuminated by the sun. Noctilucent clouds are mostly observed between latitudes 50° and 65° in the summer hemisphere; over the British Isles they may be identified by keen observers in most summers.

Other special clouds include condensation trails, clouds from fires, clouds due to volcanic eruptions and clouds resulting from industry and explosions.

Cloud amount
The amount of cloud is determined by the number of oktas (or eighths) of the sky covered. The number of oktas of sky covered by any particular cloud layer is estimated as if no other clouds were present; this can normally be done satisfactorily during the day but at night it is more difficult, especially when there is more than one layer. For the purposes of aviation, information is required on the height and amount of all layers of cloud likely to be of operational importance.

In aviation weather reports and forecasts cloud amounts may be expressed as SCT (1–4 oktas), BKN (5–7 oktas) or OVC (8 oktas).

Cloud amounts as observed from the air do not necessarily tally with those observed from the ground. Pilots should realize that reports of cloud amount are made from a fixed position on the ground. Should a pilot fly within or near a cloud layer he perhaps may not encounter gaps which are visible from below and might report having flown through continuous cloud when actually it was broken. Alternatively, a patch of very low cloud which entirely obscures the sky from an observer on the ground might be seen from above to be merely a local formation obscuring only a fraction of the ground below.

Height of cloud base
The height of the cloud base is normally reported as its height above ground level, where this datum refers to the observation site. Observations of cloud height from aircraft are described in Section 12.3.

Visual estimation. With experience, an observer becomes reasonably proficient in estimating the height of the cloud base. This ability is developed partly by comparing the estimates with heights obtained by direct measurement and partly with the aid of inferences from the appearance of the cloud, its type and structure and the general weather conditions. The height of cloud in relation to neighbouring hills or possibly objects such as aerial masts can sometimes be noted, although it should be remembered that the height of the cloud overhead may differ appreciably from the height at a distant point. When the cloud consists of an extensive uniform sheet, an accurate eye estimate of the height is usually difficult; in such cases an instrumental determination should be made whenever possible. Aircrew sometimes can check their own estimates against an altimeter reading at the cloud base, although care should be taken to avoid errors due to instrument lag.

Cloud-base recorder. This is now the primary instrument for measuring the height of the cloud base at airfields. The equipment in current operational use operates by day as well as by night, is fully automatic and is capable of unattended continuous operation. The complete system comprises transmitter, receiver and a recording unit.

The system operates by measuring the angle of elevation of a light beam, scanning in the vertical plane, at the instant at which a proportion of the light scattered by the cloud is received by a vertically pointing photoelectric cell, a known distance (about 100 m) from the light source. The transmitter emits a nearly parallel beam of two degrees divergence; the beam sweeps in a vertical arc and is modulated to ensure that the receiver is sensitive only to light emitted by the transmitter. The receiver unit comprises a photoelectric cell and an angle-of-view restrictor to ensure that light reaches the photocell only from vertically above. A pen in the recording unit, moving in sympathy with the intersection of the transmitter beam and the 'cone of acceptance' of the receiver, writes when a cloud signal is received, a current being passed through the pen tip to burn a trace on the chart. Reflection takes place from within the cloud as well as from its base as may be seen from Fig. 81. Since the recorder is primarily designed with the needs of aviation in mind, with emphasis on the faithful recording of the lower cloud detail, the maximum height measured is restricted to 4000 ft and the chart scale is arranged so that the lowest 1000 feet is expanded to cover half of the chart. The cloud-base recorder (CBR) is usually calibrated so that any cloud or fog (visibility less than 100 m) will be recorded; the sensitivity can be reduced so that only visibility of 350 m or less will give a mark.

A newer development is the laser CBR. This is a modular, solid state, low powered optical radar (LIDAR) using a gallium arsenide laser diode in the near infrared (0.91 μm). The unit measures the effective intensity of the returned beam and the time taken for a vertically projected pulse of light to be reflected and to return to the collocated receiver. It is capable of recording overhead cloud through the range 50 to 25 000 feet. The installation is completed by a remote display unit and a colour chart printer.

Cloud searchlight. Cloud searchlights provide a rapid and accurate method of cloud height determination at night. A beam of light is projected vertically on to the base of the cloud and the angular elevation of the spot of light so formed is observed by the aid of a sighting device known as an alidade. The distance of the

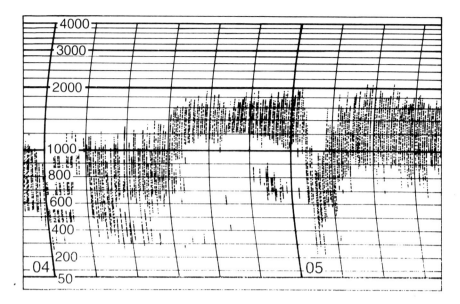

Figure 81.   Diagrammatic representation of the trace from a cloud-base recorder at London (Heathrow) Airport on 16 March 1992.

alidade from the searchlight is known and the height of the cloud is determined by simple trigonometry.

Balloon observations.   Balloon ascents are sometimes made solely for the determination of the height of low cloud. A small hydrogen- or helium-filled balloon is used, its free lift being controlled to give a rate of ascent of about 500 ft min^{-1}. The time from release to cloud entry gives the height of the cloud base. Mostly used by day, it can also be adapted for night use by attaching a small lantern and candle.

Accuracy of cloud height measurements
   The height of the base of low cloud may vary considerably both in space and time. The topography of the ground affects the cloud base which usually becomes lower over hills. Even over comparatively level ground, variations in the degree of turbulence and changes in the intensity of any precipitation falling out of it will produce variations in cloud base. At a given place the cloud base often fluctuates rapidly with time about a mean height which itself may also be changing. The Meteorological Office practice is to attempt to report the lowest point of the fluctuation.

Cloud thickness
   The vertical thickness of a layer of cloud is a matter upon which both forecaster and pilot would often welcome information, but there is no ready means of determining this from the ground. Information may be available from in-flight reports from pilots, while the forecaster is also helped in his assessment of this element by radiosonde data. The height attained by convective cloud can sometimes

be estimated visually, while radar viewing of the clouds may also give some indication of vertical development. A further source of information is the cloud-base recorder, described above, which can give some idea of the density of the cloud and may indicate the top of the lowest layer in multi-layered cloud.

11.7 VISIBILITY

The relationship between the meteorological visibility and one's ability to see any particular object in given circumstances depends on several factors which have been discussed in Chapter 9. Among others, the visibility between air and ground and the measurement of runway visual range, or the visibility along an airfield runway in conditions simulating those experienced by a pilot about to land an aircraft, have been described. The present section is concerned only with observations of the horizontal visibility at ground level; in any weather report or forecast the term 'visibility', when unqualified, has this restricted meaning. In practice it may be interpreted as the greatest horizontal distance at which a person of normal sight can recognize prominent objects under normal conditions of daylight illumination.

Determination of visibility by day

To aid the estimation of visibility, it is necessary to select a number of suitable objects located approximately at certain standard distances from the observation point, ranging from 20 m to the visible horizon. The visibility distance is then easily determined by reference to the furthest objects visible and may be expressed as so many metres or kilometres. In addition, or alternatively, to the actual distance, descriptive terms are also employed. Full details of the standard visibility ranges and descriptive terms will be found in the *Observer's Handbook* (Meteorological Office 1982a). As examples, we may note that 'fog' is used to describe visibility less than 1000 m, the obscurity being due to suspension in the air of very small water droplets or ice particles, while mist describes a visibility of 1000 m or more when the relative humidity is between 95 and 100%. The term 'haze' on the other hand, is used when humidity is less than 95%; in these circumstances the reduction in visibility is usually due to the suspension in the air of extremely small dust particles. It is frequently impossible to select a set of visibility objects for all the required distances; at sea it is never possible. In such circumstances the observer must make an estimate based on such objects as are visible and on the apparent clearness of the atmosphere.

Determination of visibility at night
In daylight the visibility as defined above is determined almost entirely by the transparency of the atmosphere and at night it is desirable that the same property should be made the basis of the estimate of visibility.

Visibility meter. One instrument that may be used to provide an estimate of night visibility is the Meteorological Office visibility meter. This consists of a simple visual photometer which measures the apparent brightness of a distant light of known intensity and hence the transparency of the intervening air. The light is observed through a variable filter (optical wedge) until it is only just visible, the setting of a slide is noted and the reading converted to the equivalent daylight visibility by means of a nomogram. A separate calibration needs to be carried out for each observer using the slide, in order to eliminate errors caused by individual variation in visual acuity. Before using the meter, observers need to allow about two minutes for their eyes to become adapted to the darkness.

Fixed lights. In the absence of visibility meter measurements, where use is made of a particular light of known distance and intensity, visibility may be judged by observation of other suitable lights at known distances, but for good results it is necessary to be aware of their luminous intensity. Tables are available showing the relation between daylight visibility and the distance at which white lights of known luminous intensity may just be seen.

Transmissometer. This instrument is used to record the optical transparency of the air by measuring the decrease in brightness of a horizontal light beam after it has travelled a certain distance through the atmosphere, usually about 200 m. A photocell receiver is used to detect the light. The air is sampled several times each minute and the transparency recorded on a chart. At locations where these instruments are available, the measurements are used by the observer as an aid to assessing the visibility. There can be marked spatial variations of visibility and the relatively short path of the atmosphere sampled by the transmissometer may not be representative of the general visibility in the locality. Furthermore, if there is a marked variation of visibility in different directions, the observer is instructed to report the lowest visibility.

Eye estimate. In circumstances when none of the above aids is available, the visibility can be estimated only from the general clearness of the night; when the visibility permits, it is surprising how much of the landscape can be seen once the eye has become accustomed to the darkness on a really dark night.

11.8 PRECIPITATION

For the sake of uniformity in the practice of observing and reporting precipitation, it is necessary to establish conventions relating to matters of detail, but most of the terms used in describing the nature of precipitation are sufficiently well known to require no further explanation; it is sufficient here merely to draw attention to two particular aspects which do sometimes cause confusion.

Drizzle and rain
The distinction between these two types of precipitation is based not upon the quantity or rate of precipitation but upon the size of the droplets which are being precipitated.

Drizzle is defined as fairly uniform precipitation composed exclusively of water droplets of less than 0.5 mm diameter. The impact of drizzle droplets falling on a water surface is imperceptible but continuous drizzle may produce a run-off from roofs and road surfaces. Visibility is inversely related to both the intensity of precipitation and the number of droplets: the density of drizzle droplets may more than compensate for the lightness of the precipitation to seriously impair visibility, even in the absence of any pre-existing mist or fog.

Rain is defined as the precipitation of liquid water droplets, either in the form of drops of diameter greater than 0.5 mm or of smaller but widely scattered droplets. If individual drops make a distinct splash on striking the ground or a water surface, then the precipitation should be recorded as rain.

Showers and intermittent precipitation
Showers, whether of rain, snow, hail, snow pellets or ice pellets are always associated with convective clouds. After a shower there is a tendency for breaks to appear in the cloud, even if the sky does not entirely clear. If precipitation falls from time to time from extensive layered clouds with no marked clearances, it is reported as intermittent. Precipitation is reported as continuous if there have been no breaks for a period of at least 60 minutes. The distinction between showers and intermittent precipitation is important if the report is to be given its full significance, for the causes of the two types of precipitation and, indeed, the accompanying flying conditions, are essentially different.

Precipitation intensity
The intensity of precipitation is reported using the scale 'slight', 'moderate', 'heavy' or, in the case of showers, 'violent'. These terms are related to specific rates of rainfall accumulation as shown in Table 11. Note that in terms of water equivalence the scales for snow and non-showery rain are similar, with 1 cm of snow yielding 1 mm of water.

TABLE 11. *Precipitation intensity. Note that the water equivalent of snow is usually about one tenth, i.e. 1 cm of snow yields about 1 mm of water.*

	Rainfall rate (mm h^{-1})		Snow accumulation (cm h^{-1})
	rain	rain/hail showers	
slight	<0.5	<2	<0.5
moderate	0.5–4	2–10	0.5–4
heavy	>4	10–50	>4
violent		>50	

Some stations are equipped with rate-of-rainfall recorders which provide a quantitative measure of intensity; at others the intensity must be estimated. Experienced observers soon acquire proficiency in forming realistic assessments of the correct subjective term by noting, for instance, the deterioration in visibility: in the absence of any other visibility impairment the relationship shown in Fig. 60 may be helpful.

11.9 WEATHER

In such terms as 'weather report' or 'weather map', the word 'weather' is taken to cover all of the meteorological factors concerned, but the word is also used in a more restricted sense where it refers only to the state of the sky and the accompanying precipitation or other phenomena — thunderstorms, fog, etc. When reporting a weather observation it is usual to give both the 'present weather', referring to conditions at the time of observation, and the 'past weather', conditions during'the interval since the previous routine observation or some other predetermined earlier observation. The observer needs therefore to keep a close watch on weather changes between the routine times of observation so that significant changes can be recorded for the 'past weather' reports and so that updated information can be supplied to aviation users when specific changes have occurred.

11.10 OTHER ELEMENTS

Sunshine
The duration of bright sunshine is measured by a recorder in which a glass sphere is used as a lens to burn a trace on a card whenever the sun is shining. During a day of continuous sunshine the burn traces out a continuous line on the card as the position of the sun alters. When sunshine is intermittent the line is broken, the combined length of all the parts gives a measure of the daily duration.

Electrical instruments are used at some locations to record quantitatively the intensity of incident solar radiation,

State of ground
State of ground is reported by selecting the most suitable of twenty standard descriptions for either the condition of a prepared bare plot of level ground which is considered representative of soil in the vicinity, or of the general condition of open ground which is easily visible from the station and no more than 100 feet different in altitude. Ten of the descriptions apply only to occasions with snow or measurable ice cover.

Snow depth
The undrifted depth of any lying snow is measured using a ruler graduated in centimetres.

State of sea
Certain coastal stations report the state of sea and the visibility out to sea. Aeronautical stations established on off-shore structures in support of helicopter operations may be required to report state of sea and sea-surface temperatures. Ship reports may include the height of the swell and wind waves, the direction from which they are coming and their period (i.e. the time interval between successive waves).

Icing, turbulence and wind shear
Although strictly not 'surface' reports, aircraft observations of severe icing and severe turbulence during climb-out or approach phases of a flight should be added to the special and routine aviation weather reports prepared at the aerodrome. Since July 1993, reports of wind shear have been included as supplementary information in METARs intended for international dissemination.

Runway state
In accordance with regional air navigation agreements, information on the state of the runway when contaminated with lying precipitation, ice, etc. should be included

when appropriate as an 8-figure group appended to the aviation weather report disseminated off the aerodrome (METAR). The provision and encoding of such information is usually the responsibility of Aerodrome Operations, not the meteorological staff, and the group must not be confused with the comprehensive SNOWTAM reports disseminated by Aeronautical Information Services (AIS).

11.11 AUTOMATIC WEATHER STATIONS

There is a continuing programme of development and installation of automatic weather stations. These stations are able to measure many of the 'surface' parameters and they therefore provide an important addition to the observing network. They are sited at locations from which manual observations are not available, these often being in remote places, or at stations which are not manned continuously throughout the 24 hours.

Special equipment, at certain continuously manned offices, is used to interrogate automatic stations at regular intervals by means of telephone or telegraph circuits. The observations thus obtained, which are already in the international code format, are then transmitted on the normal circuits used for the collection of observations.

Observations from automatic stations are valuable for synoptic meteorology. However, information from these stations is of limited direct benefit to aviation as no observations of weather or cloud amount and type can be made at present and very few automatic stations are equipped with instruments for the determination of cloud base or visibility. Any observations of cloud or visibility from automatic stations need to be examined carefully.

CHAPTER 12

UPPER-AIR OBSERVATIONS

12.1 INTRODUCTION

Observations of meteorological conditions in the free atmosphere are of obvious importance for the operation of aircraft. However, it must be remembered that they also form an essential part of the meteorologist's basic data, variations of wind, temperature and water content occurring well above the ground being at least as important for weather analysis and forecasting as variations in these parameters at the surface. Information about the state of the upper air may be obtained in many ways but this chapter will concentrate on two of the more important routine methods, observations from balloon-borne equipment and from aircraft in flight. Of course, meteorological satellites, radar and acoustic sounders now play an increasingly important role in the acquisition of upper-air data; some of these methods are discussed in Chapter 13.

12.2 BALLOON OBSERVATIONS

These still provide the most valuable source of upper-air data, especially as routine soundings are made simultaneously by an established worldwide network of land-based stations, supplemented by a few observations from ships.

Radiosonde observations
The standard method of obtaining values of temperature and humidity at upper levels is by use of a balloon carrying a small radio transmitter known as a radiosonde.

In a typical radiosonde, the incorporated transmitter produces a carrier wave which is modulated, in turn, by three audio-frequency oscillators, the resonant frequencies of which are controlled by sensors which measure pressure, temperature and humidity. Pressure is measured by an aneroid capsule, temperature by a resistance thermometer unit of fine tungsten wire, and humidity by a piece of gold-beater's skin. The temperature and humidity elements are exposed but the remainder of the instrument is enclosed within an insulated container. A small electric motor turns the switch which couples the individual oscillators that are controlled by the meteorological elements to the transmitter circuit. A small battery supplies power for all of these purposes. The modern radiosonde has a good performance, particularly in regard to its accuracy, sensitivity and the response time of its elements.

The heights attained by radiosonde balloons vary from about 65 000 ft for small balloons to 115 000 ft or more for large balloons. A 1200 ft min^{-1} rate of ascent is needed to ensure that the meteorological sensors are properly ventilated and to keep the balloon in radar range even if it comes within the influence of strong winds.

Equipment is required at the ground station to measure and record the fluctuations of the audio-frequency of the sonde. In Britain ground equipment consists of a radio receiver and a computer-controlled processor which measures and decodes the signals from the receiver so that the meteorological information may be extracted from them. The sensors which are incorporated into the radiosonde are calibrated before the launch and these calibration factors are applied by the computer to the received signals during the flight, together with various other corrections which are derived from reference signals, also transmitted by the radiosonde. The computer is therefore able to derive accurate values of the meteorological parameters and together with the radar-wind information it finally constructs the coded message which is required for the national and international exchange of upper-air data.

Radar winds
As a free balloon ascends, it is carried along horizontally by the winds at the levels traversed so that a series of observations of its position enables the average wind to be determined over the layers traversed between successive observations. The tracking of the balloon is usually carried out by radar. United Kingdom stations use primary radar which depends on the reflection of radio waves emitted by a ground station and for this purpose a reflector, made of metallized nylon mesh, is suspended from the balloon. The radar method enables the bearing, distance and height of the balloon to be determined at each observation, usually at intervals of one minute, regardless of weather. It is necessary to take account of the curvature of the earth in computation of the balloon height as the balloon drifts further from the release point. Some nations use secondary radar which depends upon a radio transmitter carried by the balloon. Bearings are taken from the ground on the transmissions from the balloon. Alternatively, the position of the balloon can be determined by reception of LORAN navigational signals and by retransmitting these to the ground stations for the necessary calculations to be made. This method of wind finding is used for balloons launched from ships. Radar-wind ascents may be carried out independently or in combination with temperature and humidity observations, one balloon carrying both the radar reflector and the radiosonde apparatus.

Pilot balloon observation of wind
Before the introduction of radar methods, upper winds were commonly determined by observations of a 'pilot' balloon. This small rubber balloon is filled with sufficient hydrogen or helium to cause it to rise approximately at a known rate, usually 500 ft min^{-1}. During the ascent, observations of elevation and azimuth are made at frequent intervals by means of a theodolite (essentially a surveyor's telescope but designed so that the eyepiece is fixed, despite large changes in elevation of the objective lens) and the wind direction and speed are evaluated by means of a special slide-rule. This method is still quite widely used, but it has serious disadvantages; its use is severely restricted by low visibility or the presence of cloud, while strong winds carry the balloon out of sight before it has had time to rise more than a few thousand feet. However, given good visibility and winds not too strong, a height of 10 000 ft is generally attainable, while with light winds 30 000 ft is not unusual, provided clouds do not interfere. Variations in the prearranged rate of ascent of the balloon may occur for several reasons, but a check can be obtained by measuring in the eyepiece of the theodolite the apparent length

of a 'tail' suspended from the balloon. A more accurate method uses simultaneous observation of the balloon by two theodolites at the end of a measured baseline, but this is involved and unsuited to routine use. These wind observations are recorded on charts to supplement the radar data, especially in areas from which few other observations are available.

Ascents may be made at night by observing a lantern attached to the balloon. The use of pilot balloons to determine cloud height has already been noted (Section 11.6).

12.3 AIRCRAFT OBSERVATIONS

Although, of necessity, they are not so regularly distributed in time and space as routine balloon soundings, meteorological observations from aircraft play an important, and at times vital, role in supplementing the basic data available for analysis and forecasting. The radiosonde network is necessarily sparse, or even non-existent, over vast tracts of the earth's surface, especially the oceans and desert regions; in-flight aircraft reports and post-flight aircrew debriefs are of immense importance in filling some of these gaps in the global cover. Furthermore, routine balloon soundings are taken, at best, only four times a day; at many locations they are taken only once or twice a day. Aircraft reports at intermediate times may provide the first indication of new developments in the synoptic situation. Even where the upper-air observing network is fairly dense, aircraft reports still provide a useful check on both balloon-borne instrumental data and that sensed remotely by meteorological satellites.

The usefulness of aircraft observations for accurate short-term forecasting of conditions for subsequent flights over or near the same route is fairly obvious, but these observations have a much wider usefulness in that they help to build up a full three-dimensional picture of the global 'weather machine'.

Increasingly, wind and temperature reports from aircraft are being used as one of the data inputs to numerical forecasting models of the atmosphere. Incorporation of these data, particularly those from data-sparse regions, enables the numerical forecast models to achieve a better analysis of large-scale atmospheric motions and hence leads to improved forecasts, not just of conditions at aircraft operating levels but of the broader-scale synoptic developments.

A particular example concerns the occasion of the 'Great Storm' which devastated parts of England on the night of 15/16 October 1987. Following this storm, post-mortem studies were carried out to establish the reasons for the deficiencies in the numerical guidance which had been available to forecasters earlier on the 15th (Lorenc *et al.* 1988). Forecasts were rerun using various combinations of observational data: none was found that could precisely match the truly exceptional developments that were to follow over Britain but the forecasts would have been much improved had the data assimilation cycle been so timed to make use of 65 Atlantic AIREP reports received between 0130 and 0300 on the morning of the 15th.

A further shortcoming of the radiosonde network is that it can provide information only on wind, temperature and humidity. The forecaster may infer much from consideration of his upper-air charts and tephigrams but for direct observational evidence of icing and turbulence he relies entirely upon reports from aircraft.

Observing procedures for transport aircraft

Meteorological observing and reporting procedures, which transport aircraft engaged in international air navigation are expected to follow, have been promulgated jointly by ICAO and the World Meteorological Organization (WMO): full details may be found in the documents ICAO Annex 3 and ICAO PANS-RAC.

The basic requirement is that aircraft operating at certain altitudes over particular routes should make routine observations at certain predetermined points and should record and report these observations as prescribed. These routine reports are transmitted in the AIREP format. In addition, there is provision for special reports (AIREP SPECIAL) to be made at any time or place should certain hazardous or potentially hazardous phenomena or circumstances be encountered.

AIREPs

As well as giving the time, position and flight level (without which information the rest of the report is, of course, valueless) the AIREP message includes air temperature, wind speed and direction and information on any turbulence or icing recently encountered at flight level. These basic items may be supplemented, as appropriate, by such useful additional information as the presence of thunderstorms on or near the track, passage through a recognizable front, cloud-top information, D-value, major deviations from forecast winds or weather, or marked changes of wind or temperature along the route.

An example of the AIREP form is included in the Annex to this book. Although this form is prescribed only as a model format it is desirable that the actual form should be completed in flight and handed in at the end of the flight for eventual delivery to the responsible meteorological authority. A valuable supplement to the record of observations is the pictorial cross-section of the conditions encountered *en route*. Completion of this cross-section is to be encouraged as a worthwhile discipline, likely to lead to a better understanding of weather by aircrew as well as providing the forecaster with a succinct graphical representation of the main features encountered. It may often be possible to include important detail not revealed in the periodical sequence of observations, such as the precise location of a frontal transition.

AIREP SPECIAL

Messages with the AIREP SPECIAL prefix are accorded special handling procedures at the ground station to ensure their rapid relay to the appropriate meteorological authority where consideration will be given to the issue of appropriate SIGMET messages.

These SPECIAL reports should be made whenever any of the SIGMET criteria or, in the case of transonic or supersonic flight, SIGMET SST criteria, are encountered (see Section 21.4).

Instruments and techniques for airborne observations

Many instruments have been designed specifically for use in aircraft, some as part of the standard equipment of civil and military aircraft, others to meet the special needs of meteorological reconnaissance and research. The descriptions which follow are confined to the more commonly used instruments and aim only at illustrating the general principles of observing the atmosphere, visually as well as instrumentally, from an aircraft in flight.

Pressure

Although not included in normal aircraft instrumentation, aneroid barometers may be carried for special research or reconnaissance work. Essentially, the instrument is the same as the pressure altimeter and is subject to the same errors; it is, of course, calibrated to read in pressure units instead of height. To obtain accurate readings it is important to maintain level flight for at least a minute since hysteresis, or lag, will introduce error if the aircraft is changing height or has recently undergone such a change. If change of height has been rapid, error may amount to several hectopascals and an extended recovery period is needed before a reliable reading can be expected.

Temperature

Several types of aircraft thermometer are in use. They should be fitted with an anti-radiation housing since protection from solar radiation has been found necessary even with the high ventilation rates obtained with aircraft in flight. The thermometer element must be exposed in a position unaffected by engine heat, aircraft slipstream or by solar heating of adjacent parts of the airframe. The usual type of sensor is the electrical resistance element where the temperature is deduced by measurement of the electrical resistance of a metal element mounted on the underside of the aircraft nose or wing. All types of aircraft thermometer are subject to a certain degree of lag, though with types in current use this effect has been minimized and can usually be ignored.

Temperature readings need to be corrected for instrument error and air speed. The phenomenon of kinetic heating at the surface of an aircraft in flight has been examined in Section 8.3 where it was seen that in clear air the temperature is increased by the effects of both adiabatic compression and air friction. The result is that the indicated temperature is too high by an amount given by $\Delta T = \alpha(V/100)^2$, where V is the true air speed and α is the speed-correction coefficient. The precise value of α depends on the type of instrument and its mounting as well as on the units employed; for temperature in degrees Celsius and air speed in knots, its value is in the neighbourhood of unity. Thus the excess temperature due to kinetic heating begins to become appreciable at a true air speed of about 100 KT; in high-speed aircraft it causes large errors in the measured temperature unless the appropriate correction is applied. If the thermometer is part of an integrated flight-instrument system, all necessary corrections for instrument error and speed will be applied automatically and the reading presented by the system will be the corrected reading. In some cases there are semi-automatic corrections, so that some final manual correction is still required.

Effect of cloud and precipitation.   During flight in cloud or precipitation, if the aircraft windows become wet it may be safely assumed that an exposed sensitive thermometer element will become equally wet, and on emergence into clear air evaporative cooling at the element will reduce the apparent air temperature.

Thermometer readings may be in error by as much as 4 to 10 degC due to these effects. Ice accretion on the element similarly degrades the observation. It is recommended that, unless the aircraft is equipped with specially protected instruments, temperature observations should not be recorded during flight in cloud or precipitation and an interval of at least three minutes be allowed in the clear air before an observation is made.

Observing procedure. The recommended procedure to be followed in reading air temperature is:

(i) First ensure that the aircraft has been in level flight at constant speed or Mach number for at least one minute and has been flying in a region free from precipitation and ice accretion for at least three minutes,

(ii) tap the dial to reduce friction error (an instrument panel vibrator may obviate the need for this), and

(iii) apply instrument and air speed corrections (unless the thermometer is part of an integrated system which provides automatically corrected readings).

Accuracy of observations. If the observational procedure is correctly adhered to as above, aircraft temperature measurements should lie within ±3 degC of the true value and under the most favourable conditions the error could be less than 0.5 degC.

A joint ICAO/WMO meeting in 1964 recommended that the desirable standard of accuracy for aircraft air temperature observations should be a standard deviation of 1 degC.

Wind

Methods of determining the wind speed and direction from an aircraft in flight depend fundamentally on the triangle of velocities. Thus if an aircraft is flying on a heading and at an air speed which in still air would take it from A to B in a certain time (Fig. 82), then B is its 'air position' at that time and AB represents the heading and air speed. If, however, the aircraft arrives not at B but at C, then BC represents the mean wind speed and direction while AC is the track made good. The success of methods of wind measurement clearly depends on the accuracy with which the aircraft's position can be determined. Modern commercial and military aircraft are fitted with a computer which calculates the wind using a measurement of air speed from the pitot–static system and a measurement of ground speed from a navigational system, such as an inertial navigation system (INS) or a Doppler navigation system. 'Spot' winds derived by these means, particularly those based on INS measurements, are very accurate. In the absence of such equipment it may be possible only to calculate a mean wind between two well-separated navigational fixes; in this case it is very important that the position of the mid-point of the leg to which the wind applies should be clearly specified in any report. A wind report allocated to an incorrect position is not only misleading in itself but could throw doubt upon accurate reports from other aircraft in the vicinity.

Accuracy of wind measurements. The joint ICAO/WMO meeting recommended that the desirable standard of accuracy of aircraft wind observations should be a standard deviation of 10 KT for wind speed and a standard deviation of 10 degrees for wind direction.

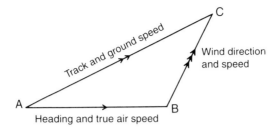

Figure 82.   Vector triangle for determination of wind from an aircraft.

Aircraft icing

Reports of ice accretion encountered by aircraft are the only direct observational material available to the forecaster regarding this potentially hazardous phenomenon. Without direct evidence, the forecaster must rely entirely upon inference from the general synoptic situation and the vertical distribution of temperature and, owing to the complexity of the factors governing ice accretion on aircraft, such inferences necessarily have to be drawn in broad terms. Any report of icing actually experienced is therefore of considerable value to the forecaster as confirmation, or otherwise, of the trend foreseen in the forecast and will assist him in providing forecasts for crews of other aircraft subsequently traversing the same airspace.

Classification

It will be clear from the discussion in Chapter 8 that from an operational point of view, both the type of ice and its rate of accretion are important factors which must be considered in assessing the potential hazard to aviation. A satisfactory method of combining both of these factors into an objective classification scheme for icing severity has yet to be devised. Instead, a simple three-tier subjective scale is used which classifies icing as 'light', 'moderate' or 'severe': this is shown at Table 12. The terms are defined by reference to manoeuvres which the pilot considers it desirable or necessary to make as a consequence of the ice formation. Such factors are obviously very dependent upon the type of aircraft and its equipment and are influenced very much by pilot judgement; the system has the merit, though, of expressing the intensity directly in operational terms which will be well understood by other pilots, for whose ultimate benefit reports of aircraft icing are primarily made.

It should be noted that the scale refers specifically to airframe icing. Any occurrence of carburettor icing or of ice accretion on jet engine guide vanes should be reported in plain language as 'supplementary information' if it is considered that the information would be of significance to other aircraft.

Turbulence

Turbulence in the free atmosphere is another factor for which the forecaster must rely upon indirect evidence and general inference unless direct observations from aircraft in flight are received; hence reports of encounters are of great value in forecasting for crews of other aircraft.

Table 12. *Airframe icing criteria*

Intensity	Description	reported as
Light	No change of course or altitude is necessary and no loss of speed caused.	—
Moderate	Change of heading and/or altitude considered desirable. Ice accretion which continues to increase but not at a rate sufficiently serious to affect the safety of the flight, unless it continues for an extended period of time; air speed may be lost.	MOD
Severe	Change of heading and/or altitude considered essential. Ice accretion which continues to build up and begins to affect seriously the performance and manoeuvrability of the aircraft.	SEV

Classification

The degree of intensity of turbulence is specified, according to the effect of the gusts upon the aircraft and its occupants, as 'moderate' or 'severe': definitions are given at Table 13. A slightly different, and rather more objective, set of definitions is printed on the reverse of the AIREP form. A number of other classification schemes have been suggested by various authorities, some of them incorporating additional 'light' and 'extreme' categories, but the two-tier scale given here is the one officially recognized for use in AIREP reports.

Cloud type

The classification of clouds seen above the aircraft presents no special difficulty to an observer who is already familiar with their observation from the ground; equally, detached clouds can be readily classified, whatever the viewpoint. Continuous cloud

Table 13. *Turbulence reporting criteria*

Intensity	Description	reported as
Moderate	Difficulty in walking through aircraft. Rather severe and frequent rolling of the aircraft; general passenger discomfort; this degree of turbulence is that usually associated with towering cumulus, passing through average frontal conditions and in the vicinity of (but not in the interior of) isolated thunderstorms.	MOD
Severe	Loose objects in the interior of the aircraft become dislodged. Aircraft tosses and it is difficult to maintain flight altitude; passenger discomfort is marked; this degree of turbulence is that usually met with in the interior of thunderstorms, either frontal or isolated.	SEV

sheets however, present characteristic surfaces which may be seen only from above and special attention should be paid to these.

Cirrus.   Very fine cirrus is often invisible from above and the ground or lower clouds are seldom obscured by it. If of great vertical thickness it appears opaque, with a milky aspect.

Cirrostratus.   Presents a milky aspect when viewed from above. The ground or lower clouds are usually visible if the cloud is thin but hardly perceptible through thick layers. During flight through either cirrus or cirrostratus, ice crystals may at times be seen glittering in the sunlight. On the other hand, it is possible to fly through these clouds without being aware of their presence.

Cirrocumulus.   Viewed from above, seen as small or discontinuous sheets, the upper surface of which generally appears fleecy.

Altocumulus.   Upper surface presents a smooth undulating layer, or is slightly fleecy. In some cases continuous, in others with distinct gaps revealing glimpses of the ground or lower clouds. Altocumulus castellanus resembles well-developed cumulus emerging from a smooth undulating layer; tops may also emerge from a haze layer. Altocumulus floccus appears as small cumulus clouds surrounded by, or emerging from, a milky white area.

Altostratus.   Nearly horizontal upper surface, appearing flat or undulating with a fairly long wavelength. Tops of cumuliform clouds may occasionally be seen projecting above the cloud layer.

Nimbostratus.   If not merged into other clouds the upper surface has a somewhat flat but diffuse aspect, unless it becomes unstable when it takes on a cumuliform appearance.

Stratocumulus.   Cloud units may be separate or merged in a continuous sheet. In the former case, upper surface resembles a sea of cloud with a fleecy appearance; more or less marked cracks appear and the surface is often pierced by heads of cumulus or cumulonimbus. When continuous, the upper surface often has undulations in the form of long parallel bands.

Stratus.   The upper surface is generally undulating with rather short wavelength, but sometimes undulations are more pronounced and follow ground irregularities. Hills often protrude. Fog may have a similar aspect when viewed from above.

AIREP reports of cloud type

The genera/species/varieties cloud type classification which was considered at some length in Chapter 6 is unnecessarily detailed for use in AIREP messages; instead a much simpler five-fold specification suffices. The descriptions and ICAO approved abbreviations are as follows:

Stratiform	(STF). The cloud formation lies mainly in horizontal layers, with little or no signs of vertical development. The standard cloud types falling in this category are cirrus, cirrostratus, altostratus, stratocumulus, nimbostratus and stratus.
Cumuliform	(CUF). The cloud formation has quite numerous and pronounced upward protuberances, indicating vertical development, but the actual vertical extent of these protuberances is not great; the cloud formation may consist of layers of cloud, showing signs of 'heaping up' or 'waviness' or separate, more or less rounded cloud masses, with clear

	intervals between them. Standard cloud types falling within this category are cirrocumulus, altocumulus and cumulus.
Towering	(TCU). Detached clouds, dense and with sharp outlines,
cumulus	towering to a considerable height in the form of a 'cauliflower head' or 'dome', but without the development of any fibrous structure at the top and not accompanied by lightning, thunder or hail; the upper part of the cloud is often brilliantly white when illuminated by sunlight. Moderate or severe turbulence may occur in towering cumulus.
Cumulonimbus	(CB). Massive and dense cloud, often very dark at the base, with a great vertical extent, in the form of 'mountains of cloud' or high towers. At least part of its upper portion is smooth, fibrous and almost flattened and usually spreads out in the form of an anvil or vast plume; almost invariably accompanied, sooner or later, by lightning, thunder or hail. Turbulence may be severe in cumulonimbus and its vicinity.
Dense upper	(DUC). Layer of cirriform cloud sufficiently dense to
cloud	obscure horizontal vision.

Cloud amount

Aircraft reports of cloud amount use a three-tier 'cloud continuity' scale of scattered, broken or continuous. Definitions and standard abbreviations are as follows:

Scattered	(SCT). The clear intervals between the cloud masses predominate, in the aggregate, over the cloud masses; an aircraft flying through the cloud formation will be in clear air more often than in cloud.
Broken	(BKN). The cloud masses predominate, in the aggregate, over the clear spaces between the cloud masses; an aircraft flying through the cloud formation will be in cloud more often than in clear air.
Continuous	(CONS). The cloud formation is one continuous sheet or layer of cloud, with no clear intervals.

In the legend of some forecast documentation it may be noticed that the abbreviations SCT, BKN and CONS (or OVC meaning overcast) are equated to cloud amounts in oktas. This equivalence is, at best, only approximate, and on occasion it can be misleading, since the perspective of a ground observer, viewing the 'celestial dome' around him, is very different from that of an airborne observer. On a day of active shower development a ground-based observer's field of view may be filled by the bases and sides of towering cumulus clouds, leaving him no alternative other than to report 7 or even 8 oktas of low cloud, whereas viewed from above (e.g. from a satellite) clear gaps will be seen separating the towers. A pilot flying horizontally just a few thousand feet above the general cloud base in these circumstances would probably judge the cloud to be scattered by the definitions above. On the other hand, a pilot flying within or just above a cloud layer may not encounter any gaps and would observe the cloud as continuous whereas an observer on the ground viewing the whole sky from horizon to horizon might be aware of significant breaks in the cloud sheet.

This lack of correspondence between the two viewpoints should be borne in mind when trying to form an assessment of in-flight conditions from a study of surface observations.

Cloud heights

In-flight observations of cloud structure can be invaluable, especially when upper layers are hidden from a ground observer by a lower overcast. The heights of the bases and tops can be determined relatively accurately from an aircraft flying at cloud level, provided that the altimeter is used properly with due regard to the effect of instrument lag during changes of flight level. However, estimation of cloud base or top from an aircraft at a different flight level does present difficulty; it is found for instance, that when viewed from above, the height of the cloud top is very often overestimated.

As was mentioned above, some high level clouds are so tenuous that an airborne observer may not be able to recognize whether he is in cloud or not, even though the cloud is clearly discernible from below. The reverse is equally true; an aircraft observer can sometimes see a thin haze or cloud layer against the background of the ground when a ground-based observer cannot distinguish the same layer against the background of the sky.

When reporting cloud heights it is important that the recipient of the information is aware of the pressure setting of the altimeter on which the determination was made. Only then will it be clear whether the heights quoted are above ground level or above sea level, a distinction which is particularly important in the case of cloud at lower levels.

ASDAR

Certain commercial aircraft have been equipped to automatically transmit AIREP information by ASDAR (Aircraft to Satellite Data Relay). Information transmitted includes positional data (latitude, longitude, flight level and time) as well as wind speed and direction, corrected temperature and turbulence. ASDAR observations are relayed from the satellite to the world centres at Bracknell and Washington. In addition to reports made during the *en route* section of the flight, observations may also be made during climb-out and approach to land, producing vertical temperature profiles for the vicinity of the aerodromes.

CHAPTER 13

OBSERVATIONS USING REMOTE SENSING

13.1 RADAR INFORMATION

In the two previous chapters, techniques were considered for the direct observation of the various meteorological parameters, both at the surface and in the upper air. In this chapter, techniques for the observation of the atmosphere by remote sensing will be outlined; that is to say, methods by which measurements of the atmosphere can be made at remote locations but without physical sensors being located there. One powerful technique for the derivation of information remotely is the use of radar.

Principles of radar
The location of distant objects by radar depends upon the emission of a suitable short-wave radio pulse from a transmitter, and the reception of the return pulse after reflection from the object. The time interval between the emitted and received pulses provides a measure of the distance of this object, while its bearing is related to the direction of the maximum reflected signal. Radars which have been developed specifically for the detection of precipitation are now in use throughout the world.

The intensity of the radar response from a cloud of n drops, each of diameter d, is proportional to nd^6, so that one drop of diameter 2 mm can give an echo equivalent to that from a million drops of diameter 0.2 mm. Although any cloud consists of drops of various sizes, the echo from a cloud containing raindrops is far greater than that from other clouds, so much so that it is true to say that precipitation, and not cloud, is detected by the normal weather radar apparatus, which uses transmissions at wavelengths of 10, 5 and 3 cm (3 cm radars are now falling out of favour because they suffer unduly from attenuation of the beam through rain).

The maximum range of any radar depends, amongst other things, on the power transmitted, the narrowness of the transmitted beam-width (typically about 1°), the pulse repetition frequency and the sensitivity of the receiver. In practice the range of a weather radar under normal propagating conditions does not exceed 400 km. Radar waves follow slightly curved paths as a result of refraction; in normal conditions, however, they do not curve as much as the earth's surface. Because of this the radar beam centred at zero elevation cannot 'see' much below 40 000 ft when the range reaches 400 km. Often, a poor radar horizon will restrict the range considerably; however, the range of the radar beam may be increased during conditions of anomalous propagation (see Section 10.8).

Conventional radar displays
Two conventional forms of radar display are in use. The more common is the PPI (plan position indicator) which shows the azimuth and the range of the received echoes from the station. A transparent overlay showing the local geography may be used on the screen to illustrate the location of the rain more readily. Normally the range scale of the display can be selected from several alternatives, e.g. 50, 100, 200

and 400 km. The other form of display is the RHI (range–height indicator) which gives a useful cross-section of the precipitation in a chosen direction and enables the observer to gauge its height and to see the shape of the leading edge. Even in PPI mode, information about the vertical extent of precipitation echoes can be obtained by small changes in the elevation at which the antenna is scanned in azimuth.

The PPI type of display is also used in aircraft weather radars, although the radar scan is restricted to about 70° either side of the aircraft heading. These aircraft radar sets are designed to assist aircrew in the detection of thunderstorms located near to the intended flight track and hence permit avoiding action to be taken. The flight crew can vary the elevation of the radar antenna allowing information to be gained on the vertical as well as the horizontal extent of storms. These displays often incorporate a contouring facility which gives a rough assessment of the intensity of the indicated echoes.

It should be noted that radars which are used for air traffic control purposes are designed to minimize or eliminate the response from weather. This aim is achieved by use of radar frequencies which are not strongly reflected by rain drops and by use of various signal processing techniques such as the elimination of echoes with small Doppler frequency shifts. On some air traffic radar sets, the weather suppression is switchable so that the controller may derive weather information if required.

Modern radars
In order to obtain the best coverage, modern weather radars are usually installed on hill tops; they are therefore designed to operate unattended in remote locations. The output from these modern radars is digitized so that further processing of the signals can be undertaken. In this way it is possible to obtain semi-quantitative rainfall data from the radar measurements. However, to achieve this aim a number of different processes and corrections need to be applied. In particular, the following are undertaken: the correction of echo intensity with range, the removal of echoes produced by the local terrain ('ground clutter'), and the calibration of rainfall rates by comparison with 'ground-truth' data received in real time from remotely sited automatic rain-gauges within the radar's area of coverage. The final result of this processing, which is performed by a mini-computer at the radar site, is a colour-coded display in which rainfall rates over a matrix of square areas, typically 5 × 5 km, are depicted on a television monitor. Such displays can be reproduced at meteorological offices and other locations remote from the radar site.

Radar network
With weather radar data available in digital form, it has become feasible to collect together the output from a number of radars and to produce in real time a composite radar rainfall pattern from these data. The whole of the British Isles is covered by such an integrated network.

Various techniques for the improvement of the quality of radar data are being explored, especially those which involve the use of human intervention. In particular, some of the problems which are being tackled are: false echoes resulting from anomalous propagation, residual 'ground clutter', effects of orography, missing rainfall areas at long ranges because of the height of the radar beam and finally, the possibility of improving the coverage by use of satellite data for areas for which no radar data are available.

13.2 ATMOSPHERICS

It is well known that atmospherics originating from lightning discharges interfere with radio reception. When a lightning flash occurs, radio waves are emitted over a wide frequency band, the most intense waves having frequencies less than 50 kHz (wavelength greater than 6000 m). This was realized by Watson-Watt in the years following 1920 and led him to build the first thunderstorm cathode-ray direction finder. In this apparatus the bearing of the discharge is displayed visually on the cathode-ray tube, and by taking simultaneous observations on the same lightning flash from widely separated receivers, the source of the discharge can be located with reasonable accuracy. Such a system was successfully operated by the United Kingdom Meteorological Office until as recently as 1988; thunderstorms could be monitored within a radius of about 1500 km from Britain.

This system has now been replaced by what is known as the ATD (arrival time difference) system. In this scheme, the location of the lightning flash is deduced from the time difference of the atmospheric arriving at various pairs of detector stations. These time differences need to be measured very precisely and it is necessary to use atomic clocks to achieve the necessary stability and synchronization between the measurements from the detector stations. The new system is run automatically with the various communications and computing tasks being handled by small computers.

13.3 SATELLITE IMAGERY

The Meteorological Office first received pictures from weather satellites in 1964 and routine operational use of these became possible in 1966 with the introduction of the automatic picture transmission (APT) facility. Since then, there has been a great increase in the number of satellite images received and a very marked improvement in their quality, enabling weather patterns to be monitored over a large part of the earth's surface.

Satellite orbits
Meteorological satellites are launched into one of two types of orbit; geostationary or near-polar. In a geostationary orbit the satellite maintains a fixed position relative to the earth; of necessity, the satellite must be located at about 36 000 km over the equator. A satellite in this position commands a view over about one third of the earth's surface; a series of five such satellites equally spaced around the equator can monitor all but the polar regions. Sequences of images obtained at frequent intervals for all or part of the area in view can be processed to provide repeatable 'movie loops'. The evolution of cloud patterns discernible on such movie loops has been found to give a far better perspective of developments than single 'snap-shot' pictures.

Meteorological polar-orbiting satellites are launched into orbits at altitudes of only 600–1000 km and can therefore provide higher resolution pictures, albeit of rather limited areas; they give particularly good coverage over polar regions where, because of the earth's curvature, geostationary satellites can provide only limited information. The orbits are sun-synchronous (i.e. each equator crossing is at the same local time) and successive equator crossings advance westwards by about 25°.

With orbital periods of rather more than 100 minutes about 14 orbits are completed in a day and full global coverage is obtained every 12 hours.

Types of imagery

Radiometer packages on the satellites typically sense radiation at two wavelengths; visible (0.6–0.9 μm) and infrared (IR 10.5–12.5 μm). A further channel which may be monitored is the water vapour (WV) channel at 5.7–7.1 μm.

The visible channel measures the reflected solar radiation from either the earth's surface or from intervening cloud. The portions of the field of view with high reflectivity appear as white and those parts with low reflectivity as black, various shades of grey being used for reflectivities between the two extremes. Most clouds are shown clearly on visible pictures except when the background is a snow or ice covered surface or when thin cirrus is viewed against a light background such as a lower cloud layer or desert.

The chosen IR wavelength is near the peak energy emission for the earth's surface (see Section 3.2) as well as being one at which the clear atmosphere has a minimum absorption (termed an 'atmospheric window'). The intensity of infrared radiation received is a measure of the temperature of the body which is emitting the radiation. The highest radiances (the warmest areas) appear as black and the lowest (coldest) as white, with intermediate temperatures being shown by a variable grey scale. With IR pictures it is easy to distinguish between low and high clouds although low clouds are not always so easy to distinguish from their background if this has a similar temperature. By use of simultaneous visible and IR pictures during daytime, it is possible to derive a great deal of information concerning the various cloud features. An example is shown in Figs 83 and 84 with corresponding surface chart in Fig. 85.

The WV wavelength is a region of the spectrum where water vapour absorbs strongly: the images show differences in the temperature of upper atmospheric water vapour. Highest radiances, representing the warmest areas again appear black and the lower radiances as white. The darker shades indicate that emission from warm, and hence low, levels is able to reach the satellite and so the upper atmosphere must be dry. Lighter shades show that the emission is from water vapour in the colder, upper atmosphere. WV images tend to be fuzzy, lacking the clear delineations of cloud features at the other wavelengths, but there are two notable exceptions in which sharp water vapour discontinuities do occur. One is where the tops of cumulonimbus penetrate the dry environment of the upper troposphere, especially noticeable in the tropics, and the second is at the poleward side of polar-front jet streams where the moist cirrus-laden air beneath the tropical tropopause abuts the dry stratospheric air overlying the polar tropopause.

An additional wavelength which may be sensed is at about 3 μm; comparison of these images with infrared images has been found useful in detecting and distinguishing between areas of fog and low cloud.

Processing of the imagery

Before distribution to users, satellite pictures need to be subjected to a number of processes, all of which are nowadays performed automatically by computer. Two most important processes are the addition of a background latitude and longitude grid with coastline (if there are no distinguishing landmarks the imagery is useless

Figure 83.   NOAA-12 visible image at 09 UTC on 23 April 1992.

without a grid), and enhancement of picture quality to take account of the changing visible light levels with time of day and season.

Use of satellite imagery

Since its inception, satellite imagery has been seen as an invaluable aid in weather analysis over data-sparse areas; its importance over the oceans has increased with the withdrawal from service of the dedicated, and strategically placed, weather ship fleet. In data-rich areas, close study of the imagery in conjunction with information from other sources has enabled the development of conceptual models by which particular patterns may be identified with particular atmospheric structures; these relationships may then be used to infer the existence of typical structures solely from the imagery in regions where other observations are completely lacking. The location of surface fronts, upper ridges and troughs, and jet streams can be determined, as can the stage of development of extratropical depressions and tropical cyclones. It is possible to make inferences about wind structure and atmospheric stability and the existence of lee waves; the extent of snow cover and

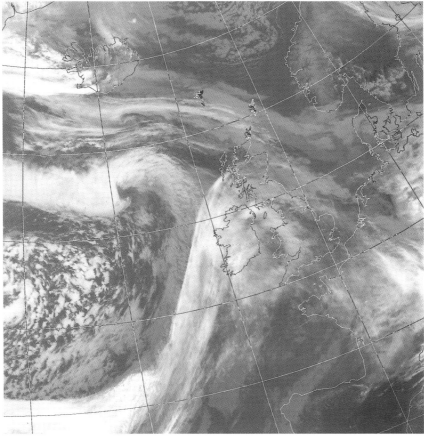

Photograph by courtesy of University of Dundee

Figure 84.   NOAA-12 infrared image at 09 UTC on 23 April 1992.

sea ice may be mapped, and the extent and movement of fog banks and low cloud sheets may be monitored and extrapolated.

Most forecast charts today are computer products or are based upon such products and it is clearly important that the numerical processes on which these are based should start from as accurate an analysis (or initialization) as is possible. To achieve this end, use is made of satellite imagery to fine-tune the machine initialization. Four particular situations in which satellite imagery can provide a sound basis for modifying the model analysis have been identified (McCallum 1992):-

(i)   Surface or upper-air vortices may be identified, deepened or relocated. The model sometimes seriously underestimates, mislocates or loses a discrete circulation which is clearly in evidence on satellite pictures.

(ii)   Through the use of conceptual models, phase and amplitude errors in upper-ridge/trough patterns may be identified and corrected.

(iii) Important small-scale features, such as new frontal developments, may be inferred and passed to the model.

(iv) Model humidity patterns may be found wanting and modified.

221

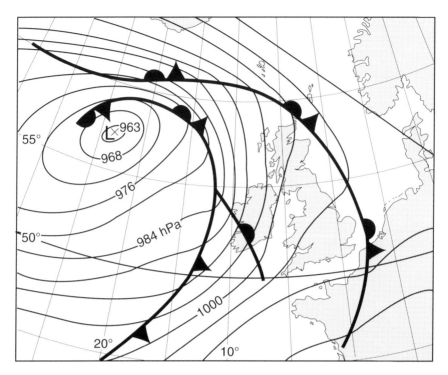

Figure 85.   Surface analysis at 12 UTC on 23 April 1992, shortly after the satellite images depicted in Figs 83 and 84.

13.4 MEASUREMENTS FROM SATELLITES

Since the 1960s there has been a considerable research effort by the meteorological community to develop techniques for the derivation of various meteorological parameters from satellite measurements. Some of these techniques have been introduced operationally whilst the search continues for new methods to improve the accuracy and resolution of those parameters currently derived, and to extend the range of parameters measured to include such other variables as surface pressure.

The impetus for the research work stemmed from a number of requirements. Firstly, the need to improve the observational network, particularly in oceanic and other areas from which few observations had previously been available. Second, satellite data provide an important input for numerical forecasting models. Thirdly, satellite observations would allow limitation of expenditure on conventional observations, such as the Ocean Weather Ships.

Principles
Essentially, all satellite-borne instruments for meteorological use monitor radiation from some part of the electromagnetic spectrum. Most instruments are 'passive' sounders for which the radiation detected is emitted by the atmosphere or earth's surface or is radiation (visible or ultraviolet) emitted by the sun and reflected by the atmosphere or earth's surface. Some instruments are 'active' sounders which generate radiation (e.g. microwave) and detect the reflection of it from the earth and

atmosphere. It is necessary to interpret these measurements and any temporal changes of them in terms of meteorological phenomena and these computations are normally carried out on earth-based computers, the basic data having been transmitted from the satellite to a suitable ground station.

Measurements are made from both geostationary and polar-orbiting satellites.

Measurements used for synoptic purposes

A number of parameters are derived and used for synoptic purposes, the necessary calculations being performed automatically by computer. However, some limited human monitoring is performed to ensure the quality of the output is acceptable. The various parameters concerned are detailed below.

Thickness (temperature). Measurements are made at a number of different wavelengths in the infrared and microwave regions of the spectrum in order to derive temperature profiles of the atmosphere. Wavelengths are chosen at which carbon dioxide or oxygen strongly emit and absorb radiation. As these gases are evenly distributed throughout the atmosphere the amount of radiation received is dependent on the temperature of the emitting gas. The height in the atmosphere from which the radiation at a particular wavelength mainly originates is dependent on how strongly absorbing the atmosphere is at that wavelength. It is therefore possible by judicious choice of suitable wavelengths to derive the temperature profile of the atmosphere, although of necessity the determined profile is rather smoothed in the vertical so that sharp inversions are not detected; this is especially so in the boundary layer and near the tropopause. If there is cloud present this affects the measurements and special processing needs to be performed. The instruments which are used to make these measurements are radiometers which are designed to scan the atmosphere below the satellite so that temperature profiles can be derived over a wide area. The height–temperature relationship (see Appendix I) is used to derive layer thicknesses from the temperature profiles; these data are regularly used for the initialization of numerical forecast models; they are particularly valuable in the southern hemisphere because of the shortage of other data.

Water vapour content. Similar methods to those described above are used, radiation being detected at those infrared wavelengths which are particularly sensitive to water vapour emissions. Since the temperature profile has already been derived, it is possible to relate the strength of these emissions to the quantity of water vapour in the atmosphere.

Wind. Winds can be derived by tracking the movement of clouds from consecutive geostationary satellite images and by assuming that the cloud or cluster of clouds has moved with the appropriate layer wind. Inaccuracies in these derived winds can arise for a number of reasons:

(i) as clouds are constantly developing and decaying, there can be ambiguity in deriving cloud movement,

(ii) some clouds which may be orographically generated will not move with the wind, and

(iii) there can be difficulty in assigning the height at which the derived wind is supposed to apply, particularly for thin cirrus cloud which is not completely opaque and therefore may yield an incorrect cloud-top temperature, leading to an erroneous height value.

Considerable progress is being made in eliminating these problems by use of both computer methods and human scrutiny. Satellite-derived winds are very valuable for initialization of numerical forecast models, particularly over the oceans.

Cloud-top height. This is determined by comparing IR measurements of the cloud top temperature with the derived temperature profile.

Sea surface temperature. Sea surface temperatures can be derived from IR measurements at 11 μm, 12 μm and 13 μm where no cloud intervenes. It is necessary to determine which areas have no cloud and to make a correction for the small contribution of the atmosphere.

Other measurements
Other parameters which may be derived from satellite measurements, but which are not routinely used for synoptic purposes, include ozone concentrations, concentrations of other trace gases, sea state (significant wave height, period and wavelength), surface wind speed and direction, extent of pack ice, surface moisture and land use. Space altimetry allows sea level changes and river levels to be monitored.

13.5 OTHER TECHNIQUES

A number of other instruments and techniques for remote sensing are under development though not yet in widespread operational use. These include acoustic sounders to deduce the height of low-level temperature inversions (hence fog tops), the use of ground-based radiometers to deduce atmospheric composition and temperature profiles, and Doppler scattering laser anemometers to measure wind speed remotely, e.g. on a runway approach.

CHAPTER 14

COLLECTION AND CHARTING OF
OBSERVATIONS

14.1 INTERNATIONAL CO-OPERATION

The rapid collection of a large number of synchronous observations from stations scattered over a wide area is an essential requirement for any meteorological service. The speed of modern aircraft and the long distances travelled necessitate the production of weather maps covering large areas, and hemispherical charts are a usual feature in central forecasting offices. The exchange of this volume of information between countries requires close international co-operation and this is achieved through the World Meteorological Organization (WMO). This organization was incorporated as a specialized agency of the United Nations Organization in 1951, and took the place of the International Meteorological Organization which had been formed in 1878.

In the specialized field of aeronautical meteorology, the standard procedures necessary for the safe, economic and regular operation of international air services are formulated by the Meteorological Division of the International Civil Aviation Organization (ICAO). This body works in close collaboration with WMO in order to ensure common procedures and to avoid unnecessary duplication of services. In general, ICAO accepts the recommendations of WMO concerning general meteorological questions. These organizations have standardized the meteorological procedures used in making and disseminating observations so that weather reports and forecasts can be exchanged internationally in a coded form, without the complication of language difficulties. Amendments to codes and procedures are agreed and brought into operation to meet changing conditions.

A network of meteorological observing stations has been established which provides a selection of weather reports required internationally for the preparation of weather maps. The density of the network is influenced by difficulties of terrain and climate, by large areas of ocean and by the differing degrees of organization.

Land stations
Main reporting stations make full observations of the weather elements at three-hourly intervals throughout the day and night, and a high proportion make hourly reports. Additional stations make abbreviated observations for limited periods of the day, or in some cases at hourly intervals throughout the 24 hours. Abbreviated observations are also made by automatic weather stations and these are available throughout the 24 hours.

Each synoptic meteorological observing station throughout the world is allocated a unique station index number of five digits. The first two figures, called the block number, represent the country or zone and the last three the serial number of the station within the national list of the country concerned. A worldwide list of station index numbers is given in the WMO Publication No. 9, Volume A (WMO 1992).

Aeronautical stations

These stations are responsible for making official weather reports for aviation at fixed times, either half-hourly or hourly as routine, supplemented by special reports whenever specific changes in value of one or more of the observed weather elements occur. When encoded into METAR form they are identified by the ICAO location indicator. At those airports manned by Meteorological Office staff, both synoptic and aviation reports are made, but at most aeronautical stations in the United Kingdom only the latter are available, prepared while the aerodrome is open by air traffic services staff who have completed an approved course of training in meteorological observing.

Ship stations

Reports from most ocean areas of the world are obtained through the voluntary co-operation of ship's officers. Regular observations are made on selected ships and the reports are transmitted to the appropriate shore radio station designated by international agreement to accept such messages. Recent technical developments have led to the introduction on some ships of equipment which automatically compiles the report and transmits it to an appropriate meteorological centre by use of satellite communication links. A few commercial vessels are equipped to carry out automated radiosonde ascents.

Ocean weather ships. The advent of satellites has seen a reduction in the number of dedicated ocean stations but a few are maintained by interested maritime states to provide regular surface and upper-air observations.

Buoys. Since the early 1970s, increasing use has been made of instrumented buoys for obtaining observations from sea areas. Two types are deployed; moored and drifting. Moored buoys are normally deployed within a few hundred kilometres of the coast and use a radio telemetry link for transmission of the data to the shore. Drifting buoys are used successfully to obtain observations from areas with little sea traffic. These buoys use satellites not only to transmit their data to the shore but also for determination of their position with standard satellite navigation equipment.

Weather reports from aircraft

Meteorological information from aircraft in flight or from aircrews after flight is used to supplement the synoptic weather data. Bulletins of in-flight reports from aircraft (AIREPs) are assembled by meteorological collecting centres and are exchanged nationally and internationally using normal meteorological communications circuits. Some aircraft are fitted with ASDAR (Aircraft to Satellite Data Relay); at regular time-intervals throughout the flight this equipment transmits data already available within the aircraft data-handling systems, such as position, altitude, air temperature and wind. The data are relayed via satellite and are inserted into the normal meteorological telecommunications channels for general distribution. In areas where the network of observations is sparse, meteorological reports from aircraft are particularly valuable.

Satellite data

The types of data and information available from meteorological satellites were described in the previous chapter. Coverage of the majority of the globe is maintained by five geostationary satellites. Each satellite not only transmits data from its own instruments but also relays data from the adjacent geostationary satellites. It is therefore possible to obtain data from satellites which are not in direct line-of-sight of the receiving station.

Imagery from polar-orbiting satellites is available when the satellite is in direct line-of-sight of the receiving station. Derived products from these satellites, such as temperature profiles, are computed at a controlling ground station and distributed via standard meteorological communications circuits.

14.2 CODING OF SURFACE OBSERVATIONS

The internationally standardized form of weather message which has been adopted is one of figure codes arranged in groups, mainly of five figures.

A detailed description of the codes employed can be found in *WMO Manual on Codes* (WMO 1988). In the Annex, a brief description is given of the code form which is used for surface weather reports from land stations (the SYNOP code). This code illustrates the general principles on which all meteorological figure codes are based. Aviation routine weather reports are coded in METAR format and a brief description of this code is also given in the Annex.

14.3 TRANSMISSION OF OBSERVATIONS

Observations from a country or region are collected regularly, in many cases each hour, by a collecting centre for the area; the 'collectives' are exchanged between countries which then retransmit the exchanged information to stations in their own region. The existing system for routine international exchange of meteorological information is based on a vast network of land-line, cable, radio and satellite transmission channels which are used to carry teleprinter and facsimile broadcasts and, more recently, direct computer-to-computer communications links.

SYNOP observations and other meteorological reports from United Kingdom observers are transmitted over the Civil Rented Data Network (CRDN) to the Meteorological Telecommunication Centre (Met TC) at Bracknell. The collected data are then retransmitted in bulletins to home meteorological offices and to other national centres overseas within about 30 minutes of the time of origin. This communication centre acts as a Regional Telecommunication Hub in the WMO Global Telecommunication System, and an average of 10 million 5-figure groups of surface data are handled per day. Data from Greenland, Iceland, Belgium, Holland, Denmark, Republic of Ireland and North Atlantic shipping are collected and distributed by Bracknell. Exchange of information between Bracknell and other European sub-centres takes place by dedicated computer-to-computer links and by land-line teleprinter. Information is exchanged between Europe and North America by radio, cable and satellite links; in particular, a segment of the WMO Main Trunk Circuit operates between Bracknell and Washington. Facsimile transmissions by land-line and radio allow British and overseas stations to receive charts and diagrams prepared by the Central Forecasting Office, Bracknell.

Coded aviation weather reports (METAR) are sent, usually via the Aeronautical Fixed Telecommunication Network (AFTN), from civil aerodromes in the United Kingdom to the Civil Aviation Communications Computer (CACC) at London

(Heathrow), where every half-hour they are assembled into bulletins of 'surface actuals' (SA) for broadcast on OPMET. METARs from government-owned aerodromes are input from the Meteorological Office Communications Centre. Bulletins containing reports from major airports are exchanged internationally over the Meteorological Operational Telecommunications Network — Europe (MOTNE), and are held in the Brussels and Vienna meteorological data banks for access by aerodrome Flight Briefing Units (FBU). A selection of METARs covering the United Kingdom and near Continent is available from the AIRMET telephone service and from the METFAX facsimile service, and a much smaller selection is broadcast on VOLMET.

The organization of communications is continually undergoing improvements and details of current procedures can be found in the latest edition of the *Handbook of Meteorological Telecommunications* (Meteorological Office 1993) and in the MET section of CAP32, the *United Kingdom Air Pilot*.

14.4 PREPARATION OF SURFACE CHARTS

Weather reports are received in large numbers at forecasting offices and before they can be comprehensively viewed by the forecaster they need to be plotted on a suitable geographical chart. On the working charts used for this purpose the position of each reporting station is marked by a small circle with its three-figure station index number alongside. The coded message is represented by entries in and around the appropriate station circle, some in figures, some as symbols, but all in a standard form which for the most part is agreed internationally in order that charts may be interpreted with equal facility by persons of any nationality. On the few points on which international agreement has not yet been reached, the British practice is adhered to in this book.

An outline of the method of plotting is given in the Annex in order to aid the reader in the interpretation of charts such as those which appear in the Annex, but for full details of plotting procedures reference should be made to *Guide on the global data-processing system* (WMO 1982). It is not expected that all aircrew will seek to become expert at plotting a weather chart but they should be sufficiently versed in the methods used to allow ready interpretation of the completed charts. Proficiency in this respect is very desirable at briefing and is required of candidates presenting themselves for meteorological examinations; it can perhaps best be attained by actual practice in the plotting of charts from coded weather reports. Unless the candidate is attached to a recognized school of instruction, it is advisable for him to seek access to a meteorological forecasting office in order to see the work in progress. Specimen synoptic messages may usually be obtained for practice purposes and the completed charts may subsequently be compared with those prepared officially.

It should be noted that today the majority of working charts used by forecasters are plotted by machine. Some main forecasting centres have automatic plotting equipment for this purpose and other offices receive facsimile copies of charts plotted at one of the main centres, such as the Central Forecasting Office at Bracknell. Charts which are plotted by machine do not normally have the station index or block numbers printed on them as the main purpose of these is to aid the human plotter.

The technique of plotting land station reports is based on the station model which is shown in the Annex. A brief description of this plotting model is given there together with details of the additional elements which are plotted from a ship report.

The plotting of charts is a mechanical process which may be learned without any consideration of meteorological science, but to pass from the plotted chart to the completed weather map it is necessary to have a good understanding of both physical and synoptic matters. Although the full consideration of the technique of chart analysis is necessarily deferred to a later chapter, many students will benefit by acquiring some experience in chart drawing at an early stage in their training. It is recommended that after some familiarity with plotting has been obtained, the student should attempt the drawing of isobars on his first charts, regarding them to start with simply as lines of equal pressure. If he has studied Chapters 2 and 5 he will be familiar with their general properties including their relationship to surface wind speed and direction, and care must be taken to draw the lines in conformity with those properties. For full instructions, reference should be made to Section 19.2, most of which should be assimilable at this stage without much difficulty.

14.5 HANDLING AND DISPLAY OF OTHER DATA

Upper-air data

There are numerous ways in which upper-air data can be displayed for use by forecasters. One method is to plot charts for selected pressure levels using data derived from radiosondes, aircraft reports and satellite measurements. The construction of this type of chart is discussed further in Section 19.3.

Much of the theory contained in Part I of this book has been discussed using tephigrams to illustrate the vertical structure of the atmosphere and these useful diagrams are used routinely by forecasters. It should be noted, however, that alternative thermodynamic diagrams are used by forecasters in some other countries for presentation of the data. Forecasting offices in the United Kingdom receive radiosonde data in coded format which can be used for the plotting of tephigrams; copies of tephigrams which have been machine plotted are also received by facsimile from the Central Forecasting Office at Bracknell .

Satellite imagery

In Britain, one ground station in southern England is used for the reception of satellite imagery. After some processing, as described earlier, this imagery is distributed to a number of forecasting offices by use of special facsimile equipment capable of reproducing an adequate range of grey shades. Some national meteorological centres produce cloud analyses from satellite pictures and distribute these by facsimile, the advantage being that only black and white shades need to be reproduced.

Miscellaneous reports

Various other reports are distributed by teleprinter. These include reports from the atmospheric (ATD) network, radar reports describing the location and movement of the main rain-bearing radar echoes, and plain-language reports from aircraft which have been submitted by airfield meteorological offices.

PART III

SYNOPTIC METEOROLOGY

CHAPTER 15

AIR MASSES AND FRONTS

15.1 INTRODUCTION

In Part I the physical principles underlying meteorological phenomena have been discussed and the individual factors considered independently; it now remains to adopt the point of view of the practical forecaster faced with a succession of synoptic charts and other observational data from which he has to infer probable changes in meteorological conditions over an area or route, involving an analysis of the various factors and an assessment of their combined effect in any particular situation.

Once it became possible to draw weather maps it was soon evident that in most parts of the world large-scale variations in weather conditions are associated with changes in the type of pressure field. The first step towards forecasting came with the recognition of the importance of the formation and movement of depressions and anticyclones. The next step forward was the discovery by Norwegian meteorologists of the nature of frontal zones and the development of a theory of the formation of depressions associated with a polar front. This led to a classification of air masses with fronts as boundaries between them and the frontal cloud masses being formed by the upsliding of warmer, lighter, air over colder, denser, air.

Further increase in knowledge of the conditions in the upper air and observations of finer detail in frontal zones by research aircraft have led to the realization that fronts are more complex than the idealized picture suggests. It is now considered more likely that depressions are formed dynamically, causing convergence of the isotherms into a frontal zone, rather than that the depressions form because of the existence of the frontal zone.

Whatever the cause of the frontal depression, from the practical point of view the frontal zones are very real. They may differ in detail from the idealized picture and considerably from one to another, but they have been, and still are, an exceedingly useful feature in the analysis of weather situations portrayed by synoptic charts.

15.2 AIR MASSES

The properties of the air depend primarily on temperature and humidity; the study of synoptic charts shows that these factors are often broadly the same over wide areas measuring many hundreds or even thousands of kilometres across. When air of substantially the same characteristics covers a large area it is called an 'air mass'. It is to be noted that, since there is little horizontal difference in temperature through the mass, there is little variation of wind with height above the friction layer (cf. Section 5.4), so that the air moves as an almost solid current.

In order that a mass of air shall assume uniform characteristics it needs to remain tolerably stagnant for a period of many days in a region where the earth's surface is itself reasonably uniform. The subtropical belts of high pressure, the polar anticyclones associated with the arctic fields of snow and ice, and the large highs

233

which form over the continents in winter are areas of this kind. Whilst air remains over these regions it becomes more or less homogeneous and when, under the influence of wind, it eventually moves away to another area it largely retains its source characteristics although these become slowly modified.

Classification and characteristics of air masses

The basis of the classification of air masses is the source region last occupied by the air mass. Since there is perhaps no part of the world which might not on occasion act as a source region, the different labels given to the variety of air masses affecting any particular place are largely a matter of the geography of the surrounding areas and especially of the distribution of land and sea. Here we shall in the main confine ourselves to a general classification determined primarily by the latitude of the source regions; thus in order of increasing latitude we shall speak of equatorial air, tropical air, polar air and arctic (or antarctic) air. The factor most affected by the latitude of the source is the temperature. As the difference in humidity between two air masses of the same basic type depends essentially on whether they have originated over land or over sea, a secondary classification is made into continental and maritime air masses.

The properties of the air as it arrives at any place depend on the characteristics acquired while at the source and on the changes which have subsequently taken place during transit. These changes are due mainly to surface heating or cooling and to evaporation and condensation; their effects have already been studied in Part I. When a polar current penetrates to lower latitudes it undergoes surface heating; this tends to cause convective currents, a steep lapse rate of temperature and perhaps cumulus or cumulonimbus clouds with instability showers. Moreover, surface heating raises the temperature further above the dew-point and, unless moisture is freely provided by evaporation, the air near the surface becomes relatively dry. Conversely, when a tropical or equatorial current moves to higher latitudes it undergoes surface cooling. Surface cooling inhibits convective currents, the cooling is confined near the surface and the lapse rate becomes stable, often with an inversion above the surface layers. Cooling may lead to condensation in the form of dew, mist, fog, low cloud or drizzle, although if the humidity is too low, condensation may not occur and the sky will remain clear.

On the basis of these well understood principles it is a simple matter to infer in broad terms the probable characteristics of any air mass on arrival in another part of the world, account being taken of the differences in temperature between land and sea according to the season of the year.

Air masses of temperate latitudes

In temperate latitudes of the northern hemisphere, the polar and tropical air masses with their subdivisions into maritime and continental varieties are the usual types at all seasons, while arctic air is also experienced occasionally in winter. The source regions and typical properties of these air masses and the modifications they undergo in their passage from the source to the temperate latitudes will now be described. A similar basic terminology applies also in the southern hemisphere; the air masses there will not be described in detail but incidental references to them are made in discussing the climatology of these regions in Part IV.

Tropical maritime air.   The source regions of this air mass are the subtropical anticyclones of the Atlantic and Pacific Oceans. The air accordingly starts with a high temperature, high relative humidity and high dew-point, and it largely retains these characteristics as it moves towards neighbouring regions. In the North Atlantic, as the tropical air moves north-eastwards towards Europe it is continuously cooled from below and if the wind is light the lower layers become increasingly stable, perhaps with an inversion; with stronger wind, the lapse rate is steepened within the frictional layer and the base of the inversion is lifted. The high relative humidity acquired in the source region is maintained or intensified by the subsequent surface cooling, saturation is often reached and low stratus or stratocumulus, fog, drizzle and orographic cloud form readily. Over the sea the air temperature is characteristically higher than that of the sea itself, and over land in winter the air is mild. In summer, as it passes over land, surface heating by day usually disperses any stratiform cloud or fog, but the pronounced stability usually prevents the development of large convective currents, even if there is orographic or frontal lifting, and visibility is usually moderate or poor.

Different conditions are found on the southern side of the North Atlantic anticyclone where the air is moving westwards towards the United States. This movement brings the air over the still warmer waters of the Gulf Stream giving instability so that convection there often gives rise to cumulonimbus with showers and thunderstorms.

Tropical continental air.   The source region in winter is north Africa. In summer the source occupies a vast area extending across north Africa and southern Europe to eastern Asia; another source region in summer is the arid region of North America to the west of the Mississippi. Tropical continental air is warm at its source, with low relative and absolute humidity. In moving to higher latitudes the lower layers become cooled, and over the sea the air temperature is higher than the sea temperature. Humidity tends to remain low, particularly when the track is over dry land, but when it passes over water, evaporation increases the humidity, both relative and absolute; if the process continues long enough, the air mass becomes changed into a maritime type. Generally, however, the dryness of the air and the effect of surface cooling in stabilizing the lapse rate, combine to prevent cloud formation even if the air is subsequently subjected to intense surface heating. This air mass affects the British Isles only in summer; after crossing Europe, high temperatures are maintained by insolation and hot cloudless weather results. Since there is nothing to remove the fine dust which enters the air mass in its source region or in its later passage over land, the visibility usually is reduced due to haze.

Polar maritime air.   The source regions of this air mass are the northern parts of the North Atlantic and North Pacific Oceans. At the source, the air is characterized by low temperature, low dew-point, high relative humidity and stable lapse rate, at least in the lower layers. In moving towards warmer regions, the air mass is heated from below but its surface temperature remains less than that of the sea surface. Thermal instability spreads upwards from the lower layers and the lapse rate becomes steep up to high levels. This permits development of convective cloud formations and often leads to large cumulus or cumulonimbus. Instability showers are associated with the well-developed clouds and at times they are accompanied by thunderstorms, strong gusts or squalls. On occasions the lapse rate aloft is stabilized by a general subsidence of the air mass and cloud development is then restricted to fair-weather cumulus or possibly stratocumulus. Except in showers, visibility is good since, at its source, the air is usually clear and any impurities subsequently carried into the air are dispersed by the convective currents or removed by showers.

If this type of air mass moves from sea to land in summer, the advective surface heating is accentuated over land by insolation and convection is at first intensified. However, after the air crosses the coast the absorption of water vapour by evaporation at the surface is greatly reduced and the increasing dryness of the air makes it more difficult for convective cloud to form. In winter, polar maritime air is relatively mild as it moves over land cooled by radiation. The air mass then undergoes surface cooling and becomes stabilized in the lower layers, thus taking on some of the characteristics of tropical maritime air; showers decrease in intensity, clouds tend to spread out into layer types, while fog can form readily under a clear sky when the pressure gradient is slack. A somewhat similar situation occurs when the air mass, after moving to lower latitudes, again moves northwards as 'returning polar maritime' air. The surface layers then become stabilized and resemble tropical maritime air, but the upper layers remain unstable, so that once convection is initiated, as for example over land in summer, it is apt to develop freely.

Polar continental and arctic air. The source regions of these air masses are the northern parts of the Eurasian and North American continents and are more extensive in winter than in summer. The arctic regions, situated between these two areas, constitute the source region for arctic air. Since at the source the polar continental and arctic air masses are in contact with a surface mostly covered with ice or snow, the air and dew-point temperatures are low; the lapse rate is stable in the lower layers and perhaps also aloft due to subsidence. Except over the continents in winter, these air masses arrive in temperate latitudes only after travel over a warmer surface with absorption of heat and possibly moisture, so that the lapse rate becomes gradually steeper from the surface upwards.

In winter over the land the convective developments are absent on account of weak insolation and low humidity; clear skies are then the rule. If the air subsequently moves over the sea, evaporation and heating produced by the relatively warm sea surface result in cumuliform cloud with perhaps wintry showers. In fact, the air mass in this process takes on a transitional character and becomes transformed more or less completely into polar maritime air. Thus polar continental air from North America in winter is transformed into polar maritime air as it travels eastwards across the Atlantic Ocean. Another example, in which the process of transformation is not carried so far, is provided by polar continental air which reaches the British Isles in winter after crossing the North Sea; showers commonly occur near the east coast but on moving further inland the source of heat is removed and cloud and showers die out.

In summer the polar continental air, while moving to a warmer part of the land, is at first dry and cloudless. It is therefore subject to surface heating by insolation; some of this heat is transferred upwards by convection, and thus in time the air becomes converted into a warm mass, sometimes called 'transitional' polar continental air. If this mass then moves over the sea, which is cool compared with the heated land, it is stabilized and moistened in the surface layers so that fog or low stratiform cloud may form. This is experienced for example on the east coast of England and Scotland provided the track across the North Sea is long enough to produce a high humidity in the originally dry air. Genuine polar continental air does not reach this country in summer, since the air necessarily undergoes transformation into the polar maritime variety if it travels over the sea, or into warm continental air if it travels overland.

Such, in brief, are the typical features of the principal air masses in temperate latitudes. In practice, no two air masses of the same type are exactly alike, nor is any one air mass strictly homogeneous. The character of an air mass undergoes more or less continuous transition by such processes as loss or gain of heat, changes in humidity and in the vertical motion to which it may be subjected during its history. The effect of subsidence in stabilizing the lapse rate has already been mentioned; this process also dries the air and dissipates cloud; if the air undergoes ascent then it becomes cooled, the relative humidity increases, the lapse rate may steepen and clouds form easily. The association of slow ascent or descent with the pressure distribution and the barometric tendency have been noted in Section 5.5 and it will now be appreciated how the character of an air mass becomes modified when it moves into a different pressure system.

It should be emphasized that there is no meaning in stating the characteristic properties of an air mass unless it is also stated to what part of the world it refers. The above characteristics refer to temperate regions; it is clear, for example, that what is classed as polar air may develop some properties of warm air on penetrating to even higher latitudes, and that stable tropical air may become unstable on moving nearer the equator.

Equatorial air masses
The belt contained between the two trade wind zones forms an extensive source region of equatorial air which for the most part is warm, moist and often unstable, especially after lifting. Subdivisions are conveniently made according to the modifying effects of the different wind systems — the trades and monsoons — each of which has its own characteristics according to the locality and season.

15.3 MAIN FRONTAL ZONES

It is implicit in the concept of air masses that in moving from one locality to another the characteristics of the air change slowly, for example, polar air on penetrating the tropics and remaining there must undergo a gradual modification before it may be relabelled as tropical air. Since it is therefore not always possible to draw any definite boundary line between air masses, a zone of transition, more or less wide, must often be recognized. Where different air masses are brought close together the transition may be rapid enough to be represented by a continuous line on a weather map. The change from one air mass to another is never absolutely abrupt but occurs over a transitional zone which may be many kilometres across, although on the scale of a synoptic chart a line is a suitable marking. Such a line is termed a 'front' since it marks the limit of advance or retreat of an air mass in its movement over the earth. The term 'frontal zone' may be used when it is desired to emphasize the gradual nature of the change from one air mass to another. It will be seen later that the interaction of two air masses at a front or frontal zone is often responsible for much cloud and precipitation.

We can now indicate the mean position of the fronts, or rather the frontal zones, which mark the transitions between the principal air masses.

Polar front

This marks the boundary between adjacent polar and tropical air masses. Over the North Atlantic its mean position in January extends north-eastwards from Florida towards the south-west of the British Isles, but in summer it lies further north from the neighbourhood of Newfoundland to northern Scotland. Often it extends eastwards into Europe and occasionally it becomes displaced southwards into the Mediterranean. The front usually has a wave-like form and it commonly oscillates during a period of a few days over many hundreds of kilometres, following the movement of air mass boundaries when disturbed by travelling pressure systems. A similar front is found in the North Pacific Ocean.

Arctic front

This is the boundary between arctic and polar air masses. It lies further north than the polar front but is often displaced southwards into temperate latitudes in winter.

Intertropical convergence zone (ITCZ) or equatorial trough

This lies within the tropics and marks the rather broad zone of separation between air masses conveyed by the trade winds from source regions on opposite sides of the equator, an arrangement which is, however, subject to modification by monsoonal winds, particularly those of Asia. This convergence zone was formerly referred to as the 'intertropical front' or ITF, but such a term was hardly appropriate since temperature and density differences across it are generally small and it has little in common with the frontal systems of higher latitudes. Its position normally varies little from day to day but there are changes in its activity and hence in cloudiness along its length. The ITCZ undergoes a regular seasonal shift in its position during the year and this is described in more detail in Section 19.10.

15.4 SOME GENERAL PROPERTIES OF FRONTS

A detailed study of the transitional regions between adjacent air masses was first carried out by Norwegian meteorologists during the First World War and it was then that the present terminology was introduced. The differences between the two masses are exhibited by both temperature and humidity as well as other characteristics but the most significant parameter is, as a rule, temperature. Where the warmer mass is displacing the colder, the front is called a 'warm front'; where the colder air is gaining ground, the front is named a 'cold front'. At other times there is little change in position and the front is said to be 'quasi-stationary'. The front, represented by a line on the chart, marks only the dividing line on the earth's surface; the two air masses, however, extend upwards and the division is really a surface in space; this is the 'frontal surface'.

Normally the two air masses come from different source regions, but sometimes from the same source by different paths so that some differences in characteristics have developed by the time they are again brought together. It will now be explained why it is possible for two air masses to flow side by side without the colder, heavier mass necessarily flowing under the warmer and lighter mass.

Equilibrium at a front.

When a light and a heavy fluid, as for example oil and water, are placed together in a vessel, equilibrium is reached only when lighter fluid floats horizontally upon the heavier. On the other hand when two air masses of different temperature, and so of different density, are in proximity, the surface of separation is usually found to be sloping with the cold air mass beneath as in Fig. 86. If it is assumed for the present that the surface pressure in the warm air is uniform, then since the cold air becomes gradually deeper from F towards C, the surface pressure, being equivalent to the weight of air above, gradually increases at the same time. The surface isobars will therefore run as in Fig. 87 where FF marks the position of the front. Pressure is uniform on the warm side, where there is no wind. On the cold side the pressure gradient force is directed towards the front and would be exactly balanced by the Coriolis force associated with the geostrophic wind blowing parallel with the front. The sloping frontal surface then remains in equilibrium with no tendency for the cold air to flow further under the warm.

Now the equilibrium of the front would be maintained if the same uniform velocity were added to both the warm and cold air masses. For example, if in the situation illustrated in Fig. 87 with the cold air moving from south a uniform westerly wind were superimposed, then the warm air would be moving from the west and the cold air from say, south-west. The isobars would then appear as in Fig. 88. If we now proceed along an isobar in the direction AB, then after crossing

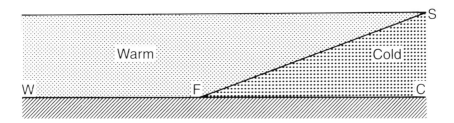

Figure 86.   Vertical section through a frontal surface.

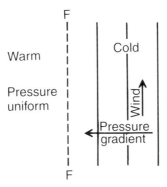

Figure 87.   Motion of cold air parallel with a front balancing the pressure gradient.

the front at B the depth of cold air increases and so the surface pressure must rise along BC. Consequently the isobar AB cannot continue in the same direction after crossing the front but must change counter-clockwise to some such direction as BD. Thus from whichever side the front is approached, the isobars on the further side appear to be refracted towards the centre of low pressure — in other words, the isobars turn cyclonically on crossing the front. It is seen too that the isobars are sharply kinked where they cross the front.

It follows that a front always lies along a trough, unless it happens to lie parallel with the isobars. The fronts shown on the weather charts in the Annex should be examined as examples of this rule. The rule applies also to the southern hemisphere although the wind direction there must be such as to keep the low pressure on the right.

Other diagrams like Fig. 88 may be drawn but with the isobars differently inclined to the front, or with the positions of the cold and warm air masses reversed. In this way it can be seen that although the wind direction necessarily changes at a front, the wind speed may either decrease, remain steady, or increase, according to the spacing of the isobars on either side.

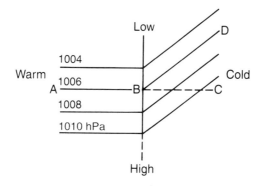

Figure 88.   Refraction of isobars at a front.

Theoretically, the slope of the frontal surface could have any value if the wind velocities and temperatures were suitably adjusted, but experience shows that the slope is rarely steep and in most cases is extremely gentle; it is usually about 1:100, ranging from 1:50 to 1:200 or even flatter. An average frontal surface therefore rises 1000 feet in about 100 000 feet or 30 km, and always slopes upwards from the warm to the cold side.

Movement of fronts
In Fig. 88 and similar cases where there is motion at right angles to the front as well as relative motion of the air masses parallel thereto, the front is carried along with the winds. In order to estimate the speed of translation it is necessary to determine the component of wind at right angles to the front. The simplest method of measuring the geostrophic component at right angles to any line is that explained in Section 5.2, namely by laying the geostrophic wind scale along the line and reading off the speed corresponding to the interval between successive isobars. This is

illustrated in Fig. 89 where the speed is seen to be about 12 KT. The method gives the correct speed of translation of a front only in so far as the winds are geostrophic, but this is generally a useful approximation. Since the isobars are necessarily continuous on crossing a front, the wind component found in this way is the same in both air masses, whence it follows that with geostrophic winds there can be no convergence at the front.

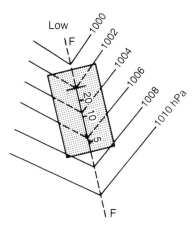

Figure 89.   Estimation of frontal speed using the geostrophic wind scale.

Convergence at fronts
The discussion of equilibrium at a front leads to the conclusion that if the winds are geostrophic then there is no tendency for the warm air to rise over the cold and therefore no cooling by ascent and no cloud formation. This fact is fundamental to a proper understanding of fronts; the mere presence of a front does not imply clouds and rain. The essential property of a front is the difference in temperature between the two sides; disturbed weather is due to disturbed conditions at the front and we must now consider how these may arise.

A discussion of vertical motion in relation to convergence and divergence is included in Section 5.5 where it was seen that among the factors concerned with upward displacements are departures of the wind from geostrophic, frictional effects and falling barometric pressure. These processes commonly affect the whole area of a depression, especially when it is deepening, and they are often localized or accentuated in the vicinity of a frontal surface which then becomes the scene of extensive cloud and precipitation.

While the frictional convergence of surface winds at a front causes a net inflow of air near the ground, the magnitude of the effect outside the tropics is insufficient to give more than very slight rain and so cannot be the main cause of frontal precipitation.

With regard to the convergence and ascent which occur in association with falling pressure tendencies, it has been seen that these may result in widespread cloud and precipitation. In a depression it is not difficult to see why the convergence and rainfall tend to be localized near the fronts. Take a frontal trough such as that represented in Fig. 90 and suppose the depression deepens so that the gradients increase; it is clear that the effect of falling pressure is to cause a flow of air into the depression roughly at right angles to the isobars as indicated by the arrows, and that the convergence is localized near the front. A word of caution is required here, for as a trough moves, pressure must fall ahead of it and rise behind; this gives a system of pressure tendencies due merely to the motion but with no general change of pressure, that is with no development and no convergence. In interpreting the tendencies it is necessary to distinguish real development and deepening from the effect of simple displacement of the isobars without change of gradient; a matter not altogether easy in practice.

It is important to stress that in general a front does not necessarily produce rainfall; for this there must always be some factor setting up convergence and the illustration shows how this occurs in the deepening depression. In regions remote from depressions, convergence is often slight or absent, so that fronts in these regions may produce little or no rainfall.

Frontogenesis and frontolysis
The effect of convergence towards a front is generally to narrow the transitional zone between the adjacent air masses, in other words to sharpen the front. This process is illustrated in Fig. 91 in which it is supposed that there is a gradual fall of temperature across the transitional zone from 12 °C in the warm air to 8 °C in the cold. The effect of the ageostrophic wind components directed towards the front on both sides is to bring the 8 °C and 12 °C isotherms closer together, the intervening air being squeezed upwards; the transitional zone thus becomes narrower and the front sharper. The process whereby the frontal zone is narrowed and the change of air mass takes place more quickly is known as 'frontogenesis'; it is the method by which the sharpness of the front is increased or maintained against the natural tendency towards a diffuse mixing zone. The opposite process which assists the smoothing out of a discontinuity and perhaps leads to a complete disappearance of a front is known as 'frontolysis'. This usually occurs in association with high or rising pressures, with descending air and divergence. The effect of divergence would be illustrated by a diagram similar to Fig. 91 but with the directions of all the wind

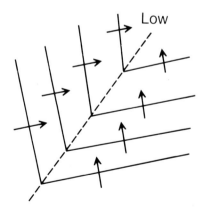

Figure 90.   Convergence towards a front in a deepening depression.

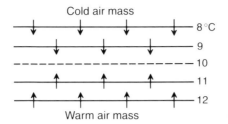

Figure 91.   Frontogenesis — a concentration of isotherms by convergence.

arrows reversed so that the isotherms would become more widely separated. Convergence and divergence are not the only factors which may lead respectively to frontogenesis and frontolysis but they are important, and the above considerations show why in a depression the fronts are usually clearly defined; in other circumstances without convergence they are often difficult to identify and may perhaps disappear altogether.

CHAPTER 16

FRONTAL DEPRESSIONS

16.1 FORMATION OF A FRONTAL DEPRESSION

The preceding chapter introduced the concept of air masses and indicated how frontal zones develop when differing air masses approach one another. Such frontal zones may become preferred regions for the birth or development of depressions.

Consider, for instance, a stationary or quasi-stationary polar front of the type shown in Fig. 92 and, in order to correspond with normal conditions in north temperate regions, let us take the warmer air to lie to the south and the colder to the north as in Fig. 92(a).

It was explained in Section 15.4 that such a front may be in equilibrium if the winds are geostrophic. Now the surface of discontinuity between two air masses is, like the surface of the sea, subject to the formation of waves. In light winds, ocean waves are of the stable kind, limited in size and moving without change of form; when the winds are strong, the waves are unstable and increase in height until the

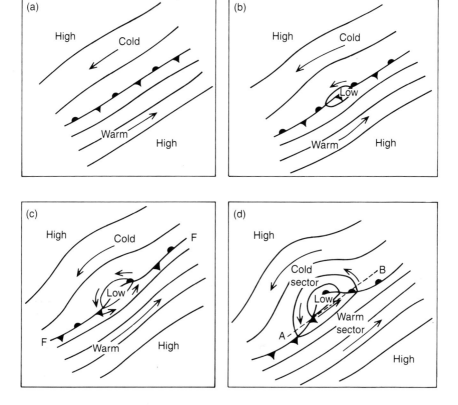

Figure 92.   Formation of a warm-sector depression on a stationary front.

244

tops are eventually sheared off by the wind. Both stable and unstable waves occur in a somewhat similar manner at the gently sloping frontal surface between two air masses, except that the wavelengths are very much greater. Because of the slope of the surface of separation, the wave motion gives rise to a horizontal oscillation in the line where the frontal surface meets the ground so that the warm air at the ground forms a bulge into the cold air. When the wave motion is unstable, the amplitude increases and a depression is formed. In the formative stage the depression enlarges and deepens but eventually it begins to fill up and decay, as will be explained later. Investigation shows that frontal waves are unstable only if their wavelength lies between about 1200 and 3000 km and if there is a sufficiently rapid change (or shear) of wind between the two air masses. In other cases the front merely oscillates without the development of a depression.

With the unstable waves a fall of pressure occurs where the warm air intrudes into the cold and a cyclonic circulation is then created. The front, being displaced with the wind, passes through the stages of Figs. 92(b) and 92(c) to the very much distorted shape of Fig. 92(d). In the original state the front is almost stationary, but as the depression develops the fronts move with the circulating winds; the section in advance of the centre, where warm air is displacing cold, is therefore marked as a warm front, the section behind as a cold front. The region between the warm and cold fronts on the warmer side is occupied by the warmer air and is referred to as the 'warm sector'; the remaining and larger portion is less frequently referred to as the 'cold sector'.

In addition to the process of deepening, or development, there is a general translation of the system, for the winds have everywhere a velocity roughly equal to the geostrophic value and the fronts are carried along with them. The depression itself, travelling with the fronts, usually has a velocity roughly equal in speed and direction to that of the geostrophic wind in the warm air.

Continuously falling pressure implies convergence into the depression so that air is forced to rise. It was noted in Section 15.4 that the upward motion tends to be localized near the fronts. In attempting to explain the process by which the air ascends at the fronts, it is frequently said that the warm air slides upwards over the cold air at the warm front and that the cold air undercuts the warm at the cold front, as though the cold air at either front were a solid wedge. This simple description may be made more explicit by stating that in a direction at right angles to the warm front the warm air moves faster than the cold, while at right angles to the cold front the cold air moves faster than the warm. At both fronts this relative motion is associated with convergence and upflow. Sections 16.2 to 16.4 follow this treatment, but it is as well to emphasize that it is only a description of events and does not provide an explanation of the convergence at fronts, which is a normal condition within a developing frontal depression but not a necessary condition of all fronts. The structure of a front is consequently related to the local pressure distribution and its changes, and the following descriptions apply in general only to conditions within a depression.

16.2 WARM FRONT

Fig. 93 illustrates a vertical cross-section through the fronts of a depression along the line AB on Fig. 92(d) and intersecting the warm front at W and the cold front at

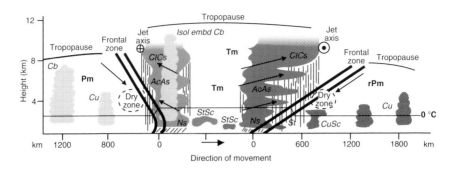

Figure 93.   Cross-section through a frontal-wave depression showing schematic cloud structure in relation to the frontal zones. Arrows show air movement relative to the fronts.

C. The tropopause is higher over the warm air than over the cold air. If a jet stream is associated with the fronts it will be about the positions marked in the diagram. Even if the wind speeds are not of jet stream values the strongest winds are likely to be found in a similar position. Ascent near the warm front produces adiabatic cooling and clouds are formed above the frontal surface. The highest clouds are cirrus, often at 30 000 ft or above, and as the height of the frontal surface decreases the cloud type passes through cirrostratus to altostratus and finally to nimbostratus. Rain or snow begins to fall from the higher altostratus, perhaps from 20 000 ft, but is slight at first and evaporates before reaching the ground; as the clouds lower and thicken, the rain becomes heavier and ultimately reaches the ground some 200–300 km in advance of the front. From then onwards rain is likely to be continuous until the front arrives, after which the rain clouds quickly clear. Apart from the true frontal clouds there is generally considerable low fractostratus (scud) formed by turbulence within the cold air below the altostratus and nimbostratus, for the cold air becomes very moist by evaporation of the falling rain. The depth and extent of the cloud varies considerably from one front to another; it may extend in a solid mass from the ground to the tropopause, or on other occasions it may be layered with clear lanes between the layers. Research flights through fronts have demonstrated clearly the variability of cloud structure, and the not uncommon existence of tongues of very dry air in or near the frontal zones. Usually the slope of the forward edge of the cloud mass is steeper than that of the frontal surface. The transition from cold to warm air usually occurs over a distance of several hundred kilometres, with a belt of more rapid temperature change in a narrow frontal zone which may be as little as 40 km across or as much as 150 km.

  In addition to the cessation of continuous rain, the passage of the surface front brings a veer of wind (a backing of wind in the southern hemisphere), as is common to all fronts, together with an increase in temperature and dew-point corresponding with the change in air mass. Normally the pressure falls steadily ahead of the front; after the passage the fall ceases, or it continues at a slower rate. The lighter winds within the friction layer cause the frontal surface to advance more slowly near the ground than aloft; this in turn produces a very shallow frontal slope near the ground which, combined with vertical mixing, means that the surface changes at the frontal passage are seldom sharp. This description applies to a somewhat idealized warm

246

front from which the actual fronts usually differ in one or more particulars. For example, with low humidity in the warm air the frontal cloud may be patchy or may develop in a number of separate layers and the pre-frontal rain may be slight or even entirely absent. Exceptionally the warm air may become unstable as it ascends the frontal surface and then warm front thunderstorms become possible. In fact real fronts show important departures from the ideal on most occasions but the idealized model nevertheless forms an essential background to any discussion of fronts.

16.3 COLD FRONT

The relative air motions at a cold front are usually of the kind shown in Fig. 93. The warm air ascends only in the lower levels; at high levels it descends along the frontal surface while at middle levels there is a horizontal component away from the front. The cold air behind the front is generally subsiding. If the warm air is convectively unstable, the ascending motion ahead of the cold front may lead to outbreaks of instability (Section 6.5) with the formation of towering cumulus or cumulonimbus clouds and heavy rain of short duration, perhaps with hail or thunder. In these circumstances the rain belt may extend on both sides of the surface front and be heralded by altocumulus clouds carried forward by the increased wind at that level. The frontal surface, sloping upwards behind the surface front, is usually marked by some layer cloud of altostratus type but the descending motion of the cold air below the front as well as of the warm air above the upper part ensure that the cloud mass breaks quickly to the rear of the front.

In Fig. 93 the cold frontal surface is drawn with an overhanging nose some 2000 ft above the surface. This is caused by frictional retardation of the surface air and is a transient feature, which is alternately formed by the overrunning of the air above and destroyed by convective mixing. This process often results in a characteristic roll of low cloud extending along the line of the front. The advance of the surface front thus takes place in an unsteady manner and may give rise to severe gusts. Above the friction layer the slope of the cold frontal surface averages about 1:50 and so is usually steeper than that of the warm front.

The phenomena of the cold front are liable to wide variations. Some fronts pass with little disturbance, some are accompanied by a line squall, sometimes the passage is not immediately evident in the cloud structure as seen from the ground because of the presence of low rain cloud. Often the squall is the most striking feature. The passage of the front is accompanied by a veer of wind sometimes preceded by pre-frontal backing. On occasions the direction may veer temporarily by as much as 180° before settling back to the new direction in the cold air. For example, the general pre-frontal wind may be south-westerly but with the approach of the front the direction may back to south, veering in the squall to north and later settling back to north-west. Temperature falls more or less suddenly and the drop in dew-point is generally well marked. Pressure normally falls somewhat in advance of the front but begins to rise rapidly after the front has passed. When the instability conditions are well developed the front may bring a sudden jump in pressure of 1 hectopascal or more, clearly observable on the barogram trace.

The wide differences between individual cold fronts have been observed by research flights. The cloud masses usually occur in the warm air with the slope of the cloud surface steeper than that of the frontal surface; dry areas in or near the frontal zone are sometimes observed. Although there are large differences in cloud and weather associated with different cold fronts, most of them can be placed in one of two main types termed cold anafronts and cold katafronts. The cold anafront is one in which the warm air is ascending and moving forward less rapidly than the frontal surface. Heavy rain usually occurs at the frontal passage with steady slight rain for some time behind the front. It is usually accompanied by a large fall of temperature and a sharp veer and sudden decrease of wind. A cold katafront is characterized by descending warm air which is moving forward faster than the frontal surface; rainfall is usually very slight at the front, there often being more rain some 100 km ahead of the surface front, the temperature drop is slight and gradual and the wind may veer only very gradually with little change in speed.

16.4 OCCLUSION

As the air of the warm sector is gradually moving upwards above the warm frontal surface and to a less extent over the cold front, the amount of warm air lying on the surface, and therefore the area of the warm sector, gradually decreases. This process appears on the weather map as the overtaking of the warm front by the cold front and when eventually there is no more warm air left at ground level, the two fronts coalesce. The surrounding or enclosing of the depression by cold air is called the 'occluding' process; when complete the depression is said to be 'occluded' and the single composite front is known as an 'occlusion'. If the cold air in advance of the warm front and that behind the cold front had identical properties there would be no surface front at the occlusion, but having been widely separated the two cold masses are likely to have been subjected to noticeably different conditions since the depression began to form; there is therefore, in general, a contrast between them although which is the colder is a matter of circumstances. In either case the occlusion lies along a trough extending outwards from the depression usually in a curved path, for the fronts are carried round more rapidly by the stronger winds near the centre than by the weaker winds in the outer parts.

Following from the warm-sector depression of Fig. 92(d) the further stages are normally as in Fig. 94 although the precise position and shape of the line of occlusion is subject to much variation. In Fig. 94(a) the occlusion is about to appear at the centre; in Fig. 94(b) the occlusion extends from the centre to O while the portions OW and OC remain as warm and cold fronts respectively; in Fig. 94(c) the occlusion extends further, the portion near the centre has become twisted round and there is a trailing end caused by the displacement of the centre along the occlusion. This trailing end which continues to travel round the centre is sometimes referred to as the 'back-bent' occlusion. The occlusion is said to be of the cold-front type or the warm-front type according as to whether the air behind the front is colder or warmer than that in advance of it. The vertical section through the front along the line AFB of Fig. 94(b) is represented in Fig. 95 for each type. The two types are distinguished primarily by the position of the rain area which in the warm type is in advance of the front but in the cold type largely in the rear. The rainfall is caused partly by the interaction of the two cold masses near the surface. The occlusion therefore usually continues to give low cloud and rain for some time after its formation, although the tendency is towards a gradual cessation except when the two cold masses have very different characteristics; then the rain may be persistent. Over western Europe the

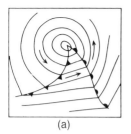
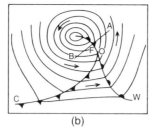
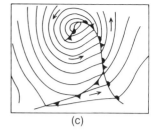

(a)   (b)   (c)

Figure 94. Occluding of a depression.

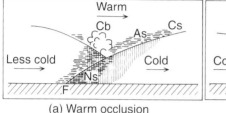
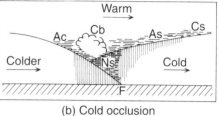

(a) Warm occlusion   (b) Cold occlusion

Figure 95. Vertical sections through idealized occlusions.

warm-front type is normal in the winter, for the cold air in the east is of continental origin and therefore colder than the maritime air from the west. In summer, conditions are reversed and the polar maritime air is generally the cooler.

It is difficult to give what may be called characteristic features of an occlusion apart from a more or less clearly marked trough of low pressure. The mere information that an occlusion lies along a route is little indication of the weather conditions to be encountered. Sooner or later an occlusion degenerates and disappears from the weather map and in its later stages may present no noticeable features other than perhaps a little cloud.

16.5 SUMMARY OF FRONTAL CHARACTERISTICS

The normal features associated with the warm and cold fronts of a depression are summarized in Table 14. It is, however, important to remember that in practice depressions and fronts rarely, if ever, agree exactly with the 'ideal' model in all respects and that, of the characteristics described above and now tabulated, some are sure to be more or less modified in any particular case.

The characteristics of the occlusion are very variable. They may be similar to those of either the warm or cold front (according to type) but are often ill-defined.

16.6 GENERAL DISTRIBUTION OF WEATHER IN A FRONTAL DEPRESSION

In regions away from the weather intimately associated with the fronts, the warm and cold air masses display their own characteristic features. A distinction is therefore made between the frontal weather and the air mass weather of a depression and some account of the latter follows.

Warm-sector depression
Warm sector.   The air within the warm sector is typically tropical maritime or continental and the conditions are as described for those air masses in Section 15.2 with appropriate variations according to locality and season. Over the Atlantic and north-west Europe the warm air is usually tropical maritime and widespread low stratus or stratocumulus with perhaps fog or drizzle are common, but clear skies can occur when the humidity is comparatively low. When the air mass is tropical continental, as for example with a Mediterranean depression, clear skies would be the rule while even the warm front cloud and precipitation may be unable to form because of the extreme dryness of the air. Isobars within the warm sector are usually straight and parallel but not necessarily equally spaced. Pressure falls slowly or remains steady depending on whether or not the depression is deepening.

Cold sector.   This includes the greater part of the area covered by the depression and conditions within it are those typical of a polar air mass, either maritime or continental,as given in Section 15.2. There are, however, modifications because of the frontal developments. In the cold air in advance of the warm front when the sky becomes covered with high and medium cloud, surface heating by the sun is reduced and the diurnal cumulus type of cloud is either very restricted in the vertical because of the shallow depth of cold air or does not form at all. There may also be some pre-frontal subsidence of air, making the lapse rate more stable than in a typical cold air mass. This clearance of low cumuliform clouds on the arrival of the high clouds of a new depression is often very noticeable. In the cold air behind the cold front, subsidence often clears the sky completely soon after the frontal rain has ceased; there may then be an interval of clear weather lasting a few hours before the convective clouds and showers of the cold air begin to appear.

By combining the results of the preceding paragraphs a diagram (Fig. 96) may be constructed showing the distribution of clouds and weather over the area of an idealized warm-sector depression.

Occluded depression
The depression usually continues to deepen until an advanced stage in the occlusion process is reached. By then the supply of warm air has been cut off and the depth of the depression subsequently changes little. At the same time the centre, previously carried along with the warm air, becomes almost stationary. The last stage in the life of a normal frontal depression is thus a stationary or slowly moving system of circulating polar air. This decaying depression fills up only very slowly and is often very persistent unless the circulation is destroyed by the approach of a new, vigorous depression, in which case an old and deep occluded centre may fill up completely within 24 hours. During the occluding and decaying stages, the weather usually tends to improve slowly. The frontal cloud and rain become gradually less extensive but convective cloud and showers may become more general, their intensity and extent varying with the characteristics of the cold air and the thermal and dynamical processes to which it is subjected. Hence the weather in old depressions ranges from conditions of little cloud to widespread convective cloud

TABLE 14. *Idealized frontal characteristics*

WARM FRONT

Element	in advance	at passage	in the rear
pressure	steady fall	fall arrested	little change or slow fall
wind	backing, increasing	veer, decrease	steady direction
temperature	steady or slow rise	rise	little change
dew-point	rise in precipitation	rise	steady
relative humidity	rise in precipitation	may rise further if not already saturated	little change, may be saturated
cloud	CI, CS, AS, NS, in succession; ST fractus, CU fractus below AS, NS	low NS and ST fractus	ST, SC may persist, perhaps some CI
weather	continuous rain or snow	precipitation eases or stops	dry, or intermittent slight
visibility	good except in precipitation	poor, often mist or fog	moderate or poor; mist or fog may persist

COLD FRONT

Element	in advance	at passage	in the rear
pressure	fall	sudden rise	rise continues more slowly
wind	backing and increasing, becoming squally	sudden veer, perhaps squall	backing after squall then steady or veer at further squalls
temperature	steady, but fall in pre-frontal rain	sudden fall	little change; variable in showers
dew-point	little change	sudden fall	little change
relative humidity	rise in pre-frontal precipitation	remains high in precipitation	rapid fall as precipitation ceases; variable in showers
cloud	ST or SC, AC, AS then CB	CB with ST fractus CU fractus or very low NS	lifting rapidly, followed for short period by AS AC and later further CU CB
weather	some rain, perhaps thunder	heavy rain or snow perhaps hail and thunder	heavy rain or snow for usually short period, sometimes more persistent, then fine but later showers
visibility	moderate or poor perhaps fog	temporary deterioration followed by rapid improvement	very good, except later snow showers

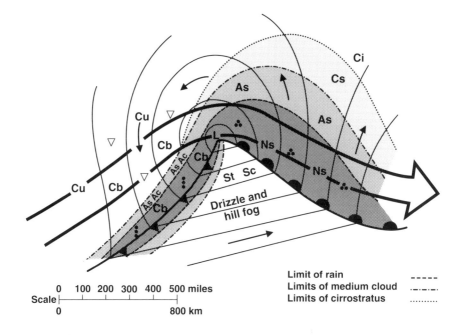

Figure 96. Distribution of cloud and weather and the position of the jet stream in an idealized warm-sector depression.

with showers and thunderstorms. During the decay of the depression the winds decline slowly and clearing skies over the land at night may permit radiation fog to develop.

16.7 FAMILIES OF FRONTAL DEPRESSIONS

As a rule the development of a frontal depression occurs on a long, slowly moving front between polar and tropical air in temperate latitudes. When one depression develops, moves along the front and finally becomes occluded, the cold front trails back from the point of occlusion. Conditions may then be favourable for a new development passing through the same stages and in this way there forms a series, train, or family, of depressions. As each occludes in turn the cold air spreads round it and penetrates to lower latitudes so that successive depressions usually follow a more southerly track until at last the cold air sweeps through and goes to feed the trade winds of lower latitudes. By this time the polar front has been displaced far to the south of its normal position and a large anticyclone builds up in the polar air, so breaking the continuity of the front and terminating the family sequence. Meanwhile a new family starts to form on the north-west side of the anticyclone and as the latter drifts away south-eastwards the whole process may be repeated. There is no regularity about the number of individual depressions in a family but there are often three, four or five. The weather changes associated with the passage of the depressions, alternating with brief fine periods in the high pressure ridges dividing them, are typical of 'unsettled' conditions in the British Isles.

252

16.8 UPPER WINDS OVER FRONTAL DEPRESSIONS

The winds at an upper level can be estimated by adding to the low level geostrophic wind a 'thermal component' determined from the horizontal distribution of mean temperature in the intervening layer (Section 5.4). As a frontal depression is essentially a phenomenon of temperature contrasts, it is to be expected that marked changes of wind with height will occur within it. Over a frontal depression in the northern hemisphere, the mean isotherms or thickness lines between the surface and 500 hPa are usually distributed somewhat as shown in Fig. 97. Since a cold region acts as a region of low pressure in the upper atmosphere the thermal winds blow in the directions indicated in the figure, and when these are added vectorially to the geostrophic wind near the surface a good indication of the upper winds is obtained. In advance of the depression, the upper winds at a high level tend to become north-westerly above the warm front surface. When the air to the north-east is very cold, as is often the case with North Atlantic depressions in winter, the thermal north-westerlies may be strong. A rapid movement of the cirrus clouds from this direction is often a valuable indication of the approach of a warm-sector depression from the west. Similarly, to the rear of a depression, the thermal effect accounts for south-westerly winds at high levels above the cold frontal surface. Thus when the thermal effects are pronounced, strong upper winds are found blowing approximately parallel with the surface fronts but displaced towards the cold air side of the surface frontal position; these are the jet streams of temperate regions which were described in Section 5.7.

With regard to the pressure distribution aloft, it will be seen that at a level high enough for the surface distribution to be overcome there is a ridge of high pressure just ahead of the ground position of the warm front and a trough of low pressure just to the rear of the cold front. Alternatively the contours of a given pressure surface aloft will be seen to be elevated in advance of the warm front and depressed in the

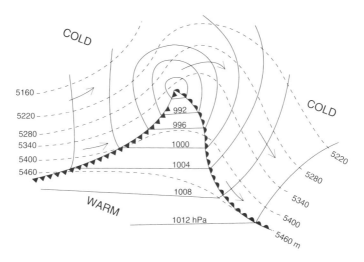

Figure 97. Thermal winds in a warm sector depression. The broken lines show the distribution of mean temperature by means of the thickness of the 1000–500 hPa layer; arrows show the direction of the thermal wind.

rear of the cold front, as illustrated in Fig. 98. Within the warm sector little change of wind with height would be expected since the thermal gradients are slight, as illustrated in Fig. 97. North of the centre, the superposition of the thermal westerlies on the surface circulation often eliminates the weak low-level easterlies so that the distribution of the isobars or contours aloft then shows no closed centre but merely a wave-like deformation of the prevailing westerlies.

In an old occluded depression entirely surrounded by polar air, the horizontal temperature gradients are relatively weak and the variation of wind with height is less pronounced than it is in the warm-sector depression. The roughly circular form of the isobars (or contours) near the surface is often maintained up to high levels and forms what is known as a 'cold pool', since an area of low contour heights implies a low mean temperature of the air column.

Thus when a frontal depression is regarded as a circulation in three dimensions, it is observed that the formation, development and final occluding transform the circulation from an asymmetrical system, with marked surface troughs and large changes of wind speed and direction with height, to a roughly circular symmetrical depression with the air simply rotating round the centre and the wind varying little with height. While the conception of a depression as a column of rotating fluid extending upwards through the atmosphere may apply to an occluded centre, it has no application to the active frontal depressions responsible for most of the bad weather.

The above discussion takes no account of the frictional effect at the ground, which gives a veer and increase of wind with height through the friction levels in all normal circumstances (backing and increasing in the southern hemisphere).

16.9 FLIGHT THROUGH FRONTAL DEPRESSIONS

It is a useful exercise when studying synoptic charts to lay off specimen routes and to write out accounts of the weather likely to be experienced along them. The

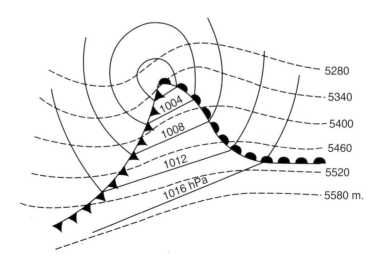

Figure 98.   Warm sector depression and 500 hPa contours.

254

following notes apply to the idealized depression in accordance with the frontal theory and are not likely to represent any actual case faithfully, for there are always minor (and sometimes major) differences and allowances must be made for diurnal and seasonal variations. Thus each chart must be examined in detail before a reliable forecast can be made.

Flight at low levels

To fix ideas, suppose that, in the northern hemisphere, a warm-sector depression is approaching from the west and a flight from east to west is made at about 5000 ft from well in advance of the depression, through the warm sector and out into the cold air beyond. To begin with, in the ridge, winds are probably light and variable with perhaps some broken cumulus. The first sign of the depression is the cirrus of the warm front perhaps 800 or 1000 km in advance of the surface front; as this thickens to cirrostratus the low clouds clear, except for local orographic effects, the wind becomes southerly and increases but away from the surface turbulence the air is not bumpy. A period of good flying weather is to be expected at first but the cloud above gradually thickens to altostratus and later nimbostratus while rain starts to fall and eventually becomes continuous (sleet or snow if the temperature is near or below 0 °C). The cloud base lowers continuously and may ultimately reach almost to the surface: low flying is then hazardous as winds are probably strong and turbulent, while high ground is obscured by cloud. A period of instrument flying should be expected and the flight level must be chosen to give adequate clearance of high ground. In this connection allowance should be made for any overreading of the altimeter on account of falling surface pressure. A previous study of the weather map should have given a useful indication, or a report may be obtained while in the air; but failing such help a considerable margin of safety is necessary, for the drop of pressure from the ridge to the trough may be as much as 30 or 40 hectopascals, causing the altimeter to overread by more than 1000 feet if the sub-scale setting has not been adjusted.

The passage into the warm sector will usually be made evident by the cessation of rainfall and although the warm sector may be cloudy, clear air will almost always be found at a moderate height, usually above 4000 ft, except perhaps over high ground. Temperature observations are also helpful in confirming that the warm air has been entered.

As the wind may have veered during the passage through the front, it is important to fix position. Flight through the warm sector usually presents little difficulty except perhaps in regard to navigation when low cloud obscures the ground. The pilot should avoid descending through the clouds to fix position unless the altimeter correction is accurately known, for the cloud base may be very low with drizzle or fog on the surface. Normally on a long flight the warm sector will be traversed in the smooth clear air above the low clouds.

The approach to the cold front will be recognized by the pre-frontal high or medium clouds, usually altocumulus, thickening and lowering to a heavy bank on the horizon. An attempt to fly below the clouds may be successful if the front is not severe but unless information is available to the contrary it should be assumed that the front will have line-squall characteristics with violent turbulence, heavy thundery rain and possibly hail from embedded cumulonimbus, patches of very low cloud and severe icing if the temperature is below 0 °C. Cloud flying in these conditions is clearly not to be recommended. If the clouds are thick and unbroken, the pilot should consider the advisability of flying above them, which would probably mean climbing to at least 15 000 or 20 000 ft. If conditions are severe and a climb is impracticable, it might be advisable to consider reversing course or perhaps making a landing.

The width of the belt of violently disturbed weather does not usually exceed some 30 km and after this has been negotiated a complete clearance is likely to follow. A veer of wind usually accompanies the passage of the front and allowances should be made for this in navigating. Conditions in the cold air will remain bumpy and secondary cold fronts or squally showers may be encountered but, generally speaking, flying conditions will improve.

Flight at medium levels

The conditions encountered when flying through a depression vary considerably with the altitude. We consider now a flight in the vicinity of 500 hPa (about FL180) on a track similar to the one already described. The pre-frontal cirrus thickening to cirrostratus will again be the first visual indication of the approach to the warm front, while below the aircraft the cumuliform cloud will become less frequent. At flight level the winds will be westerly at first, but ahead of the surface warm front they will veer perhaps as far round as north-west. At the same time a slow increase in air temperature and the presence of stratiform cloud will indicate that the upper frontal zone is being traversed. The total horizontal distance through the frontal cloud may amount to about 150 or even 300 km, and since the temperature will be below 0 °C, airframe icing may be encountered.

Once the upper frontal cloud has been left behind, conditions will usually be clear except that the ground is likely to be obscured by low stratocumulus or stratus cloud or fog. As the flight continues westwards, the wind will slowly back and decrease until the aircraft reaches a point over the surface position of the warm front when the upper wind will again be approximately westerly; from this point on there will be little change until the aircraft passes over the surface position of the cold front, when the wind will back further and increase.

In the clear air, the cloud system of the cold front will be visible from a great distance. It may be desirable to increase height in order to fly above the pre-frontal altocumulus or altostratus, since flight in these would cause the cumulonimbus immediately ahead to be obscured. For the same reason, any anvil cirrus should in general be avoided. Provided the cumulonimbus clouds are kept in view they can often be avoided at this altitude even though individual peaks may be much higher; but if the front is very active, a climb is likely to be required before a gap can be found. If, after due consideration, it is decided to fly through the clouds, then appropriate precautions should be taken as described in Section 7.5 to safeguard against the effects of severe turbulence, lightning and other hazards. During the approach to the cold frontal surface, the wind at flight level gradually backs to about south-west and increases. Within the frontal zone, the wind again begins to veer and decrease and this process continues in the cold air until wind direction finally becomes westerly once more. The passage through the frontal zone is a gradual process marked by a slow decline in temperature and usually by dispersal of the cloud system.

Flight at high levels

With increase of height above the medium levels, the disturbance caused by the clouds and wind of the depression becomes gradually less marked; the warm-front cloud would then be flown through at cirrus levels while the only disturbance from the cold front would be isolated peaks of cumulonimbus, which could be easily avoided, unless obscured by anvil cirrus. At these levels the general wind is westerly and the modification produced by the depression would be expected to take the form of a broad north-westerly current east of the surface position of the warm front and a broad south-westerly current to the west of the surface cold front. The conditions become very different, however, if a jet stream exists where the warm or cold frontal surfaces approach the tropopause. This case together with other aspects of high-altitude flight has been discussed in Sections 5.7, 5.8, 10.3 and 10.4.

CHAPTER 17

OTHER DEPRESSIONS

17.1 CAUSES OF DEPRESSIONS

The discussions of the two preceding chapters have emphasized the relation between air temperature or density and the pressure field in the neighbourhood of fronts and frontal depressions, but even in these cases the development cannot be attributed solely to changes of temperature or density. In order that a depression shall fall from, say, an average of 1012 hPa to perhaps 970 hPa, some 4% of the air must be removed, for pressure is given by the weight of the air above. The development of the depression leads, however, to inflow towards the centre which tends to an accumulation of air and to a rise of pressure. It is evident, therefore, that air must be removed somewhere in the upper atmosphere and that convergence near the surface is to be regarded as a result of changing pressure and not as the cause of the depression. Similarly, with an anticyclone, the outflow of air near the surface tends to destroy the high pressure. Thus in many cases the cause of the formation of depressions and anticyclones must be sought in the upper atmosphere. This is a fundamental problem which is still far from being completely solved, but with adequate upper-air observations it is often possible to identify areas in the middle troposphere where theory indicates that the form of the thickness pattern is associated with cyclonic or with anticyclonic development at lower levels. Such considerations however, are more appropriately discussed under the heading of 'weather forecasting' and an account will be found in Chapter 19.

Frontal depressions are predominant only in temperate latitudes and the impression that all depressions are associated with warm sectors or occlusions is to be avoided, even in temperate regions.

Other types of low pressure area are:

(a) frontal secondary depressions,
(b) orographic depressions which form in the lee of mountain ranges,
(c) thermal lows, associated with surface heating,
(d) cold air lows, associated with instability,
(e) tropical cyclones, and
(f) tornadoes and waterspouts.

17.2 SECONDARY DEPRESSIONS

When a relatively small depression is enclosed within the circulation of a larger or primary depression, it may be termed a 'secondary'. Any process which leads to the formation of a depression may be responsible for the formation of a secondary. Generally speaking a secondary moves around the primary in a cyclonic sense, being carried along by the larger circulation. Some of the more common types are described here.

Frontal secondaries

A common place of origin of a secondary depression is on a trailing cold front from an occluded primary depression. If the new disturbance forms well outside the primary circulation it may develop to form the next member of the family (see Section 16.7), eventually taking over as the major centre. A development of this type is illustrated in Fig. 99. In Fig. 99(a) the new centre is shown as a small wave disturbance on the cold front without a definite circulation but in Fig. 99(b) it has moved along the front and deepened to appear as a secondary circulation. Not infrequently the new formation becomes deep while the old occluded centre fills up and the new system then becomes the dominant and controlling depression of the two. An old primary which becomes involved in the circulation of a new vigorous development eventually behaves as a secondary itself, rotating around the new centre in a cyclonic direction. When the two centres are of similar depth they tend to rotate around each other, a process often referred to as 'dumb-belling', as in Fig. 100.

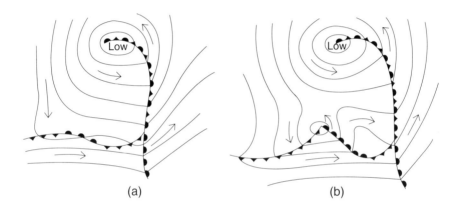

(a)   (b)

Figure 99.   Development of a frontal secondary depression.

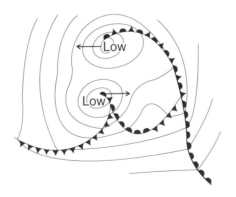

Figure 100.   Movement of two neighbouring depressions.

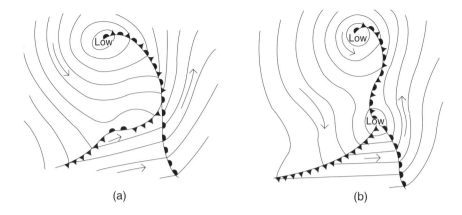

Figure 101. (a) Secondary depression well within the primary circulation, and (b) secondary depression at the tip of the warm sector of a partly occluded depression.

Sometimes, small disturbances form on the cold front well within the primary circulation, as in Fig. 101(a). Such a development may be recognizable only by a local widening of the isobars near the front. It moves along the front, but usually without much further development and soon becomes absorbed again into the primary circulation. Although apparently of minor significance, such a disturbance often delays or even temporarily reverses the movement of a slow-moving cold front. The accurate timing of the passage of the front is then a matter of considerable difficulty.

A third position favourable for the formation of a secondary is the tip of the warm sector of a depression which is already partly occluded. This position is known as the point of occlusion or as the 'triple point'. The remaining warm air acts as a warm sector for the secondary which develops while the primary centre continues to fill up. The development is illustrated in Fig. 101(b). Experience shows that this development is most probable when the primary depression and occluded front are retarded by a mountain barrier, for example in southern Greenland or Norway; in either case the secondary develops and moves away eastwards to the south of the obstructing land mass.

17.3 OROGRAPHIC DEPRESSIONS

When a current of air meets a mountain barrier at a sufficiently large angle, energy is usually required if the air is to rise over the obstruction and there is a tendency, often very marked, for much of the air to sweep around the ends of the barrier, so avoiding the ascent. Something in the nature of a lee eddy is formed but the problem cannot be treated in quite the same way as that of the eddy formed by a building, for when the obstruction is a large mountain range the dimensions of the disturbance are such that the earth's rotation exercises an influence and the winds must obey Buys Ballot's law. The result is a shallow depression to the lee of the mountains and a ridge of high pressure on the windward side with the sea level isobars and winds distributed as in Fig. 102. The low may be maintained as long as

260

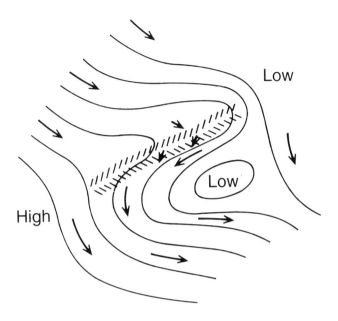

Figure 102. An orographic low. The effect of a mountain range on isobars and winds.

the wind persists but, apart from the local strong winds which blow around the ends of the range, the only disturbance in weather may be limited to cloud and rain of orographic origin. Within the depression itself weather may be fine and warm as a result of the föhn effect due to some of the air passing over the barrier.

An important case arises when a cold front reaches a mountain range after being more or less parallel with it and when there is warm stagnant air on the lee side. The lower part of the front is obstructed by the barrier with the result that the slope of the front becomes steeper and a lee depression begins to form. The upper part of the front may then pass over the crest of the range and overrun the warm air below. This results in severe instability with heavy showers and thunderstorms until the warm air is finally displaced by cold air sweeping over the barrier. Alternatively, if the cold air can sweep round the ends of the barrier, a bulge is formed on the front with the air in the lee of the range acting as a warm sector and an intense depression may then develop. A large proportion of the disturbances which occur over northern Italy are formed in association with a cold front held up by the Alps — the associated strong wind down the Rhône valley is the well-known mistral. Similar developments are recognized in various other parts of the world, for example the desert depressions which form to south of the Atlas Mountains when polar northerlies penetrate across the Iberian peninsula. The preference for triple point secondaries to form over the Skagerrak, in the lee of the Norwegian mountains, is also largely due to topographical control.

The barrier effect of mountain ranges is important in controlling and modifying the movements of all winds in their vicinity; just one of the many meteorological problems posed by mountainous terrain.

17.4 THERMAL DEPRESSIONS

There is a tendency for the warmer regions to become areas of low pressure. This comes about somewhat as follows. As the air is heated it expands and the overlying isobaric surfaces are lifted. At any given upper level, the pressure becomes higher than over the surrounding parts with the result that the air starts to move outwards. This in turn reduces the surface pressure and an inflow takes place at low levels which, under the influence of the geostrophic force, is converted into a cyclonic circulation. Since the higher pressure and outflow aloft imply an anticyclonic circulation at high levels, the thermal depression or 'heat low' weakens with height; the cyclonic winds decrease and are often reversed in the upper atmosphere. However, much depends on the vertical stability and on conditions in the upper atmosphere, so that situations in which warm surface air is associated with high surface pressure can also occur; indeed, the hottest weather in western Europe is almost always anticyclonic. In such cases the lapse rate is so stable that surface heating results at most in shallow lows of little significance. On the other hand, if the lapse rate is unstable or becomes so as a result of continued heating so that instability showers break out, then there is an increased likelihood of a fall in surface pressure and development of a depression. In these cases additional energy is provided by the liberation of latent heat of condensation of water vapour and if this takes place on a large scale the resulting depression may become a major feature of the weather map.

Monsoon low
The most obvious example of a thermal low is that which tends to develop over a large continent in summer; the south Asiatic monsoon low which controls the general circulation over that area is the outstanding example. The weather in a monsoon low does not follow any regular pattern, being very dependent on topography and on the characteristics of the air masses which are drawn into the area of the depression. Some account of the associated weather over the areas concerned will be found in Chapter 20.

Equatorial low-pressure belt
This may be regarded from the present point of view as a permanent heat low encircling the earth in tropical latitudes. The lapse rate is generally steep and there is heavy showery precipitation. For further details see Chapter 20.

Shallow lows over land in summer
When the pressure gradient is slight, surface heating over any land mass in summer may lead to the formation of shallow depressions. Sometimes these are of little significance but when associated with vertical instability or with pre-existing old frontal zones they may result in deteriorations such as squalls, widespread rain or outbreaks of thunderstorms. Central and western Europe are particularly vulnerable to this type of thundery breakdown.

Lows over inland waters in winter
The temperature of inland waters in winter is relatively high compared with that of the surrounding land mass. Almost invariably when a current of polar air spreads

over large inland seas such as the Mediterranean, the Black Sea and the Great Lakes of North America, the air becomes unstable and local depressions may develop. The arrival of the cold air is marked by a cold front but low pressure areas often persist long after the whole region has been flooded with polar air and continue to give local showers and squalls. Winds circulate in the ordinary cyclonic manner but there are often large deviations caused by orographic and katabatic effects, especially noticeable on coasts; both gales and calms are typical of the coastal areas in these conditions.

17.5 COLD AIR LOWS

Polar air depressions
In temperate latitudes depressions showing no obvious fronts sometimes develop within a large mass of apparently homogeneous polar air — there seems little doubt that their formation is associated with the development of vertical instability. They are roughly circular in shape and generally move in the direction of the general current in which they form. Near the British Isles the development is usually in a northerly or north-westerly airstream around a parent depression over the Norwegian Sea or Scandinavia. Precipitation is often limited to local showers but when there is a greater degree of instability and horizontal convergence, thunderstorms and areas of continuous rain or snow may develop. There is a tendency for precipitation to become more organized along a trough extending from the centre on the side opposite to that of the parent depression, typically to south-west of the centre in the case of polar lows approaching the British Isles. These polar lows are particularly a feature of the winter months when they can bring appreciable snowfall to windward coasts and high ground of Scotland. Satellite imagery is invaluable in identifying these features.

PVA areas
PVA is an acronym used in reference to regions of positive vorticity anomaly, i.e. regions in which there is a secondary maximum of cyclonicity. Such areas commonly occur within broad outbreaks of polar air; in the North Atlantic they are often found in the mainly north-westerly flow around deep lows centred near Iceland or over the Norwegian Sea. They appear as small-scale features, perhaps no more than 100 km across, and would often escape detection but for satellite imagery on which they characteristically show up as a comma-shaped cloud mass. Not all of these PVA areas are associated with discrete low centres; in some cases it is possible only to draw a trough in the isobars, but they all appear to represent regions of enhanced convective cloud. Their movement is controlled, as with all secondary features, by the broad flow around the parent depression; when a PVA is swept far south to approach the cold front which trails back from the parent low, its approach often induces the formation of a wave on the front and the tail of the PVA 'comma' may link up with the wave to appear as an 'instant occlusion'.

17.6 TROPICAL CYCLONES

Intense depressions occur in some tropical regions during certain periods of the year. They are known by the generic name of 'tropical cyclones', but individual storms will usually be referred to by a regional name such as 'hurricane' and 'typhoon'; a distinction is also made according to the maximum sustained surface wind speeds within the storm. The nomenclature is often confusing; the main regional alternatives are listed in Table 15. Table 16 is a more detailed summary of the terminology employed for North Atlantic and eastern north Pacific storms.

Tropical cyclones are warm-core low-pressure systems around which the air circulates in the usual cyclonic sense; counter-clockwise in the northern hemisphere and clockwise in the southern. In the more intense storms, the central pressure is commonly less than 950 hPa; the lowest on record is the 870 hPa reached by Typhoon 'Tip' in the western north Pacific on 12 October 1979, whilst the lowest recorded in the western hemisphere is 888 hPa measured by a reconnaissance aircraft in the centre of Hurricane 'Gilbert' over the Caribbean on 13 September 1988. A fully developed tropical cyclone consists of a rotating mass of warm, humid, air, anything between 300 and 1500 km in diameter; the strongest winds, which may approach 200 KT, blow around a central 'eye', a region of light winds and clear sky ranging from a few kilometres to over 100 km in diameter.

TABLE 15. *Tropical cyclones — regional terminology*

Region	Range of maximum sustained wind speeds (KT)	
	34–63	≥64
Western north Pacific	tropical cyclone	typhoon
Bay of Bengal and Arabian Sea	cyclone	severe cyclone
South Indian Ocean	tropical depression	tropical cyclone
South Pacific	tropical depression	cyclone
North Atlantic and eastern north Pacific	tropical storm	hurricane

Tropical cyclones draw their energy from the convective overturning of the atmosphere. Warm, moist air spirals over the tropical seas towards the storm centre and ascends in a cloud 'wall' surrounding the central eye. The inflowing air gathers speed as it draws towards the storm centre and produces winds of destructive violence. The storms invariably form over the sea, their initiation and survival being dependent upon a plentiful supply of warmth and moisture; a sea surface temperature of 26 °C is usually considered to be a necessary prerequisite for storm formation. The rate of movement of the storm centre (as distinct from the speed of the winds in its circulation) is generally less than 15 KT.

Global distribution
Preferred tropical cyclone tracks are shown at Fig. 103. It will be noted that tropical cyclones form over all the tropical ocean areas except the South Atlantic and south Pacific east of about 140 °W. They are most commonly observed in the northern hemisphere from May to November and in the southern hemisphere from December

TABLE 16. *Tropical cyclones of the North Atlantic and eastern north Pacific.*

WMO nomenclature		Maximum sustained wind		Representation on	
		Force	KT	analyses	WAFS forecasts
Tropical depression		≤4	≤16	X	
		5–7	17–33		
Tropical storm	(moderate)	8, 9	34–47	૬	૬
	(severe)	10, 11	48–63		
Hurricane		≥12	≥64	🌀	

to June though a significant number occur during other months in the western north Pacific. Most storms develop deep within the tropics though not usually within about 5° of the equator; it is only in the western North Atlantic and western north Pacific that a substantial number have their origin poleward of latitude 22 °N.

Tropical storm origins
Scrutiny of satellite imagery has revealed that a tropical storm 'seedling' initially appears as a cloud cluster comprised of a number of thunderstorm cells developing independently. These cells join together to form what may be described as an atmospheric heat pump which becomes the cyclone. The pump consists of a spiralling influx of warm, moist air at its intake in the lower boundary layer and an equally large-scale spiralling outflow at the exhaust end or top of the storm system. Exactly what determines whether the initial seedling will grow into a major storm remains a mystery; it is estimated that about 100 hurricane seedlings originate over the Atlantic Ocean per year but only about 10% succeed in developing into tropical cyclones.

Convergence near the ITCZ is probably an important factor in cyclone formation and the so-called 'easterly waves' may often provide a suitable trigger for storm development. Globally, over 80% of tropical cyclones which reach storm intensity have their origin at the poleward side of the equatorial trough as it moves into the summer hemisphere. The remainder, less than 20% of the global total, develop from disturbances which are deeply embedded within the trade wind flow. In the North Atlantic, however, storms of such origins comprise a substantial percentage of the total; a 5-year study revealed that about 90% of North Atlantic storms developing from purely tropical systems in the western North Atlantic could be traced back to westward moving disturbances in the trade wind belt, some of them being traced to mesoscale cloud clusters over West Africa.

Once formed, storms move initially in a generally westward direction along the equatorward peripheries of the large subtropical anticyclones. Many turn poleward as they reach the western sides of these anticyclones and recurve toward the east if they move into the higher-latitude westerlies. The storms dissipate and eventually

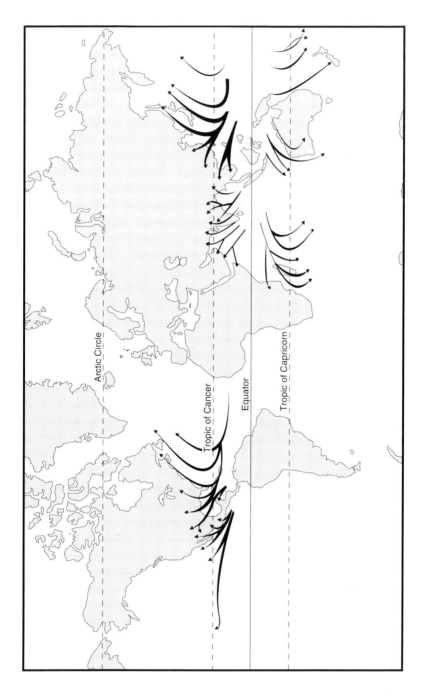

Figure 103.   Preferred tropical cyclone tracks. Arrow widths are proportional to storm frequencies along indicated paths (from Crutcher and Quayle 1974).

266

die once deprived of the plentiful supply of moisture; those that make a landfall quickly dissipate whilst those that move over colder waters weaken and may eventually engage polar air to continue as an extratropical depression with a conventional frontal structure.

Occasionally, depressions reaching the British Isles have been traced back to a tropical origin; these are not necessarily accompanied by strong winds when they reach Europe; it is more likely that the very warm tropical air which is retained aloft contributes to heavy rainfall. On the other hand, some intense frontal depressions may develop surface winds that reach Beaufort force 12 (hurricane *force*) without being of tropical origin; the 'Great Storm' of October 1987 was such a case.

Flying conditions in relation to tropical cyclones
Tropical cyclones have been successfully traversed by aircraft on many occasions — indeed, they are flown through regularly on certain meteorological reconnaissance flights. These flights have shown that conditions within the storms up to at least 10 000 ft are extremely unpleasant and even hazardous. In general the only reasonable course is to avoid the storms as far as possible. As these cyclones are easily visible on satellite pictures and advisory messages are issued which detail their position and expected movement, it should normally be possible to avoid flying through a tropical cyclone. The most severe weather is usually found in the quadrant towards which the centre of the cyclone is expected to move and it is possible to avoid this sector by a deviation in the flight track of a few hundred kilometres.

Cloud and precipitation. The instability conditions usually associated with the ITCZ become intensified in the earliest stage of the development of a cyclone, when compact masses of convective cloud are present with heavy showers and thunderstorms. After the cyclonic circulation has started, the cloud formations tend to become arranged in bands along the wind and more or less concentric with the centre but spiralling inwards so that the central area of the storm (outside the eye) forms an extensive unbroken cloud mass. Subsidence takes place between these cloud bands in the outer part of the storm, as well as in the eye. The vertical extent of the clouds appears to be greater over the inner core of the storm — apart from the eye, which may be cloudless — and commonly reaches to cirrus levels. If flight is above cloud, the approach to a storm may be indicated only by thick bands of cirrus, but while the existence of a storm may on occasions be revealed by the upper or lower cloud formations, these are apt to be misleading as a guide to the position of the centre. The cloud base is often about 1000 ft and occasionally on the surface in heavy rain. Visibility below the cloud base is poor in strong winds on account of spray.

Turbulence. This occurs in two ways; severe turbulence present in the active convection clouds within the storm and the frictional turbulence generated in the lowest layers by the strong winds. This of course increases in intensity with the strength of the wind; it becomes severe when the wind exceeds 50 KT and is considered dangerous if the wind exceeds 80 KT. The extremely strong low-level winds produce huge wave development which together with the turbulence just described makes low-level flight through tropical cyclones very dangerous.

17.7 TORNADOES

The name tornado is applied to two distinct phenomena which form over land. In West Africa, particularly in the countries bordering the Gulf of Guinea, tornadoes are thunder squalls generally accompanied by heavy rain but occasionally without precipitation. They often advance across the country from east to west as a line squall and are most frequent at the beginning and end of the wet season, that is in March, April, May, October and November.

The other kind of tornado takes the form of a violent whirlwind and it is this type of disturbance which is more commonly identified with the name 'tornado'. Tornadoes are most frequently thought of as a phenomenon of the USA east of the Rocky Mountains, especially in the central plains of the Mississippi region. However, they also occur in other parts of the world and it is estimated that they occur over Britain on about 30 days a year; although not as violent as some of the North American examples these British tornadoes may nevertheless be responsible for substantial damage.

The whirl or vortex has a diameter varying from a few metres to some hundreds of metres and so is much too small to be represented by a system of isobars on a weather map, although the central pressure may be extremely low. Paths of violent tornadoes may be marked by uprooted trees and the explosive destruction of buildings, brought about by local pressure differences that occur in the intense horizontal pressure gradient near the centre. Tornadoes may occur in a wide range of synoptic situations but most United Kingdom occurrences are associated with the passage of sharp fronts or troughs associated with rapidly deepening depressions; deep instability appears to be a requirement, hence occurrences are often associated with thunderstorms, heavy rain and hail. Wind speeds in some North American tornadoes have been estimated to reach about 200 KT.

17.8 WATERSPOUTS

The structure of a waterspout is similar to that of a tornado except that the occurrence takes place over the sea and the phenomenon does not reach the same intensity. It is associated with heavy instability cloud. In the incipient stage a funnel-shaped extension, point downwards, projects from the base of the cloud and at the same time the sea below becomes agitated by a whirling vortex of air, so forming a cloud of spray. Sometimes this stage is all that is seen, at other times the so-called 'cloud pendant' develops downwards until it forms an unbroken column of cloudy whirling air joining sea and cloud; this is the waterspout. The dimensions of the vortex are quite small; the figure of 20 or 30 ft is sometimes quoted for the diameter and 200 to 300 ft for the height, but the maximum possible dimensions are no doubt considerably greater. In the early stages the column is generally vertical but later it becomes distorted and breaks away at the base, after which it quickly disappears; the whole phenomenon rarely lasts more than half an hour. Waterspouts are most common in low latitudes although they are occasionally seen off British coasts. They frequently occur in groups.

CHAPTER 18

ANTICYCLONES

18.1 TYPES OF ANTICYCLONE

A convenient classification divides anticyclones into two types. In the first the high pressure is accounted for by the low temperature and high density of the air in the surface levels and through the lower troposphere; it is known as a 'cold anticyclone'. In the second type or 'warm anticyclone', the air in the troposphere is warmer than the average; the high pressure cannot be explained by the greater weight of the lower atmosphere and is due to an excess of air at higher levels.

A subdivision of each type may be made into 'permanent' (or 'quasi-permanent') and 'temporary' or migratory anticyclones. A permanent anticyclone constitutes a persistent feature of a given area over a period of months. For example, the subtropical belts of high pressure are regarded as permanent features even though in places they may be occasionally interrupted or displaced by low-pressure systems; similarly the Siberian high is a more or less permanent feature throughout the winter months. On the other hand the temporary or migratory highs are transient features which often pass over any one place within a day; occasionally one remains stationary for several days or even weeks, but then it is usually found to form an extension of a permanent high.

18.2 GENERAL PROPERTIES OF ANTICYCLONES

An anticyclone is a region of high pressure with the winds circulating in the direction given by Buys Ballot's law. It may be shown on theoretical grounds that the wind speeds over the central regions must in general be weak compared with those possible in a depression. An anticyclone is, then, a region of light winds, although there is no reason why on the outskirts, away from the centre, winds should not be strong.

When surface pressure is rising within a mass of air, divergence is set up and the air must subside (Section 5.5). The development of an anticyclone therefore involves subsidence and even when the system has reached its maximum development there is still slight outflow near the surface due to surface friction (which causes the surface winds to drift across the isobars from high pressure to low) and slight subsidence continues. Since a necessary condition for rain is ascending motion, it follows that an anticyclonic region is generally dry.

In broad terms, an anticyclone is, then, a region of quiet weather.

18.3 COLD ANTICYCLONES

Permanent or quasi-permanent cold anticyclones
Maps of average pressure over a long period show weak anticyclones over the polar regions but daily charts show that these regions are frequently invaded by travelling

depressions so that the high pressure is not a permanent feature. Nor are the polar anticyclones, when they do form, necessarily of the 'cold' type — they can be of the 'warm' type.

The only example of a permanent cold anticyclone is that over Siberia in the winter, and even this is not immune from disturbances. There is, however, a predominating tendency for high pressure to be maintained throughout the season and the same is true to a less extent over the North American continent. In the Siberian high the air subsides, surface cooling more than compensates for the adiabatic warming and the air in the lower atmosphere is maintained at a very low temperature with a marked surface inversion. There is no precipitation except when the anticyclone is temporarily displaced by travelling depressions and fronts, but conditions are very favourable for fog or low stratus when the moisture content of the air is adequate. In the central region the air is generally too dry for fog and brilliant frosty weather is common, but in the outer regions, particularly near the sea coasts, dull foggy weather is common. Flying conditions, apart from the extreme cold, are good; even when low cloud and fog obscure the ground, clear skies and smooth air may be found at a height of a few thousand feet.

These seasonal anticyclones play an important part in controlling the general wind circulation of the atmosphere, which is described in Chapter 20. The area affected by the circulation varies from time to time. For example, towards the end of the winter, if the British Isles come under the influence of the Siberian anticyclone (this occurs occasionally) the wind direction is easterly and either the clear and frosty or the dull foggy type of weather occur. Frequently the air leaves the continent clear and dry but picks up considerable moisture over the sea; as the sea is warmer than the air, fog formation is prevented but a layer of stratus or stratocumulus may be formed. Often in south-east England the easterly winds have not picked up sufficient moisture in their short sea passage, particularly if the wind is fresh or strong, and the weather remains bright; further north, however, easterly winds in winter almost invariably bring cloudy skies to the east coasts; heating over the sea may even be sufficient to give local instability showers of snow or sleet.

Temporary cold anticyclones
Cold anticyclones of a temporary nature are common features of the changeable weather of middle latitudes. When a family of frontal depressions travels eastwards, each member is necessarily separated from its successor by a ridge of high pressure or a small anticyclone in the cold air which moves along between the two centres. The ridge brings a short break of dry weather lasting perhaps one day between the instability showers behind one depression and the warm front cloud and rain ahead of the next; it is a transitory pressure feature which usually collapses as the new depression advances. When polar air finally breaks through and terminates the family, the cold air builds up into an anticyclone of considerable size. Such developments may occur anywhere in temperate latitudes; in winter over the land the anticyclone may merge into, or become an extension of, the seasonal continental anticyclone, being maintained as a cold anticyclone by continuous radiative cooling at the surface. Over the sea, and over the land in summer, a cold anticyclone is never of great persistence; it either collapses within a day or two or is gradually transformed into a warm anticyclone by the adiabatic heating associated with subsidence.

The type of weather depends on many factors. In the summer, polar air is subject to surface heating over both land and sea. Fog is, therefore, exceptional and clouds of a cumulus type may develop. In the winter the air may undergo surface cooling over the land and radiation fog becomes probable where the winds are light, and stratus or stratocumulus clouds where the wind is stronger. The cold anticyclone is, however, associated with a large measure of bright and dry weather. In accordance with the general rule that a region of low temperature tends to become a region of low pressure in the upper atmosphere (Section 2.3), the cold anticyclone is not deep and the easterly winds on its equatorward side are generally shallow, decreasing with height and changing to westerly at moderate altitudes.

18.4 WARM ANTICYCLONES

Permanent warm anticyclones
The subtropical oceanic belts of persistent high pressure are areas of subsiding air which do not undergo any appreciable surface cooling. They are subject to a seasonal variation in position, moving north and south with the sun, and in the winter season they extend over the land areas where they are partly intensified by some degree of surface cooling. They are also subject to temporary variations in sympathy with the development and movement of depressions and anticyclones in higher latitudes; and lastly they are liable to be invaded in certain localities by tropical cyclones originating nearer the equator. In general, however, they are remarkably stable systems, being composed of warm and dry subsided air; the weather is fine with usually excellent visibility. These anticyclonic areas are the main source regions of tropical maritime air masses which give much low cloud, fog and drizzle on moving to higher latitudes.

Temporary warm anticyclones
In temperate latitudes, warm anticyclones are a temporary phenomenon and it is possible to distinguish two varieties:
   Extension from the subtropical high.   The air mass in this type of anticyclone is tropical. In summer it gives fine warm weather over the land but in autumn, whenever the air is of maritime origin, nocturnal radiation fog becomes likely where the winds are light. Sea fog may occur at any season but especially in spring and summer. Above the fog or low cloud there is invariably an inversion of temperature, often with no cloud above. This type of anticyclone seldom affects temperate regions in winter since the subtropical high itself is then shifted towards the equator, but in other seasons the anticyclone, when once established, may persist for periods up to a few weeks.
   Development from a temporary cold anticyclone.   The more common type of temporary warm anticyclone is evolved from a temporary cold anticyclone by the adiabatic warming which results from subsidence. When one develops over the land in summer the air becomes dry and the result is bright dry weather. Over the sea the air absorbs moisture by evaporation while an inversion of temperature builds up as the result of subsidence. Fog may then develop over the western side where the air is moving towards lower sea temperatures and also over the land as a result of cooling by radiation. Alternatively, a layer of stratocumulus often forms within the inversion and if the air moves from the sea over land during the summer, daytime

insolation may be sufficient to break the cloud into small cumulus or even to clear it completely. Long spells of settled weather are often associated with this type of anticyclone. During such spells of settled summer weather there is frequently a build-up of pollutant under the subsidence inversion which results in an extensive haze layer.

18.5 RIDGE OF HIGH PRESSURE

A ridge may extend in any direction outwards from an anticyclone and movement can vary from almost stationary to fast moving. The most reliable indication of the motion of a ridge is the barometric tendency; the direction of motion is, of course, towards the rising pressures and away from the pressure falls. A ridge is generally a passive feature and when it projects between two depressions its motion is controlled by that of the depressions. The weather is generally good and particularly fine and clear in the ridge behind a frontal depression, a consequence of the subsidence in the polar air.

18.6 COL

The col is not an entity in the same way as a depression or anticyclone; the winds do not circulate round it but flow towards and away from it. If, as in Fig. 104 a quadrilateral is drawn centred at the col, the air flows in across two opposite sides and out across the others, remaining stagnant in the centre. No special type of weather is associated with a col and almost any phenomena can occur except for strong winds at low levels. This does not mean, of course, that the probable weather cannot be anticipated, but only that each col needs to be considered on its merits. A col is frequently traversed by a front, and as the front is more or less stationary, any rain from it may be long-lived. If pressure is rising in the col (a frequent occurrence) the front will usually degenerate. On the other hand, if pressure begins to fall the inflowing currents from opposite directions may tend to develop a new

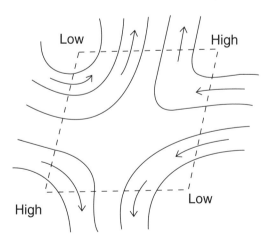

Figure 104.   Isobars and geostrophic winds in a col.

272

front or intensify an old inactive one, and the convergence may then cause rain. In autumn and winter over the land the col is associated with low cloud and fog; in summer thunderstorms are frequent although to assess the likelihood of their occurrence on any particular occasion it is necessary to study the upper-air observations.

CHAPTER 19

ELEMENTS OF FORECASTING

19.1 INTRODUCTION

It is not possible within the limits of one chapter to give more than a very general outline of forecasting methods. Indeed, since the synoptic chart is the main tool of the scientific forecaster, no course or book of instruction on practical forecasting can claim to be comprehensive unless it is accompanied by reproductions of numerous actual charts. That good treatises on practical forecasting are so few is mainly because of the difficulty in providing, either within the text of the work or in folder or album form, a sufficiently large number and variety of charts bearing all the necessary observations and analyses. For the purposes of the present work the Annex includes small-scale reproductions of surface charts for a few situations and these enable a number of points of general and particular interest to be studied. No more than this can be done within the compass of the present volume, but it should be sufficient to demonstrate how weather charts are constructed and used, and to illustrate some of the points discussed in the present chapter. Only by long experience and close examination of successive weather charts and particularly of current ones, which can be related by the forecaster to the existing weather in his own area, can ability be acquired in applying to actual weather forecasting the physical principles and other meteorological information which have been discussed in this book.

However, pilots or navigators are not required to become accomplished forecasters, though it has long been recognized that they should have sufficient acquaintance with synoptic charts and with the methods of aviation forecasting to enable them to derive the maximum benefit from meteorological briefings by professional forecasters and from documentation and other data made available by meteorological services; moreover, in cases of necessity or emergency they should be able to make good forecasts during flight on the basis of all available information. The syllabuses for the technical examinations for civil pilots' and navigators' licences and for corresponding qualifications in the Royal Air Force have accordingly provided for these requirements.

It has been the aim of ICAO to secure the maximum possible uniformity of practices in the meteorological services of the world in regard to facilities provided for aviation, so that aircrew may readily understand the flight briefing and documentation which they receive in any member country. Some differences in procedure between meteorological services in equatorial regions and temperate latitudes must remain, however, particularly in regard to the attention paid to frontal analysis on surface charts and to modes of displaying the distribution of winds at high levels. Variations there will also be in the methods of forecasting; in some regions seasonal and diurnal effects must be given particularly careful consideration, whilst elsewhere the trends of movement and development of pressure systems will figure prominently in the technique of forecasting. Nevertheless, in what follows in this chapter the main emphasis will be on practices and procedures in temperate latitudes in general and in the United Kingdom Meteorological Office in particular.

19.2 ANALYSIS OF THE SURFACE CHART

By analysis is meant the dual process of locating the fronts and drawing the isobars. Before either of these steps can be taken it is essential for the analyst to be so familiar with the symbolic method of plotting the observations that the meaning and significance of each entry is at once evident, except perhaps for a few symbols of infrequent or rare occurrence. It is also useful if the analyst is readily able to discern any reports which are clearly erroneous, since errors, although infrequent, may arise at any stage, but particularly during the transmission. In addition to the obvious errors there are the reports which appear inconsistent with neighbouring reports or with previous observations from the same station. On these suspected reports an open mind may have to be maintained until a confirmation can be obtained from the station originating the report or until the report can be compared with a subsequent one which may enable its accuracy to be properly assessed.

The best procedure to follow in analysing a chart varies with circumstances. An experienced forecaster working against time and being interrupted by requests for forecasts is normally handicapped in following a systematic method and in giving concentrated attention to every detail. The pilot or navigator who is learning analysis mainly for examination purposes should accustom themself to a sequence on the following lines:

(i)   If possible, obtain an analysed chart for the previous hour of observation. For an analysis to be satisfactory it must be consistent with that of the preceding chart. This is the fundamental principle of 'historical sequence'. It is usually an advantage if the previous movement of depressions and anticyclones has been indicated on the earlier chart. This is commonly done by marking the positions of the centres of the system at the 6-hourly chart intervals and joining the successive positions by a broken line. From a brief inspection of the resulting tracks a preliminary idea of the main features of the synoptic situation is gained.

(ii) If an illuminated tracing or 'light' table is available, place the chart to be analysed on top of the previous chart, ensure correct registration and lay the two on the light table. By extrapolation from the tracks on the previous chart deduce approximate positions for the centres of the depressions and anticyclones and mark them lightly on the top chart. Also estimate and lightly mark approximate positions for the main fronts: these too must follow on logically from the previous chart, their displacement being estimated by means of the geostrophic rule (Section 15.4). Should no previous chart be available, the positions of fronts and pressure centres must be determined solely by a careful scrutiny of the plotted observations.

(iii) Sketch in the isobars roughly and lightly, starting where the analysis is simplest. In general it is easier to draw isobars in areas where winds are strong than where they are light and variable. Where the density of available observations permit, it is often a good plan to begin by inserting the isobars for the lowest pressure in the depressions and the highest pressure in the anticyclones.

(iv) Insert the fronts as accurately as possible by making any necessary adjustments to the estimated positions with the aid of the plotted reports, applying the knowledge about frontal and air-mass characteristics given in earlier chapters. From the weather conditions at the front, the characteristics of the air masses on the two sides of the front as shown by the plotted reports and from the previous history (if available), decide the type of front.

(v) Revise the roughly drawn isobars, carefully fitting the pressure and wind observations and making appropriate kinks where they cross a front.

(vi) Finally mark the fronts in the standard colours or by the conventional markings. These standard colours are:-

warm front	red
occlusion	purple (or contiguous red and blue)
cold front	blue
stationary front	broken line, alternating red and blue.

In the monochromatic system, the nature of the fronts is depicted using conventional symbols, as shown in the Annex. The projections are placed on the side of the front towards which it is moving; for a stationary front they alternate from side to side.

Drawing of isobars

In the United Kingdom isobars are normally drawn at intervals of 4 hPa or, for larger-scale charts, sub-multiples of 4 hPa. In some countries they are drawn at 5 hPa intervals. In all cases the 1000 hPa isobar is drawn. If then, for example, the lowest pressure reported in a depression is 989 hPa, the central isobar of the system to be drawn on a chart with isobars at 4 hPa interval will be that for 992 hPa, whilst on a chart with isobars at 2 hPa interval it will be 990 hPa. By inserting the intermediate isobars between the highest and lowest pressures, a start may be made anywhere on the chart and the isobar drawn continuously in such a way that the pressures at stations near the isobar on one side of the line are always above and on the other side always below that appropriate to the isobar itself; for example the 1020 hPa isobar will pass between two stations if one has a pressure of 1018.8 and the other 1020.9 and will be rather nearer the latter than the former. When stations are far apart and there is a substantial difference of pressure it is useful to determine how many isobars lie between them and then to divide the distance between them so as to space the isobars out more or less uniformly. If however, the wind force at one of the stations is considerably greater than at the other the spacing of the isobars should be correspondingly closer near the station with the stronger wind than near the other. The following fundamental properties of isobars should be borne in mind:

(i) Isobars are simple curved lines with loose ends only at the edges of the chart, or they are simple closed curves.

(ii) Isobars never cross, touch or join (except where two parts of the same isobar join to make a closed curve).

(iii) Everywhere along an isobar the higher pressures are on one side and the lower pressures on the other, and the sides must never be interchanged on passing along the isobar. For example in Fig. 105 where the isobars form a col, the 1012 hPa isobar must not be drawn either as AB or CD, but must be drawn as two separate parts, as shown by the full lines. It is in such a region that the beginner is most likely to get into difficulties.

(iv) The pressures on consecutive isobars always differ by the same standard interval, except at a col where they have the same value in the direction across the col.

(v) Isobars should be drawn to fit the wind direction as nearly as possible, in accordance with Buys Ballot's law, allowing for a slight flow across the isobars from high pressure to low. There should, however, be no slavish insistence on this point for there are many exceptions to the rule, particularly where winds are light and in coastal and hilly districts. Isobars must also be drawn in general conformity with the wind strength, being near together where the winds are strong and well separated where they are light. In regions of somewhat sparse observations where a good deal of interpolation may be necessary, it is important in passing from an area of strong winds and concentrated isobars to one of light winds and few isobars that the isobars should be drawn to show a gradual transition and should not be unduly crowded in the one region at the expense of the other.

(vi) When the isobars are finally adjusted they should be as smooth as possible with sharp bends only at frontal troughs and possibly over mountain ranges. Small irregularities in the isobars should be avoided unless it is certain that they are caused by secondary disturbances. It is often better to assume a slight error in a pressure observation and a local cause for an irregular wind (such as a sea breeze or a mountain or valley wind) than to fit one such single observation by drawing a dubious trough in the isobars which could be mistaken for a significant secondary disturbance. Experience normally enables practised forecasters to distinguish the real from the local or spurious irregularity.

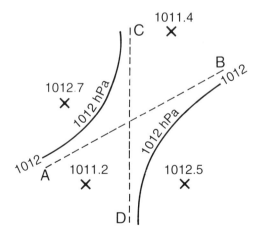

Figure 105.   Drawing isobars in a col.

This can be said to complete the usual analysis of the chart, but on occasions when pressure is falling or rising at a substantial rate it may be convenient to draw isallobars (lines joining places having the same barometric tendency) since these show clearly the areas where the main changes of pressure and movements of pressure systems have been taking place. A concentrated area of falling pressure appears as a system of closed curves similar to the isobars of a depression and is known as an isallobaric low. Likewise an area of rising pressure is known as an isallobaric high.

19.3 ANALYSIS OF UPPER-AIR CHARTS

No study of the weather situation can be complete unless it is three dimensional. The surface charts do in fact take some account of this aspect of the problem since the plotted reports include features of weather, cloud and rain for example, which may originate far above the surface layers, but a detailed analysis of observations of pressure, temperature, humidity and wind in the upper air is an essential part of the diagnosis of any synoptic situation.

The most practical way of displaying the patterns of circulation in the free atmosphere is by the construction of contour charts for selected pressure levels. The basic theory of these charts has been dealt with in Section 5.4. In analysing these charts it is not sufficient to consider each selected level independently, but rather it is necessary to ensure that the analyses of the selected levels are mutually consistent. The importance of doing this is related to the sparseness of upper-air observations in space and time as compared with surface reports.

In the United Kingdom, routine upper-air analyses are performed by computer at Bracknell (Section 19.6) and many of these analyses are distributed by facsimile to the various forecasting offices. It is therefore not necessary at most of these offices for similar analyses to be produced manually.

The standard pressure levels for which upper-air analyses are normally produced are 850, 700, 500, 300, 250, 200 and 100 hPa, the contours being drawn at intervals of 60 m at the lower levels and 120 m at 300 hPa and above. The analysis of 100 hPa charts tends to rely heavily on isotherms and isotachs as the observations of temperature and wind at this level are often more reliable than those of deduced contour height. Charts for the 300, 250 and 200 hPa levels, when drawn manually, are usually annotated with the positions of the axes of the jet streams. Analyses of thickness patterns (see Section 5.4) are normally produced for the 1000–500 hPa layer although other layers, notably 1000–850 hPa, are sometimes used. The isopleths of 1000–500 hPa (or 'total') thickness have a special application in forecasting changes in the surface pressure distribution and this application is described in the next section.

The study of contour charts soon reveals that moving patterns of airflow are as characteristic of upper levels as they are of the surface. However, whereas closed circulations in the form of depressions and anticyclones are common at the surface, such circulations tend to disappear in the upper air where they are frequently replaced by troughs and ridges. These troughs and ridges are often major features of the general circulation in the sense that a single one of them may cover a substantial sector of the whole hemisphere. Troughs and ridges, with an amplitude of about 20 degrees of latitude are common features of the upper-flow patterns; they are known as 'long waves'. The circumpolar chart reproduced at Fig. 24 shows five major waves around the hemisphere. The long-wave features are often persistent and slow-moving and a particular trough or ridge may dominate the weather of a large area for several days. It will be seen in a later section how this tendency for persistence can be a useful forecasting aid. On charts of the 1000–500 hPa thickness there are patterns broadly similar to those on the 500 hPa contour chart but, whilst the most common features are likewise troughs and ridges in the thermal pattern, there are sometimes closed areas of warm or cold air known as warm and cold pools. These are commonly very slow moving or quasi-stationary. Since the temperature in the lower stratosphere varies inversely with the height of the tropopause and low tropopauses occur over well developed surface depressions, it is usual to find warm pools in the lower stratosphere over cold pools in the troposphere.

19.4 PREPARATION OF FORECAST SURFACE CHARTS

With the advent of the computer, many of the laborious processes needed to produce analyses and forecasts have been superseded, and this is a development which will continue. This section is included, however, in order that the methods underlying the complicated process of producing forecast charts without the assistance of a computer may be appreciated.

We have seen that the large mass of data received by the forecaster in the form of individual reports is presented in systematic form on surface synoptic charts. On these charts the main emphasis is on the pressure systems, fronts and air masses and from these alone a tolerably good idea of the broad distribution of weather can be obtained even without the detailed observations. Further details of the forecasting of 'weather' are given in Section 19.7. It is clear therefore that in preparing a forecast it is necessary first of all to consider how the pressure systems and fronts shown on the current chart are likely to move and change during the period for which the forecast applies. The most natural way to develop and formulate these ideas is to sketch the forecast isobars and fronts on a blank map. This is the method adopted in most forecast offices and it is strongly recommended to the student. A forecast, or prognostic, chart may be drawn to relate to any future time within those limits for which useful forecasts can be prepared. For general purposes in Britain it is usual to prepare the forecast chart for 24 hours ahead of the current synoptic chart. Since some hours must be allowed for the plotting and analysis of the current chart, as well as the preparation of the forecast chart itself, the 24-hour forecast chart can usually be completed about 19 hours before the time to which it applies. Forecast charts may be drawn for other time intervals as required.

The main considerations in drawing a forecast chart are as follows:
    (i)   the movement of existing pressure systems,
    (ii) the evolution (formation, development and decay) of pressure systems,
    (iii) the changes of pressure in areas remote from the main centres of activity,
    (iv) the movement of fronts, and
    (v)   the formation and disappearance of fronts.

It must be emphasized that much of the movement and development of surface pressure systems and fronts has to be deduced from upper-air charts and that this separation into distinct steps is made solely to avoid confusion in the written description. In practice the process must be considered as a whole, each step affecting the others to a greater or lesser degree. The aim is to build up a coherent and self-consistent picture which follows logically from the current charts. Moreover, not only the surface charts but also the upper-air charts must be studied in the process of forecasting. The considerations listed above will now be discussed in turn.

Movement of pressure systems

Extrapolation. In this connection extrapolation means the continuation of the recent movement of the system for some further period. The motion of each anticyclone or depression over the past 24 hours will have been noted on the analysed charts and the positions of the centres at 6-hourly intervals marked as already described. A first rough approximation to the position at which the centre might be expected 24 hours hence is given by assuming that its speed and direction of motion over the next 24 hours will be the same as over the past 24 hours. This would be an obvious conclusion if, in fact, over the past 24 hours the system had moved in a constant direction at a constant speed, but such is rarely the case. Usually, the track of the centre as marked on the charts is curved to some degree and the distances moved in successive 6-hour periods are not constant. Sometimes these changes of speed and direction of the centre are irregular and then extrapolation affords no help. Often, however, the track of the centre is a smooth curve and the speed increases or decreases steadily over the successive intervals. With judgement the curved track may then be continued by eye and allowance made for the changing speed; this is likely to give a better approximation to the future position of the centre than the mere repetition of the previous 24 hours movement.

With a trough or a ridge there is no central point and a track cannot be drawn. However, the axis of the system can be drawn and the process of extrapolation can be applied using the position of the axes on successive charts if the changes thus indicated have been sufficiently regular.

It should be pointed out, however, that extrapolation consists essentially of continuing past trends and can take no account of new factors which may arise during the forecast period. It should therefore be regarded as a rough approximation to be modified or even disregarded in the light of other considerations.

Tendencies. An important clue to the movement of pressure systems is provided by the pressure tendency, or isallobaric, field. The following rules apply broadly but it must be borne in mind that the tendency field is often affected by the changes of intensity of systems even more than by their movement and it is often difficult to separate the effects of these two factors.

(i) A depression or anticyclone moves roughly parallel with the line joining the largest positive tendencies to the largest negative tendencies. The depression moves towards the area of falling pressure, the anticyclone towards the rising pressure.

(ii) If the tendencies are symmetrical with respect to the centre, the system is stationary.

(iii) A ridge or trough usually moves in a direction more or less at right angles to its axis: the ridge moves towards that side on which the pressure is rising and the trough towards that on which it is falling.

(iv) Taken in conjunction with the pressure gradient the tendencies afford some indication of the speed of the pressure system. Assume for simplicity that the pressure system is moving bodily without change of intensity. Then if the isobars drawn at, say, 1 hPa intervals are 80 km apart a tendency of 30 (i.e. a change of 3 hPa in 3 hours) would correspond to a speed of 80 km h^{-1} for the movement of the pressure system; if only 40 km apart the speed would be only 40 km h^{-1}. Thus, for a given tendency, the stronger the pressure gradient the smaller the speed of the system and vice versa.

Steering. Experience shows that a depression or anticyclone often moves in the same direction as the upper winds, that is, along the contours at 10 000 ft or more above its centre; this is called the steering effect. Theory leads to a similar expectation except that the movement of the pressure system is related to the thickness lines rather than to the contours. Since, however, there is often very little difference between the directions of the upper contours and of the thickness lines, particularly in the vicinity of jet streams, it follows that the two results are in reasonable agreement. For practical purposes the thickness lines for the 1000–500 hPa layer are used in applying the steering principle and the procedure is therefore referred to as 'thermal steering'. The speed of the surface pressure system is only loosely related to the speed of the thermal wind over the centre; the two increase and decrease together but the speed of the surface system is usually less than that of the upper wind and no precise relation can be formulated.

The steering principle is most useful in regard to small systems without vigorous circulations since these can, so to speak, move through the upper patterns without disturbing them appreciably. Large and vigorous surface circulations on the other hand are associated with distorted thickness and upper-air contour patterns as the warm and cold air is twisted into spiral-shaped tongues; the steering pattern is therefore destroyed and the movement of such a system becomes slow and irregular.

Miscellaneous. A depression with an open (i.e. not occluded) warm sector moves in the direction of the isobars in the warm sector. The ratio of the speed of the depression to the geostrophic wind is variable, its average value being about four-fifths; this ratio tends to be least with the strongest gradients. Some small wave depressions move a little faster than the geostrophic wind in the warm sector.

During the process of occlusion a depression slows down and a fully occluded depression is usually slow-moving or stationary. In applying the warm-sector rule just described it is obviously important to consider how soon it will be before the depression becomes occluded.

If in any sector of a depression the wind is markedly stronger than in the remaining sectors, the depression tends to move in the same direction as that of the strongest wind (i.e. in the direction of the isobars where the pressure gradient is greatest, as in Fig. 106).

Depressions tend to move round large anticyclones in the same direction as the anticyclonic circulation of winds.

Secondary depressions often move in the direction of the circulation round the primary. This applies particularly to small secondaries on the cold front of the primary and to secondaries forming within the polar air. On the other hand,

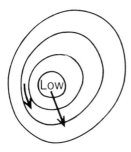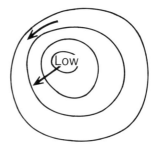

Figure 106. Movement of a depression in the direction of the strongest winds circulating around it.

secondaries on the warm front or at the point of occlusion often move along the warm front more or less radially away from the primary; an indication of the movement is then usually given by the tendencies and also by the thermal steering.

An anticyclone or ridge separating successive depressions of a family normally moves with the depressions.

An anticyclone forming in an outbreak of polar air behind the cold front of a frontal depression moves with the mass of cold air (generally towards lower latitudes).

A warm anticyclone moves slowly and tends to become stationary.

The movement of pressure systems may be influenced by topographical features. For example, a depression approaching a high plateau or mountain range is often brought to a stop or it is deflected so as to avoid the high ground; occasionally, if the ground is not too high, the upper part of the disturbance crosses the barrier and the surface depression then appears to reform on the lee side. It is difficult, however, to lay down general rules regarding topographical influences; such influences are usually introduced into forecasting practice indirectly by means of the local indications, such as pressure tendencies or through a knowledge of the tracks habitually followed by pressure systems in given situations.

Evolution of pressure systems
It has been found that surface pressure systems are likely to develop where there are certain characteristic differences between the contour patterns near the surface and those in the upper levels of the troposphere — that is when certain marked characteristics are present in the thickness pattern. In the application of these ideas the total (1000–500 hPa) thickness is normally taken as being representative of the atmospheric layer in which the development takes place. The effects occur where there are sharp changes in the direction and spacing of the thickness lines, and the development is proportional to the speed of the thermal wind. Accordingly the forecaster examines the thickness chart for sharp troughs and ridges and for spreading out (diffluence) or closing together (confluence) of the thickness lines, coupled with close spacing of thickness lines. These may occur in a variety of combinations and only a few of the simpler models can be considered here. These are shown in Fig. 107. Development is to be looked for in those parts of the

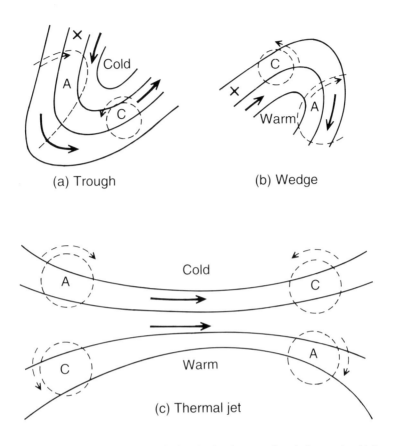

(a) Trough   (b) Wedge

(c) Thermal jet

Figure 107. Cyclonic (C) and anticyclonic (A) development in relation to the thickness pattern. Thickness lines and thermal wind directions are shown by full lines and arrows; surface isobars and wind directions by broken lines and arrows.

thickness pattern marked A (divergence and anticyclonic development) and C (convergence and cyclonic development).

Cold thermal trough (Fig. 107(a)).   Cyclonic development tends to occur on the forward side and anticyclonic development on the rear side of the trough. A depression in a position such as X will tend not to develop; rather, it will weaken and may disappear. It may however be steered along the thickness lines until it rounds the trough when it will begin to deepen in the position C. An anticyclone at X on the other hand will be steered towards A where it will settle down and intensify; it will not readily come round the trough but if it does so it will weaken in the cyclonic development area C.

Warm thermal ridge (Fig. 107(b)).   This is the opposite of the cold trough. Cyclonic development occurs at C, behind the crest of the ridge, and anticyclonic development at A, ahead of it. A depression at X is not easily steered round the ridge but moves towards C where it settles down and often deepens.

283

Thermal jet (Fig. 107(c)).   By thermal jet is meant a region of closely spaced thickness lines. C areas, favouring cyclogenesis, are located in the diffluence at the cold exit of the jet and in the confluence at the jet warm entrance. A areas, favouring anticyclogenesis, occur at the warm exit and the cold entrance regions. Cyclonic and anticyclonic development occur respectively at C and A; in the exit regions, since the thermal wind over C and A is weak the systems developing here are often slow moving. A depression steered through the jet towards C will tend to slow down and deepen. A depression on the warm side of the flow, on the other hand, would tend to weaken as it is steered towards A. Systems developing at the jet entrance regions will tend to accelerate as they are steered through the jet. In particular, a depression located in the C area at the warm entrance region will tend to accelerate through the jet; ascent generated as it deepens will lead to cooling aloft and a lower thickness value over the centre so that it will appear to cross the thickness lines to emerge later in the cold exit region where further deepening is favoured.

By combining the conceptual thermal jet model with either the trough or ridge model, it will be found that certain areas are particularly favourable to development. For instance, if the flow to rear of the trough in Fig. 107(a) is replaced by a thermal jet it will be found that the C areas from both models coincide; the region just ahead of a diffluent thermal trough is thus particularly favoured for cyclogenesis.

Tendencies.   The following rules, though almost self-evident, are given here in some detail owing to their frequent application in forecasting.

(i)   A depression is deepening if pressure is falling all round the centre or if the rate of fall on one side is greater than the rate of rise on the other.

(ii)   A depression is filling up if the pressure is rising all round the centre or if the rate of fall on one side is less than the rate of rise on the other.

(iii)   The intensity of a depression or anticyclone does not change if the tendency is zero all round the centre or if a fall on one side is balanced by an equal rise on the other.

(iv)   An anticyclone is intensifying if pressure is rising on one side more rapidly than it is falling on the other. Conversely it is weakening if pressure is falling at the centre or falling on one side more rapidly than it is rising on the other.

New depressions and secondaries.   In addition to estimating the movement and development of features already on the chart, it is always necessary to consider the possibility of new formations. The various ways in which depressions may form has already been discussed. The first sign of a new disturbance is usually a local fall of pressure not accounted for by the movement or development of the system already present and for this reason the closest attention should always be given to the pressure tendencies. If the tendencies indicate the development of some recognized type of depression the forecast chart should be modified accordingly. If for example, pressure begins to fall locally on a slowly moving or stationary front a new frontal depression is indicated; if the fall occurs in a broad current of polar air a non-frontal depression (polar low or developing PVA) is indicated, and so on. Experience alone will enable the probable degree of development to be estimated and much depends upon the part of the world and the season of the year.

The following points are also useful:

(i) A warm sector depression usually starts as a wave on the cold front of an existing (primary) depression. It may remain in wave form for some time without deepening but on moving into a favourable position, usually forward of a thermal trough, it may deepen rapidly.

(ii) A wave disturbance on a warm front usually moves fairly quickly along the front away from the main depression; it is unusual for such a system to deepen.

Changes of pressure in areas remote from the main centres of activity

In preparing a forecast chart it usually happens that there are some areas, remote from pressure centres and fronts, in which the existing features of the synoptic chart afford little guide to the likely pressure changes. It is best to estimate the probable pressures at a few selected points and to draw the forecast isobars to fit these values, joining them smoothly with the isobars already drawn for the more active regions. For estimating the pressures, the plotted 3-hour tendencies are obviously useful but they should be used in conjunction with the pressure trends (changes in the past 24 hours) which can be read off the appropriate charts. In low latitudes and to a less extent in temperate latitudes the normal diurnal variation of pressure needs to be allowed for, especially when the tendencies are small. For example a tendency of -20 (fall of 2 hPa in 3 hours) at the Azores is not to be regarded as significant if it occurs on the afternoon chart since this is about the normal diurnal fall of pressure; in the absence of a nearby depression or front it is usually followed by a corresponding rise during the evening. On summer afternoons similar falling tendencies often appear over France and central Europe but if they are no greater than about -15 they are not as a rule synoptically significant.

Movement of fronts

The first approximation to the velocity of a front is given by the geostrophic component of wind at right angles to it, which may be measured by means of the geostrophic wind scale. The following additional rules are also of assistance:

(i) The speed of a warm front is generally considerably less than the geostrophic component (roughly two thirds of this value), particularly within an occluding depression or when the isobars in advance of the front are inclined at a small angle to it (Fig. 108).

(ii) The speed of a cold front is generally about equal to the geostrophic value or a little greater.

(iii) When the geostrophic wind across the front is small the direction of motion may be determined by other considerations, for example, a flow of air across the isobars will occur from an area where the pressure is rising to one where it is falling and this isallobaric component may occasionally be sufficient to neutralize or reverse the geostrophic component on the front.

The speed of a front is often given most accurately by measuring its movement between successive charts. This should always be done if possible as a check on the

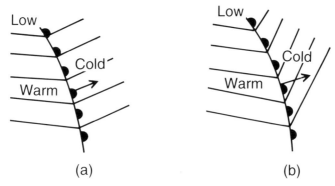

Figure 108. Movement of a warm front. (a) The front moves in the direction of the arrow with a speed of about ⅔ of the geostrophic component, and (b) the front moves at about ⅔ of the geostrophic component.

foregoing rules. Appreciable departures from the movements given by the rules should be given due weight in estimating the frontal positions on the forecast charts.

The above rules can be applied in a simple direct way only if it is assumed that the geostrophic wind across the front is not likely to change much during the forecast period. In practice there are many complications of which only a few can be mentioned here by way of illustration. In the case of a straightforward deepening of a depression (that is when the main fall of pressure occurs in the central part of the system) the geostrophic wind across the front will increase and the speed of movement of the front may be expected to increase. On the other hand it often happens that a fall of pressure is concentrated along the front itself, leading either to an elongated trough along the front or perhaps to a small separate closed centre. In either case the geostrophic wind across the front will be very much reduced along a considerable length of the front and in the second case it will be reversed over a limited distance so that the front will become very slow-moving or possibly retrograde. Lastly, with an old frontal depression the occlusion often spirals outwards from the centre. The part of the occlusion remote from the centre gradually tends to become parallel with the isobars and, in consequence, almost stationary.

Formation and disappearance of fronts
For forecasting for periods up to about 12 hours ahead it is, as a rule, sufficient to consider only those fronts which are already present on the current synoptic charts. The question of the formation of new fronts as well as the strengthening, weakening or disappearance of existing ones is hardly likely to arise; it does however present a problem to the professional forecaster concerned with longer periods and the student should at least be aware of the possibilities. It may generally be assumed that fronts will weaken in anticyclones and ridges. They will weaken in those parts of the thickness patterns favourable to anticyclonic development and strengthen in the parts favourable to cyclonic development. For short-period forecasting the weakening of a front is shown by rising pressure and general decrease of rain and cloud in its vicinity, while changes of the opposite type indicate a strengthening of the front. Generally speaking a major front is associated with a close spacing of

thickness lines, that is, the boundary between two distinct air masses; if it can be seen that because of the circulation of winds the thermal gradient is likely to become strong over a considerable distance the formation of a new front should be anticipated. A front which is drawn crossing the thickness lines at a large angle should be regarded with suspicion; if it is a true front its effects are usually confined to a comparatively shallow layer of the atmosphere near the surface.

Secondary cold fronts are often a feature of an outbreak of cold air. The showers in unstable polar air often occur along an extended line more or less at right angles to the airstream, sometimes merging into an unbroken, elongated rain area, and since a shallow trough sometimes develops along the rain belt the synoptic chart shows all the appearances of a minor cold front. It is not uncommon for a series of such secondary fronts to develop and be carried round in the circulation of a large slow-moving depression after the main cold front has passed. It is not usually possible to forecast the location of such a front before its formation but once it has appeared on the current synoptic chart it should be included in the forecast chart with due allowance for its possible movement.

Drawing the forecast chart
The various considerations involved in the preparation of the forecast chart have been discussed in some detail in the preceding sections but it is perhaps desirable here to summarize the actual procedure. First the expected positions of the centres of high and low pressure and the troughs and ridges should be sketched in lightly, using extrapolation for the first approximation with modification in the light of tendencies and thermal steering. Next the forecast central pressure should be estimated for each system. After this, the forecast frontal positions should be lightly sketched in; these will be based on the geostrophic winds of the current synoptic chart and any change of speed can be allowed for only rather vaguely at this stage. A few estimated pressures at points remote from active pressure systems and fronts should now be inserted and the isobars sketched in. Generally speaking the isobars should run in evenly spaced and more or less smooth curves except for the kinks where they intersect the fronts. If the predicted pressures lead to a local crowding of isobars or simply unaccountably large pressure changes in any part of the chart they should be smoothed out unless there is good reason not to do so. Finally, each frontal position should be adjusted so that the frontal movement is not inconsistent with the appropriate geostrophic wind at both the beginning and the end of the forecast period. For example if the geostrophic wind across the front is 40 KT on the current synoptic chart and 20 KT on the forecast chart then a predicted frontal movement corresponding to a steady speed of 30 KT throughout the forecast period would be reasonable, whereas a sustained speed of 40 KT would be inconsistent.

19.5 PREPARATION OF FORECAST UPPER-AIR CHARTS

Most upper-air charts, both analyses and forecasts, are prepared using a computer (Section 19.6).

If computer charts are not available, the changes in the various thickness patterns are forecast mainly by extrapolation of the troughs and ridges on the current chart by considering how the thickness lines will move under the influence of the wind circulations in the appropriate layers. Heating and cooling of the air as it moves over warmer or colder parts of the earth's surface will affect the partial thicknesses to a greater or less degree and the experienced forecaster can to some extent estimate and allow for these effects. Studies of past records have shown that there are more or less limiting latitudes to which air masses having particular thickness values can penetrate without being modified. Charts showing these limiting latitudes (which are longitude dependent) have been prepared for each month of the year and are useful aids to forecasting.

It will be recalled that the movement and development of surface pressure systems is influenced by the thickness pattern while the thickness pattern is itself modified by (among other factors) the surface circulations. It is evident therefore that the preparation of forecast surface and upper-air charts are interrelated problems and ideally they should proceed hand in hand by a process of modifying one chart in the light of the others to bring the whole set of charts into reasonable conformity. It is therefore important to ensure that any surface forecast is compatible with the available upper-air forecasts whether these are produced manually or by computer.

The three-dimensional perspective
Despite caveats interpolated at various points, the analysis and forecasting techniques described above may leave the reader with the impression that the synoptic chart is treated like a games board across which the various systems are moved, like chessmen, according to certain fixed rules; it is inevitable that an unpractised analyst should view it in this way. Of course this is not the case at all and the analyst should endeavour to eschew such a 'cardboard cut-out' viewpoint and should try to think instead 'in three dimensions'. The lows and highs of the surface chart are not discrete 'solid' entities but are the surface reflections of vast exchanges of air at different levels throughout the depth of the troposphere; interacting in response to both horizontal and vertical air movements. Development of this 3-D perspective will not come easily; indeed a full understanding of all the dynamical processes involved will require a much deeper mathematical treatment than has been attempted in this book; nonetheless it is such a perspective that should be the goal of every analyst. Only with such an understanding will it become possible to produce realistic forecast charts with confidence.

19.6 NUMERICAL WEATHER PREDICTION (NWP)

Introduction
In Part I of this book various mathematical and physical concepts were introduced to describe and explain aspects of atmospheric behaviour. Implicit in this approach was the acceptance that the atmosphere can be regarded as a machine, performing in accordance with certain defined physical laws. The equations introduced in Part I, and those examined in Appendix I, are necessarily very simple and the circumstances of their use are often limited by restrictive qualifications. The geostrophic wind, for example, is strictly applicable only when the isobars are straight, parallel and not changing with time, when there is no vertical motion, and when there are no external forces such as friction: use of the geostrophic scale on isobaric charts is further restricted to a single value of air density. In spite of these caveats, the first approximation of geostrophic balance has proved invaluable in the

everyday practice of analysis and forecasting; its success a testimony to the belief that atmospheric motions are, indeed, capable of description in mathematical terms and nurturing the dream that a more accurate description of the atmosphere would be possible with the application of more precise and more generally acceptable equations.

More precise equations have long been known but their solution in anything approaching real time remained intractable until the development of computers during the 1950s. The equations of motion appropriate for the atmosphere are the equations for a viscous fluid — the Navier–Stokes equations. Weather forecasting may thus be regarded as a deterministic problem in which any future state of the atmosphere may be obtained by integrating the Navier–Stokes equations forward in time from some initial known state. The principle is simple enough but the problems are profound.

One major problem lies in the vast range of scales of motion that have to be accommodated in any complete system of equations: spatially, at the lower end of the scale, we are concerned with the behaviour of water droplets whose diameter is measured in micrometres (μm) and at the other extreme temperate latitude depressions extending across 2000 km. On time-scales, we are concerned with showers of duration less than an hour and monsoon wind systems with a period of some months. There is continuous, and often complex, interaction between these various scales of motion.

NWP model types
Two basic types of numerical model are used in weather prediction, finite difference models and spectral models.

In the finite difference approach, the area of concern is considered to be divided into a horizontal grid and values of those basic parameters which describe the state of the atmosphere, such as wind, temperature and humidity, are assigned to a number of different levels at each grid point. By integration of the primitive equations, conditions at each grid point are determined for a short forward time-step and the process repeated to the end of the desired forecast period.

The spectral method may perhaps be best understood by first considering the analysis of a continuous curve such as a time-series, a barogram trace for example, or a two-dimensional cross-section through a range of hills. Such curves, no matter how complex they may appear, can be reduced to a mathematical expression by the statistical procedure of harmonic (or Fourier) analysis. In a somewhat similar way, a three-dimensional surface of say, temperature, may be mathematically defined. This is the principle of spectral analysis. Many of the more recently developed computer models use this spectral approach; it is claimed that the spectral form more closely represents the true nature of real atmospheric flow and preserves the speed and shape of individual components with differing horizontal scales. However, the differences are probably quite small; any differences in the method of the mathematical representation generally have less impact upon predictive skill than other aspects of the forecasting system.

Resolution
One most important aspect of any numerical model is its resolution, especially in the horizontal. Clearly, a better definition of the spatial distribution of any

parameter will be attainable if the network of grid points is closely spaced (higher resolution) than if the grid points are far apart (lower resolution). To date it has generally been found that improving model resolution is rewarded by improvements in forecast performance but increased resolution requires increased computing power and so, in practice, a compromise always has to be accepted.

The Meteorological Office's 'unified model', introduced operationally during 1991, is a finite difference model using a global horizontal grid spacing of $1.25°$ of longitude by $0.83°$ of latitude, giving a total of 62 496 grid points at each model level. With 20 different levels this gives a grand total of about 1.25 million points for which integrations must be made for each small time-step. When it is considered that the forward time-step for the global model is a mere 10 minutes, it will be readily appreciated that to run a forecast for a few days ahead is a truly prodigious undertaking which could not be contemplated without supercomputer support.

Within the vicinity of southern Britain the grid length for the global version of the unified model is approximately 92 km in each direction. There is also a regional version (the Limited Area Model, or LAM), which covers the North Atlantic and western Europe. Additional grid-points are interpolated between those of the global model, giving the LAM a grid-point spacing of less than 50 km over the British Isles; the LAM time step for the forward integrations is 5 minutes. A further, 'mesoscale', model with a grid length of only 15 km and 32 levels in the vertical covers the immediate vicinity of the British Isles.

Parametrization

Many of the physical processes which are important for a complete forecast specification operate at scales much less than even the smallest grid length referred to above. Among these sub-grid-scale processes may be mentioned cumulus convection, stratiform precipitation, radiation and turbulence. These processes need to be described in terms of the parameters resolved and predicted by the model integrations, namely, temperature, humidity and wind. It is therefore necessary to devise what are called 'parametrization' schemes to model these processes.

Data assimilation

A necessary condition for a numerical model of the atmosphere to produce a good forecast is that the initial state should be adequately specified. This initial state can never be perfectly known and the inevitable initial deficiencies will become magnified in the successive forward integrations and will eventually destroy the accuracy of the predictions. It is therefore most important that great care is taken over the initial analysis or, as it is more usually termed, the 'initialization', in order to ensure that it as error-free and definitive as is possible.

The starting point for the initialization is a forecast chart prepared from the previous model run; at Bracknell this 'background field' will have been produced from a forecast run only 6 hours earlier. All new data undergoes an automatic quality control procedure, each observation being critically examined for such things as internal consistency and consistency with any earlier observations; the position of a ship, for example, will be compared with its previous position and if the implied movement is implausible the observation will be rejected. Observations markedly different from the background field are also 'flagged' for the attention of an intervention forecaster who will decide whether the observation should be rejected as erroneous or accepted as a correct departure from the earlier forecast expectation. The intervention forecaster also has the facility to inject additional data from sources which may not be directly available to the model, such as information deduced from scrutiny of satellite imagery.

All data which pass the quality control checks will be assimilated into the model, modifying the background field as necessary to provide the initialised field. It is this field that is the basis for the successive integrations from which the forecast fields are derived.

Forecast output for aviation

From each computer run, a series of forecast charts is produced in a variety of formats, for a number of different levels and for validity times up to about 6 days ahead. Other output is in the form of coded bulletins of grid-point data. One important data set is that provided specifically for aviation purposes to meet Bracknell's responsibility as one of the two World Area Forecast Centres designated by ICAO (Washington is the other) and as a Regional Area Forecast Centre (RAFC).

WAFS products

The role of a World Centre is to provide numerical forecasts of winds and temperatures with a global coverage. These are usually provided as coded bulletins of grid-point values and they are distributed to a network of RAFCs with responsibility for provision of planning information and flight documentation. In addition, digital data in grid-point form is supplied on direct computer-to-computer links to some individual airlines as well as to SITA (Societe Internationale de Telecommunications Aeronautiques). Main computer runs are based upon initialization times (data times) of 00 and 12 UTC. If the data time is denoted by T, then transmission of the global grid-point data typically commences at T+4 h 30 min. and comprises forecasts for validity times T+12, 18, 24 and 30 for standard flight levels from FL050 (850 hPa) to FL530 (100 hPa) as well as maximum wind and tropopause data. Further bulletins for T+36, 42 and 48 provide back-up data to cover against the eventuality of delay or failure of the subsequent forecast run.

The role of the Regional Centre (RAFC)

Regional Centres are tasked with the provision of WAFS data sets for flight planning: RAFC Bracknell's responsibility is the NAT (North Atlantic) region, covering westbound air traffic from European airfields to terminals on the North American continent. Charts are disseminated by facsimile to United Kingdom airports as well as to a number of international centres, including Paris and Frankfurt, the other European RAFCs. From a main computer run at time T the chart transmission sequence will commence at about T+5 h 30 min for a validity time of T+18 and T+11 h for a validity time of T+24. Each chart package comprises charts of wind and temperature for standard flight levels as well as a high-level significant weather chart. This latter is prepared manually but incorporates data provided by the numerical model and depicts major frontal systems, jet stream axes, areas of likely clear air turbulence (CAT), tropopause heights and any significant weather expected between FL250 and FL630. The eventual World Area Forecast System objective is for the significant weather charts also to be prepared by computer at the two World Centres for global dissemination in coded format. Further technical advances are needed before this goal is achieved; in any case an interim period is envisaged during which the World Centres will broadcast a mixture of data in coded and chart form via satellite.

Complete regional chart sets are available to users at least 9 hours before the chart validity time. Examples of RAFC charts are included in the Annex, including output from some of the other Regional Centres.

Other products

Bracknell has a dual role. In addition to its aviation function it has responsibilities as a WMO Regional Meteorological Centre (RMC) charged with the provision of numerical analysis and forecast data for Europe and the North Atlantic to other national centres; it is also the national centre, its Central Forecasting Office (CFO) providing guidance material for public sector forecasts for the United Kingdom.

Products received in the CFO

From each forecast run, the CFO receives a wealth of forecast output, not only charts of surface pressure and upper-air contour patterns but derived data such as the forecast fields of precipitation, humidity, cloud, wind, temperature and vertical velocity and forecast tephigrams. Each product is scrutinized and on a particular occasion any one may prove of inestimable use in helping the forecasters to interpret and evaluate the synoptic developments; to clothe the basic skeleton provided by the isobaric chart with the detail which is necessary to forecast the many aspects of weather which are of importance to the end user. Here it will be sufficient to draw attention to two particular products which regularly assist the forecaster in solving one of the main problems examined in the previous Section (19.4), namely, locating the forecast position and intensity of surface fronts.

The first is the total thickness chart. The 1000–500 hPa thickness is a function of the mean temperature of the lower troposphere and it was noted earlier that frontal surfaces, which of course separate air masses with differing temperatures, may therefore be expected to parallel the thickness isopleths. Furthermore, the closeness of these isopleths gives an indication of the thermal contrast across the front and hence, some idea of its activity. By associating the surface front with a particular isopleth and observing how the thickness pattern evolves through the forecast cycle, the forecaster is able to assess both the future position of the front and whether it is undergoing frontogenesis or frontolysis.

The other product is the field of wet-bulb potential temperature (or WBPT) at 850 hPa. WBPT was introduced in an earlier chapter; it is one of the most conservative of air mass properties and remains unchanged by such processes as evaporation and condensation as well as by adiabatic changes; it is therefore an ideal air mass tracer. Again, a concentration of WBPT isotherms suggests a well-defined frontal zone. By examining its distribution at about 5000 ft the forecaster is able to identify and forecast quite shallow frontal features which might not necessarily show up clearly on the total thickness chart, which of course is representative of a much greater depth of the atmosphere. Experience shows that both total thickness and 850 hPa WBPT are very well handled by the forecast model.

The man–machine mix

As a consequence of the continuous development of numerical models and data management procedures, forecast quality has undergone significant improvement. Forecasts of upper winds and temperatures are particularly skilful, justifying the direct dissemination of grid-point data to the user interests (amendment procedures do exist but they are rarely invoked).

The question may therefore be asked, why do we still need forecasters? The simple answer is that in spite of the admitted accuracy of the forecasts, they are by no means perfect; the forecast equations are not exact; computing limitations are such that we can never achieve the model resolution that we would wish and the initialized data are neither as complete nor as accurate as we would like to see. It is for this reason that forecasters continue to monitor and to adjust machine predictions and it is for this reason that manual methods of forecasting were considered at such length in the foregoing sections of this chapter. In fact, it is because the numerical forecasts achieve such accuracy, that it is more than ever incumbent upon the human forecaster to fully understand the physical and dynamical atmospheric processes in order that he will be able to spot those rare, but very important, occasions when the model is going awry. The value of this man–machine mix has been demonstrated on a number of occasions in recent years when potentially major forecast errors in the eastern Atlantic/British Isles sector were avoided by human intervention (Woodroffe 1990, McCallum 1990, McCallum and Norris 1990).

The forecaster is also required to interpret the machine products. Even with an excellent sequence of forecast surface pressure charts, skill and professional judgement are required to assess the many aspects of weather detail which concern the customer, whether it be sunshine amount for the holiday maker, frost risk for the farmer, local wind pattern for the yachtsman or cloud base for the aviator. We turn our attention to these aspects in the next sections.

19.7 PREPARING THE FORECAST

The construction of forecast charts as described in the preceding sections is merely a means to an end — the preparation of the forecast itself. To a certain extent the forecast is implicit in the charts; the forecast fronts and depressions indicate the areas of bad weather, the winds are indicated by the forecast isobars and contours, and the general character of the weather away from the pressure systems and fronts can usually be inferred from the broad air-mass properties. However, there are other considerations which enter into the forecast which are not implicit in the charts, but are dependent upon the more detailed structure of the pressure systems, fronts and air masses. These considerations are important for the forecasting of such diverse features as fog, thunderstorms, turbulence, showers, the distinction between snow and rain and so on. A physical account of these phenomena has been given in Part I and by using that knowledge in conjunction with the forecast charts the student should be able to prepare useful forecasts in some of the simpler cases. Most meteorological situations are more or less complex to a degree which cannot be adequately dealt with in a textbook. Only long experience can show how they should best be handled and so the aviator has, perforce, to rely on the professional forecaster for advice. Here we can give nothing more than a brief outline of the simpler considerations involved in translating synoptic and forecast charts into a weather forecast.

Types of forecast

The formulation of a forecast is a matter which depends upon the purpose for which it is intended. The various types of aviation forecast may be classified as follows:

General inference. A general description of the distribution of pressure and of the position of fronts based on the current synoptic chart, followed by the probable movements and developments of the pressure features and fronts based on the forecast charts. The general inference is regarded as being supplementary to the forecast charts; thus it amplifies the information which they portray, particularly in regard to the activity of fronts and the properties of air masses which cannot easily be represented cartographically, and indicates the degree of confidence and possible alternative developments.

Area forecasts. General indications of flying weather conditions to be expected over substantial areas for a stated period with little attention to detail. These forecasts may either be in a written format or a chart format, the latter being known as 'significant weather' charts.

Route and flight forecasts. The expected conditions along a specified route for a given period of time (route forecast) or for the duration of a particular flight (flight forecast).

Local forecasts. The expected conditions in some detail for the immediate vicinity of a flying centre for a stated period.

Aerodrome forecasts. Area, route and flight forecasts need to be supplemented by forecasts of landing conditions for destination aerodromes and alternates for appropriate stated periods.

The broad principles employed in the preparation of these forecasts will now be discussed. It must however, be repeated that every situation shows some variations from these broad principles which cannot be dealt with in a textbook and which only the experienced forecaster can handle.

The area, route and flight forecasts will be considered together since they are prepared almost entirely from the current and forecast charts. Local and aerodrome forecasts require, in addition, a study of the way in which the meteorological situation is modified locally by geographical peculiarities and they are therefore dealt with separately.

19.8 AREA, ROUTE AND FLIGHT FORECASTS

Frontal weather and cloud

The pilot's first concern will probably be the extent to which the area or route will be affected by bad weather and extensive cloud associated with fronts. The areas likely to be so affected can be seen at a glance from the current and forecast charts and allowance can be made for the frontal movements during the period of the forecast. Reference should be made to Chapter 16 for a detailed description of the weather to be expected on a flight through a frontal depression, and for a tabular statement of normal frontal characteristics. The expected changes in intensity of the fronts must be taken into consideration. In summer, especially, the activity of a front may be increased by the presence of a moist unstable air mass and any front, but more particularly a cold front, advancing into such an air mass is liable to give rise to an extensive outbreak of thunderstorms. With weakening fronts the cloud sheets tend to break up and the normal cirrostratus, altostratus and nimbostratus succession assumes the forms of cirrocumulus, altocumulus and stratocumulus respectively.

Air-mass weather

Away from the fronts the broad features of the expected weather will be inferred from the characteristic air-mass properties. These, as they apply to the temperate regions of the northern hemisphere, are described in Chapter 15. It will be recalled that the air masses are broadly classified into warm and cold types according to their respective origins in tropical or polar regions, with a further subdivision into maritime and continental according to their recent location over ocean or land areas. In any given situation however, the standard air-mass properties are modified to a greater or lesser degree by various factors such as heating or cooling at the earth's surface and the evaporation of moisture from the sea, vegetation or wet ground. The resulting changes in air-mass properties may to some extent be estimated but to deal with them properly representative observations of upper-air temperature and humidity within the air mass are essential; these should be plotted on a tephigram.

Clouds in relation to air masses

The broad distinction is between cumuliform clouds characterized by vertical development and layer cloud occurring in extensive horizontal sheets. The former occur with unstable air masses and are most characteristic of maritime polar air which usually contains adequate moisture for cloud formation. Layer clouds occur with stable air masses, most often with tropical maritime air, but there are widely varying degrees of stability and instability for a given type of air mass and the forecasting of cloud in a given situation is greatly helped by the tephigram. The reader is referred to Chapter 6 for a full discussion of cloud formation in relation to lapse rate; only a brief summary is given here. In general if the lapse rate is steep, clouds are mainly cumuliform; the height to which the clouds grow is roughly the same as the height to which the steep lapse rate continues. Deep unstable layers are therefore associated with large cumulus or cumulonimbus clouds; shallow unstable layers with only small cumulus. Stable layers and inversions on the other hand are associated with layer cloud which may be formed either by turbulence or by the spreading out of cumulus clouds formed in rising currents in unstable layers below. Over land, except in winter, the cumuliform clouds usually build up during the day and disperse at night; stratiform clouds on the other hand tend to increase at night and sometimes they disappear by day; these changes are clearly associated with the changes in lapse rate caused by the variation of surface heating. In this connection it is often useful to estimate the changes in the lapse rate in the lowest layers caused by the surface heating and cooling. Over the sea there is no appreciable diurnal variation of lapse rate; cumulus or stratocumulus clouds may occur at all times of the day in a polar air current whose surface temperature is lower than that of the sea. If on the other hand the air is warmer than the sea the tendency is for stratus to form.

Precipitation in relation to air masses

In areas away from fronts there are two principal types of rainfall: convectional and orographic.

Convectional rainfall occurs with a steep lapse rate and high moisture content in at least the lower layers of the atmosphere. The principal aid to forecasting this type of rainfall is the tephigram, as described in some detail in Chapter 6. In general the more unstable the lapse rate and the higher the humidity the more vigorous is the convection and the heavier is the rain associated with it; in extreme cases violent thunderstorms and heavy hail occur. Much depends also upon the surface pressure distribution. Within a depression or region of cyclonically curved isobars the convergence caused by inflow of air across the isobars not only aids the vertical motion but also increases the available moisture and the vigour of the convection is thereby increased. A shallow depression is more favourable than an intense one for vigorous convection, for a weak circulation of wind prolongs the contact of the air with the warm surface while strong winds tend to shear off the rising columns of heated air; the most intense convectional effects occur therefore in summer in shallow depressions moving slowly over land areas. Within an anticyclone or ridge there is usually subsidence coupled with the outflow of surface air across the isobars. This not only tends to diminish the instability but also brings down drier air towards the surface, and these two factors tend to dampen out the convection.

In temperate latitudes convective rainfall occurs mainly in polar maritime air, chiefly in the form of showers from detached cumulonimbus, the individual showers often being separated by areas of clear sky. Over the sea this type of rainfall is most prevalent in winter when the cold air moves over relatively warm water and surface heating leads to instability. Windward coastal regions also are subject to these showers and, with diminishing frequency, the showers may penetrate considerable distances inland, especially through gaps in mountains or hills; thus in the English Midlands with north-westerly winds showers often penetrate through the Cheshire gap, and with south-westerly winds through the Bristol Channel. In summer the sea is relatively cool and it is over the heated land that convection chiefly occurs, the frequency of showers often increasing with the distance from the windward coast. Owing to the diurnal variation of temperature, convective rainfall over land in summer occurs chiefly in the afternoon; on the other hand, over the sea convective rainfall may occur at any time, day or night. There is however, a tendency for showers in coastal areas to occur most frequently in the early morning.

Orographic rainfall. The conditions associated with orographic rainfall and the factors which cause variations in its intensity have been discussed in Chapter 6. We may summarize by saying that orographic precipitation should be forecast whenever an airstream which is saturated or nearly saturated blows against hills or mountains or a high coastline. If the lapse rate is stable and there is no front, only drizzle or slight rain is probable; if a front is present or there is instability (including convective instability) the intensity of the rainfall will be increased. To the lee of high ground there is a region of diminished rainfall, or even none at all; this is the so-called 'rain shadow'.

Drizzle is precipitation in the form of very small drops. It occurs in association with a stable lapse rate and stratiform clouds. The processes which give rise to drizzle are turbulence and the less-marked orographic effects. It is especially liable to occur when warm, moist air passes over a cold sea surface; if there is a sufficient degree of turbulence the drizzle may occur over the open sea but it is more usual on the coasts and for some distance inland where turbulence increases as the airstream passes from sea to land. It frequently occurs in the warm sector of a frontal depression but may equally well occur in the outer regions of an anticyclone if the airstream is damp enough.

Snow at the surface should usually be forecast when the surface temperature is below about 3 °C in those situations which would otherwise give rain. The exact critical temperature depends upon circumstances and there is no hard and fast rule. If the wet-bulb temperature is low, precipitation which starts as heavy rain may quickly turn to snow or a mixture of rain and snow even though the dry-bulb temperature is a few degrees above the critical value of 3 °C to begin with; the air temperature is soon lowered to its wet-bulb temperature by evaporative cooling from the raindrops. A useful rule of thumb is that rain could turn to snow if the rate of rainfall is heavy enough and if the sum of the dry-bulb and dew-point temperatures is no more than seven. On the other hand drizzle or very fine rain may occur with the temperature nearly down to freezing-point.

Visibility in relation to air masses
The factors which affect visibility and give rise to fog, mist and haze are discussed in detail in Chapter 9 and it is necessary here to consider these factors only in relation to the synoptic situation. It will be recalled that fog arises in the main from two causes: radiation and advection. Radiation fog occurs chiefly over land at night and in the early morning, with clear skies and light winds; the fog develops where the ground cools by radiation from a clear sky. The central regions of anticyclones and ridges often provide the requisite conditions, and indeed the advantages arising from the dry quiet weather of an anticyclone are often nullified by its liability to fog, especially in autumn and winter. For dense fog the air must be cooled below its dew-point, not only at the surface but also up to a height of a few hundred feet. Some of the worst fogs begin under the special conditions of light wind and clear sky at night after the air has been made damp by rain falling through it. This occurs most frequently in a depression or trough with weak pressure gradients but the type of pressure distribution does not matter so long as the pressure gradient is weak.

Advection fog occurs when moist air flows over a cold surface of land or sea; the temperature of the cold surface must be below the dew-point of the air. This type of fog occurs at any season of the year and at any time of day or night and is not restricted to occasions of light winds or clear skies. Over land it is especially liable to occur in winter with the incursion of mild damp air over a snow-covered surface or after a spell of frosty weather. Over the coastal waters of the British Isles it occurs chiefly in late spring and early summer while the sea is still relatively cold. Tropical maritime air from the Atlantic then frequently gives rise to fog near the south-west coasts of the British Isles. Similarly, heated air from the continent, after cooling over the North Sea, may give rise to fog on the east coast.

In general, visibility over land and sea is best when the lapse rate is steep; a small lapse rate and especially an inversion is often associated with poor visibility. Visibility is, however, affected also by dust, smoke and other solid impurities in the atmosphere. A steep lapse rate with its associated upward currents readily disperses the impurities while a stable lapse rate prevents this dispersal and causes the

297

impurities to accumulate near the surface. Under these conditions the visibility may be adversely affected not only near the source of the pollution but for a great distance downwind.

Ice accretion

The meteorological conditions leading to ice accretion on aircraft are fully discussed in Chapter 8. Any clouds containing water droplets will probably give rise to airframe icing if the temperature is between 0 °C and -40 °C (or even below on rare occasions) though as a general rule the risk is smaller as the clouds become colder. Cumuliform clouds and particularly cumulonimbus are the most dangerous. Airframe icing is heaviest in the more active types of cloud, that is, in clouds associated with active fronts, in cumulonimbus associated with vigorous convection and in clouds intensified by orographic uplift. Forecasting airframe icing is thus a matter of forecasting clouds, their horizontal and vertical extent as well as their type, in conjunction with the distribution of upper-air temperature over the area or route concerned. Therefore a good selection of recent upper-air ascents plotted on tephigrams is an essential addition to the synoptic chart. The degree of airframe icing is classed as 'light', 'moderate', or 'severe' according to the expected severity. Further, when rain ice is expected it should be specifically mentioned in the forecast.

Since engine icing can occur over a wide range of conditions (including clear air and temperature above 0 °C) and since its occurrence is affected by the design of the engine, forecasts of engine icing are not normally attempted.

Winds and temperatures

For area, route and flight forecasts the upper winds constitute perhaps the most important item because of their direct bearing on navigation, flight duration and payload. Temperatures have an effect on engine performance. Surface winds and temperatures on the other hand are important for take-off and landing at particular aerodromes and they are more appropriately dealt with under local and aerodrome forecasts.

While upper winds can be estimated from the appropriate contour chart using the geostrophic relationship, it is more usual, for aviation purposes, to have a chart that gives the winds at fixed locations. Forecast temperatures are presented in an analogous manner and are usually included with the winds on a single chart. Examples of such charts are given in the Annex.

Surface pressure

The expected surface pressure at any position may be obtained from a forecast chart. The importance of surface pressure lies in its effect on altimeter readings. If wrongly set the altimeter reading could be dangerously in error.

19.9 LOCAL AND AERODROME FORECASTS

The problems of local and aerodrome forecasting are at the same time more restricted but more intensive than those of area and route or flight forecasting, for while the region considered is small, the precision demanded is much greater. Whereas the area forecaster is content to specify 'local fog' or 'squally showers' for example, the local forecaster is expected to state when the fog will form, how thick it will be, when it will clear, at what time of day the showers are expected, how frequent they may be and how severe will be the squalls. The local forecast is, of course, based on the forecast chart but special attention must be given to local peculiarities. The main factors causing local variations in conditions have been mentioned in connection with the individual elements but it is convenient now to present a comprehensive summary.

Causes of local variations in meteorological conditions
Surface wind
— Stronger over the sea than over the land for a given pressure gradient.
— Diurnal variation; for the same pressure gradient the surface wind is stronger for large than for small lapse rate.
— Sheltering effect of high ground to windward.
— Deviating effect of hills on wind direction.
— Funnel effect through valleys.
— Katabatic winds down hillsides at night.
— Diurnal land- and sea-breezes.
— Variations in turbulence due to ground contour or lapse-rate differences; in particular the difference between land and sea fetches.

Cloud
— Orographic cloud over high ground.
— Lowering of cloud base to windward of high ground and clearance in the lee.
— Differences in turbulence affecting low cloud.
— At coastal sites, the effect of wind direction upon convection cloud formation and turbulence. Thus with onshore wind at cloud level stratus or sea fog may drift over the coast, or cloud may form at the coast as a result of uplift and increase in surface roughness.

Precipitation
— Orographic precipitation or enhancement of general rain by topography.
— Rain-shadow effect in lee of high ground.
— Near coasts, land- and sea-temperature differences affecting incidence of both instability showers and drizzle; diurnal and seasonal influences important.
— Tendency for thunderstorms to favour certain regions.

Visibility
— Valley fogs.
— Hill fogs (low cloud on hills).
— Land and sea differences.
— Presence of smoke sources.
— Effect of local clouds and winds on radiation fog formation.
— Effect of nature of ground on radiation fog.
— Possible drift of fog from adjacent areas, especially from lower ground after dawn; fog sometimes drifts from a direction backed by 45° or more from the geostrophic wind in slack gradients.

Temperature

— Effect of altitude.
— Low minima in valleys on clear nights.
— Effect of soil type on diurnal range of temperature.
— Effect of local clouds or fog on diurnal range.
— Föhn effect in lee of high ground.
— Difference between land and sea fetches.

All forecasters are aware in general terms of the factors that can cause local variations in meteorological conditions. However, in-depth local knowledge and experience is invaluable in compiling local or aerodrome forecasts.

19.10 FORECASTING IN THE TROPICS

Despite the fact that in some tropical regions, especially certain coastal and mountainous areas, extensive cloud and heavy rain occur quite frequently, on the whole the weather in the tropics is less hazardous to aviation than in temperate latitudes. Over both land and sea the predominating weather in most areas is fine with well broken cloud at a safe height, good visibility and light or moderate winds. Poor flying conditions in the tropics are mostly associated with one or more of the following circumstances: active portions of the Intertropical convergence zone (ITCZ) and convective conditions giving rise to heavy thunderstorms with their dangerously turbulent clouds and liability to severe airframe icing, orographic effects producing or enhancing cloud and rain, the obscuration of high ground and occasionally low-level aerodromes by low cloud, duststorms in arid areas, and tropical cyclones. Most of these phenomena are comparatively infrequent at any one location and are generally limited in extent, but they are often extremely violent.

A brief inspection of a tropical synoptic chart will show that it cannot be interpreted in the same way as the chart of temperate latitudes. The pressure gradients are, as a rule, weak and irregular; the common isobaric models — depressions, anticyclones, troughs and ridges — are rarely recognizable and certainly they cannot be regarded as distinct features which move in more or less regular fashion and carry their characteristic weather with them, a property which is fundamental for forecasting in temperate latitudes. Fronts, similarly, are an exception and when they do occur they are as a rule weak and indefinite and difficult to trace. The geostrophic wind relation does not apply in very low latitudes and winds frequently appear to be haphazard in relation to the isobars; isobars and upper contours are of limited assistance for estimating the surface and upper winds. The synoptic chart does not 'hang together' as it does in temperate latitudes and perhaps is more truly regarded as a collective representation of local weather at a large number of stations than as an ordered picture of an overall weather situation. This absence of large-scale organization does, however, make for some advantages in forecasting, at many locations the weather shows a high degree of regularity in its behaviour since the local, diurnal and seasonal effects come into full play and are barely modified by overall influences. This means that at many places in the tropics the weather is more dependent on the time of day than on any other single factor and that changes from one day to the next are small — the well known daily sequence of fine clear nights and mornings and afternoon showers or thunderstorms provides a good example. It follows that a good knowledge of local weather is an important part of the tropical forecaster's equipment. More widespread adverse weather on the other hand, since it can seldom be tied to travelling depressions and fronts, is a much more difficult problem for the forecaster than it is in temperate latitudes.

The main considerations in tropical forecasting may be classified, very broadly, under the following headings:

(a) diurnal effects,
(b) orographic effects,
(c) trade winds and monsoons,
(d) the ITCZ, and
(e) tropical cyclones.

These are not necessarily distinct from one another and in a given situation a number of them may need to considered together.

(a) Diurnal effects
At many inland places in the tropics the most significant feature of the weather is the daily build-up of cumulus or cumulonimbus cloud, often culminating in afternoon and evening thunderstorms; the forecasting problem then consists mainly in estimating the incidence, the time of occurrence and the intensity of these phenomena. The greatest single aid is the morning tephigram. Day-to-day changes in the temperature profiles are often quite subtle but with experience it becomes possible to estimate the likelihood of deep convection by applying the conventional procedures for convection cloud forecasting. It is particularly important though, that coupled with the necessary unstable lapse rate there shall be adequate moisture both in the lower and middle levels. If the air aloft is dry, the rising cumulus turrets readily evaporate.

Inland, convection starts most readily over high ground and it is common in the afternoon to see the hills topped by massive cumulonimbus while bright, sunny weather prevails over the adjacent plains. There is often a tendency for these mountain-based cloud masses to spread out during the evening to bring showers and thunderstorms to the adjacent plains, these lasting into the first part of the night before the sky finally clears. Radiative cooling of the rain-moistened air may encourage the formation of early morning fog patches but these clear rapidly after sunrise.

Over the sea, the diurnal variation of temperature is small and convection may occur at any time of the day or night. In the equatorial regions, roughly within 10° of the equator, the lapse rate is usually near the saturated adiabatic and the moisture content of the air is high. Convection is also set off by other factors of which the principal one appears to be the convergence of winds at lower levels in association with either the ITCZ, or vestiges of cold fronts from higher latitudes. Near the coasts, especially on the seaward side, there is a marked tendency for convection cloud and precipitation to occur in the early morning and to disperse during the forenoon. These coastal build-ups are often associated with the undercutting of the moist, unstable sea air by the night-time land-breeze, for land- and sea-breeze effects are a prominent feature of the weather along tropical coasts. Outside the region affected by the ITCZ, i.e. in the trade wind belts, convection over the sea is limited; a shallow, moist, inversion-capped layer supports the typical fair-weather cumulus, but a dry layer above inhibits deeper convection.

(b) Orographic effects

Extensive cloud and rain are formed orographically in the tropics wherever a broad current of air, after flowing for a long distance over the warm oceans, strikes an elevated coastline or mountain range. Such broad airstreams are seasonal features of the tropical circulation and are either monsoon or trade winds. Details regarding the incidence of these winds are given below. Here it is sufficient to note that heavy and persistent rain, often with intense cumulonimbus cloud and thunderstorms, occurs when maritime air rises over coastal hills and mountains. Inland the effects tend to become gradually less pronounced as the air dries out, although cloud and rainfall may be accentuated at times by convection due to solar heating or to uplift over further high ground.

(c) Trade winds and monsoons

Trade winds are understood to be the steady winds which blow on the equatorial side of the subtropical high pressure regions in both hemispheres. In the southern hemisphere the trade wind is well defined at all seasons. It is for the most part a south-easterly current but divergences from this direction are evident in some localities in agreement with the distribution of pressure. Thus on the west African coast the wind is deflected to a south or south-westerly direction while in places on the opposite side of the Atlantic the flow becomes north-easterly; there are similar effects in the other oceans.

The trade wind of the northern hemisphere — the north-east trade — covers a wide stretch of the Pacific. In the northern winter it crosses the equator in the vicinity of the East Indies and extends, as the north-westerly summer monsoon, to the coast of Australia. In the Atlantic this trade wind extends from the coast of Morocco nearly to the equator in January but lies some 10 degrees further north in summer. The monsoon-type variation near the Gulf of Mexico turns the trade wind into a south-easterly current in summer, an effect similar to that over the western Pacific. In the Indian Ocean there is no north-east trade wind proper but only the winter monsoon wind from that direction.

The trade winds are remarkably steady and persistent, hence their name which derives from the expression 'to blow trade', meaning to blow constantly from one direction. Since they consist of air which has subsided in the subtropical high, an inversion with its base between 3000 ft and 8000 ft usually limits the cloud type to fair weather cumulus and stratocumulus. There are occasional disturbances however, in the form of weak belts of cloud and showers; moreover, cloudiness increases as the ITCZ is approached and as the length of the sea track increases — thus the western oceans are more cloudy than the eastern within the trade wind belt. Over mountainous country orographic ascent may result in copious rain. Thus the south-east trade brings rain all the year round to the eastern coasts of Madagascar and in summer to South Africa. The north-east trade is a rain bearing wind over the mountains of the West Indies and again over the Hawaiian Islands which, at 20 °N, are in the heart of the trade wind belt. Generally speaking, trade wind rain, when it occurs, is caused by a combination of orographic ascent and vertical instability set up by surface heating over the land. It is of a local showery character, often thundery, and falls mainly during the day.

The tendency in middle latitudes for high pressure to develop over the continents in winter and for low pressure in summer is reflected in persistent seasonal winds known as monsoons, a name which is derived from the Arabic for season. These winds are most developed over southern and eastern Asia, but also occur to a lesser degree in many other areas.

In winter the outflow from the Siberian anticyclone appears as a north-westerly wind across the Pacific coasts, north-easterly or northerly across southern China, Myanmar (Burma) and India, and continues across the Indian Ocean to meet the south-east trade south of the equator. Although it is a remarkably constant wind it is not entirely free from disturbances. Both central China and north-west India are affected by shallow winter depressions which cause breaks in the monsoon. The Siberian anticyclone begins to give way in March when continental temperatures are rising rapidly, but the south-west monsoon of India does not arrive until June. Over the western Pacific the direction of the summer monsoon is southerly or south-easterly.

The winter monsoon of Asia is a cool or cold wind with dry weather predominating except where the wind has a long sea track. During the summer, moist equatorial air moves north and reaches India as the south-west monsoon. The reason for the sudden onset of the monsoon and the change in pattern of the upper winds is not fully known. Large changes occur in the high-level wind flow associated with the onset of the south-west monsoon. The axis of the subtropical westerly jet stream shifts quite suddenly from south to north of the Himalayas in early June and the high-level easterly winds spread north across India during May and June.

As the geostrophic wind relation does not apply in very low latitudes it is more convenient in the tropics to depict the wind flow direction by 'streamlines' and, where necessary, to show the wind speed by isotachs superimposed over the streamlines. Curvature of streamlines, apart from the normal cross-equator turning, may imply convergence or divergence, similarly the spiralling of streamlines into, or out from, a centre would imply upward or downward motion respectively. Thus where such changes to the trade wind flow occur in the equatorial trough they influence the weather.

(d) ITCZ

A widely accepted convention in meteorological analysis is that the ITCZ exists where the trade wind streams meet, both at the earth's surface and aloft, and that it is replaced by the northern and southern shear lines where the trades are separated by a zone of equatorial westerly winds. As can be seen from Fig. 109, trade winds are generally confluent into the ITCZ regions but occasionally winds with a westerly component separate the shear lines. Cyclonic circulations, as shown, may form on the shear lines; it can be seen that wind directions on the shear lines are either north or south. It is assumed, here, that the ITCZ is near the equator and the circulations around the depressions are drawn in the sense appropriate to the particular hemisphere.

The ITCZ is convergent where air moves into the zone more quickly than it moves away (horizontally) and hence some air must ascend. Where there is

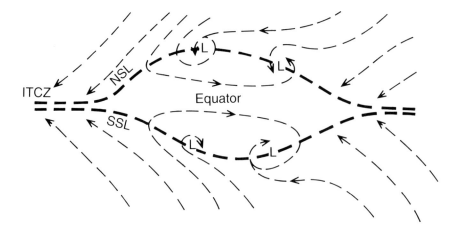

Figure 109. Bifurcation of the ITCZ to form northern and southern shear lines (NSL and SSL) separating regions of equatorial westerlies. Broken lines represent surface streamlines.

downstream acceleration (divergence) descending motion occurs to make good the deficit of horizontal inflow.

The convergent parts of the ITCZ and the cyclonic circulations centred on the shear lines are, of course, features of the equatorial trough of the general circulation model. The shear lines and the ITCZ, when actively convergent with strong upward motion are zones or belts of cloud, frequently including cumulonimbus, heavy rain, thunderstorms and squalls, but where subsidence is involved they are often marked by little more than scraps of low cloud.

The width of the belt of disturbed weather varies according to the scale of the convergence; observations have shown that the width may range from about 40 to 500 km. Outside the clouds, visibility is good except in heavy rain where it may be reduced to a few metres. The cloud base is usually 1000 ft or more above the sea but it may descend practically to the surface in heavy rain. The surface wind in the vicinity of the line of disturbance is squally, often reaching force 5 while squalls of force 8 or 9 are occasionally reported.

On occasions of vigorous development, some large rain areas occur and thick masses of nimbostratus and altostratus with embedded cumulonimbus are found, with violent turbulence within the clouds. Usually, however, conditions are somewhat patchy and there are areas of lighter rain and broken cloud.

The height of the cloud tops in the vicinity of the lines of disturbance varies considerably. On many occasions the belt of cloud may be flown over without difficulty at 20 000 ft but on occasions of active development, cloud should be anticipated well above that level, even up to or just above the tropopause, which is in the neighbourhood of 55 000 ft in tropical regions. The spreading out of the cloud tops into extensive sheets of cirrus occasionally conceals the cumulonimbus turrets with their severe turbulence; at other times the cirrus sheets may persist long after the convective cloud has dispersed. Ice accretion in active areas is liable to be serious in convective cloud at temperatures from 0 °C to −40 °C or even lower. The corresponding heights at which these temperatures are found in equatorial regions are about 16 000 ft and 35 000 ft respectively but are higher by about 2000 ft over southern Asia during the northern summer.

(e) Tropical cyclones
See Section 17.6

PART IV

GENERAL CIRCULATION AND WORLD CLIMATE

CHAPTER 20

GENERAL CIRCULATION AND
WORLD CLIMATE

20.1 CLIMATOLOGY AND THE AVIATOR

The climate of a locality may be described as the synthesis of the day-to-day values of the meteorological elements that affect the locality; its study is called climatology. By amassing and analysing meteorological statistics for a particular place the climatologist aims to identify and quantify those factors which succinctly summarize the weather at that place and so to permit comparisons to be made with other places. It then becomes feasible to subdivide the surface of the earth into zones which share particular climatological characteristics: such a simple classification is attempted in Section 20.3.

Such knowledge is of general interest to any traveller and it should be of particular interest to those who have a commercial interest in travel. To the pilot and navigator a general background knowledge of the weather peculiarities of distant localities can only be helpful in supplementing the flight forecast. In Section 20.4 we examine, very briefly, some characteristic features of a few typical areas.

The aviation route-planner must depend upon climatological data and this will be presented in some statistical format. As with any statistical data, there are possible pitfalls: statistics will yield the right answer only if the user has some understanding of their basis. In the final section of this chapter we offer some guidelines to the interpretation of meteorological statistics which, it is hoped, will be a safeguard against at least some of the pitfalls.

First though, it is useful to consider what sort of climatological framework we would expect. Throughout this book we have adopted the premise that atmospheric behaviour is determined by physical and dynamical laws; if that is truly the case then it should be possible to predict the patterns of pressure and air motion which will provide the basis for the global climatic variations. We look at this aspect next.

20.2 THE GENERAL CIRCULATION

An idealized model
We use the term 'general circulation' to refer to the global flow pattern which results from those atmospheric temperature and pressure gradients which are generated by the unequal distribution of solar radiation received at the earth's surface.

The observed atmospheric circulation is so complex, with wide variations both in time and in space, that before looking at the actual patterns it is perhaps better to consider a grossly simplified model; an earth-sized planet, with a uniform surface, orbiting the sun as the real earth does, but not rotating.

On such a body the atmosphere would circulate in response to latitudinal differences in the heat generated from the incoming solar radiation. Solar radiation would be greatest at the equator and a minimum at the poles (cf. Section 3). Air would rise above the equatorial heat source; since pressure decreases less rapidly with height in a warmer air column, pressure would be greater at high level above the equator than in other latitudes and a horizontal pressure gradient would be established leading to a high-level poleward flow. Continuity would be satisfied by descent at the poles and a compensating low-level flow from the polar (high pressure) regions towards the equatorial (low pressure) heat source.

Such a simple, gigantic, hemispherical circulation cell is not observed because, in the first place, the real earth is rotating. Once we introduce rotation we need to take account of the Coriolis effect. Because of rotation, poleward moving air is deflected towards the east and we find that instead of continuing to the poles, the high-level branches of the circulation reach only about latitude 30° before the air cools and begins to subside. Thus, in each hemisphere on our hypothetical model we find a simple thermal circulation, which is known as the Hadley cell, between the equator and about latitude 30°. At the surface, belts of high pressure mark the poleward limits of the Hadley cells, and winds with an easterly component, the trade winds, blow from these subtropical high pressures towards the equatorial trough. The conjectured polar high-pressure areas can no longer be thought of as fed by lifted air which has travelled from the equator, but their retention is physically plausible since the polar air is the coldest, and hence densest, in contact with the surface of our model planet, and high pressure must result, with a consequent equatorward flow of surface air from these polar highs. In mid-latitudes then, between the subtropical highs and the polar highs, we find a broad zone of lower pressure in which surface outflows from the high pressure areas converge, equatorward flow from the polar highs being deflected towards the west and the poleward flow from the subtropical highs towards the east. To maintain continuity there must be ascent within this region and divergence aloft both polewards and equatorwards. These longitudinal (or meridional) components of the flow are, in fact, quite small and the dominant flow between the subtropical highs and about 60° N is towards the east, hence this region is usually referred to as the region of mid-latitude, or Ferrel, westerlies.

In summary, we have described an atmosphere in which the flow in each hemisphere may be represented by three distinct but collaborative cells, the Hadley cell in low latitudes, the Ferrel cell in mid-latitudes and a polar cell polewards of about 60° latitude. The cross-section in Fig. 110 represents these main components schematically.

As yet, we have said nothing about any axial tilt of our rotating planet; if the axis is perpendicular to the orbit around the sun, then the circulation pattern will remain unchanged through the year: there will be no seasons. Once we postulate that the axis is not perpendicular to the orbital plane, then we introduce the concept of seasons with the implication of latitudinal movements of the cells and the related surface pressure systems. The tilt (or 'obliquity of the ecliptic') of the real earth is about 23° 27' and if we were to retain our fiction of a uniform surface we would thus expect the equatorial low-pressure belt or 'meteorological equator' to migrate between the tropic of Capricorn at the December solstice and the tropic of Cancer at the June solstice.

The reality
The observed distributions of average sea level pressure and prevailing surface wind for the months of January and July are shown in Figs. 111 to 114. It will

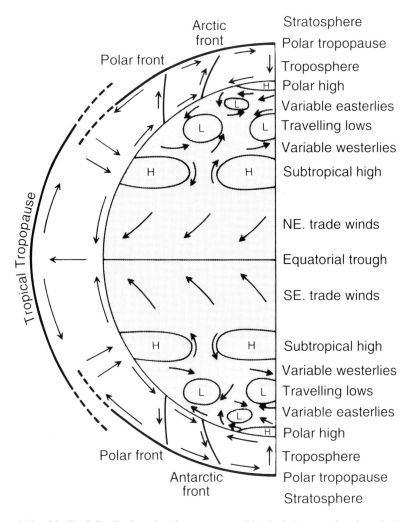

Figure 110. Idealized distribution of surface pressure which includes a section through the troposphere with idealized circulation and fronts in the vertical. Vertical scale grossly exaggerated.

immediately be recognized that, although there is some resemblance to the idealized model explored above, there are many differences too; some of them are of major importance. The one major factor which was ignored in the model is the non-uniformity of the earth's surface. The unequal distribution of continent and ocean is of supreme importance but other factors include the varying nature of the land surface: its relief: its thermal conductivity: its radiative capacity, as well as the depth and other properties of the oceans whose behaviour interacts so intimately with that of the atmosphere. It is to be noted that these factors, and others, have been built into modern numerical models of the atmosphere and the increasing realism attained as each feature is successfully modelled is convincing proof that we could have extended the physical reasoning to have included them, at least

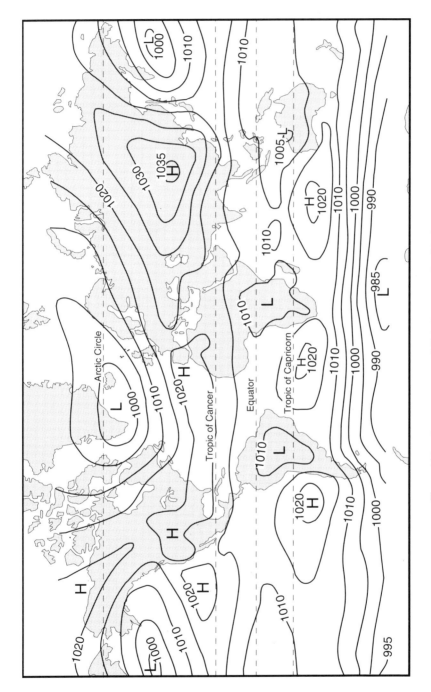

Figure 111.   Average pressure (hPa) at mean sea level in January.

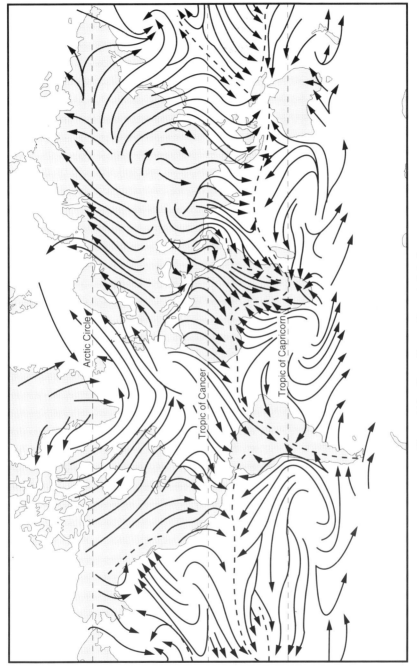

Figure 112.   Prevailing surface winds in January.

313

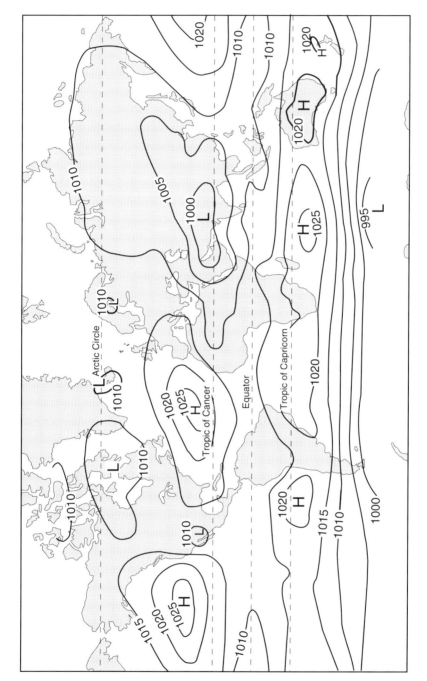

Figure 113.   Average pressure (hPa) at mean sea level in July.

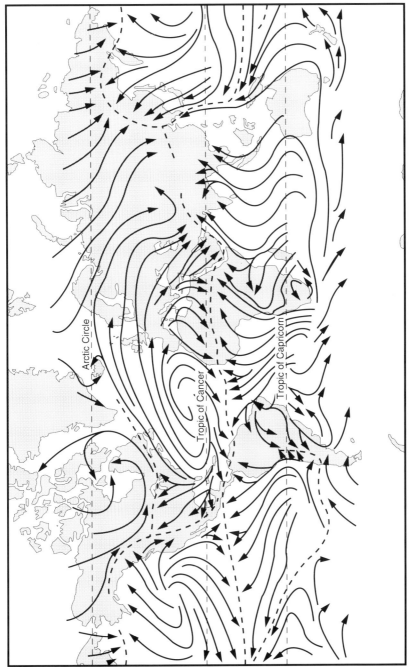

Figure 114.   Prevailing surface winds in July.

qualitatively, in our model. The development of ever more-realistic global climate models (GCMs) has become a major avenue of study in the 1990s following the increased concern about global warming.

The tropics. The model's subtropical high-pressure belts are clearly supported by the observed major anticyclones in both hemispheres at both seasons though the belts tend to be interrupted by relatively lower pressures over land in the summer season. This is seen even over the narrow southern continents but is most strikingly marked over Asia which is dominated by low-pressure at this season. From the model it was expected that the equatorial low pressure belt would migrate north and south as part of the global seasonal changes. This process is observed but with some complications. In January, the ITCZ is driven far south of the equator over Africa and over South America; these irregularities occur as a result of the extension of the north-east trades flowing into areas of low pressure over the strongly heated land masses. Strong heating over Australia results in a large low pressure system there too and there is a consequent south-eastwards surge of equatorial north-westerlies, extensions of the north-east trades which back on crossing the geographical equator. In July the ITCZ is mostly positioned as would be expected with the northward displacement of the equatorial trough most marked over the land masses and particularly so over China due to a surge of south-south-westerlies into the summer heat low there.

The westerlies. The figures generally confirm the model idea of low pressures at about latitude 60°, especially in the southern hemisphere which is predominantly ocean, but a most important exception is the large Asiatic anticyclone of January. This is a consequence of the protracted cooling of a large land mass during the winter months; a less obvious anticyclone extending northwards from the subtropical high occurs over North America. In July, prolonged heating in these same continental regions produces low pressure areas. The low centre and confluent winds over western North America are of special interest as they demonstrate not only the effect of strong insolation and mass heat storage in continental interiors but also the marked lee-trough effect produced by the Rocky Mountains, the only major north–south oriented mountain range in the hemisphere. A similar but less obvious feature is associated with the Andes in January.

It is important to realize that to obtain these 'mean' maps it is necessary to time-average observations over a number of years: typically 30 years or more. Whereas over many parts of the tropics it will be found that the situation on any particular day may bear a close resemblance to these long-term mean distributions, it is a very different story in higher latitudes. In the zone of the mid-latitude westerlies the situation will differ markedly from the mean on most occasions since the averaging process almost completely masks the existence of the travelling depressions and anticyclones which are so much a feature of these latitudes. Polewards of the subtropical high-pressure belt the meridional exchanges of air shown in the cross section of Fig. 110 are small net residuals; on a particular occasion there may be massive poleward advection of air in one or more parts of the hemisphere and compensating equatorward flow at others. Such large-scale motions belong to a series of 'long waves' or 'Rossby waves' which girdle each hemisphere in the middle and high troposphere in mid-latitudes; laboratory experiments confirm that such undulations are inherent features of any rotating fluid system which has a thermal gradient applied to it. Typically, Rossby waves have a wavelength of some

5000 km, so that four or five waves will stretch around the hemisphere. Their amplitude varies greatly: sometimes just a few degrees of latitude: more typically about 20 degrees: sometimes much more. It is these waves which are a common feature of upper-air contour charts (cf. Section 19.3); the development and movement of the travelling surface depressions and anticyclones is intimately associated with them. It is ascent at the polar and arctic fronts in the vicinity of these depressions that completes the cellular circulation envisaged in Fig. 110.

The polar regions.   Maps similar to Figs. 111 to 114 but on a circumpolar projection do, indeed, confirm that small anticyclones occur at the poles, as would be expected from the idealized model. The Antarctic high is a permanent feature, evident on daily charts throughout the year, but the high cell over the North Pole is a more transient feature: travelling depressions pass over the pole from time to time.

20.3 CLIMATIC ZONES

The classification of climates is a topic which has received a great deal of attention and there are many different schemes, varying widely in their complexity and objective. The more complex are often concerned with natural vegetation or with land use; for aviation purposes a much simpler classification will suffice.

Equatorial zone
Sometimes called 'humid tropical', this zone extends about 10° either side of the equator; rather less over the oceans where it is also known as the 'doldrums'. Winds are usually light, temperature and humidity are high. The diurnal range of temperature (difference between day maximum and night minimum) usually exceeds the modest annual range (difference between average temperatures of hottest and coolest months). There is no dry season but two wetter-than-average periods may be associated with the passage of the sun north and south of the equator. Rain falls mostly as showers or thunderstorms; the annual total varies much according to relief.

Savannah
A zone in each hemisphere extending between the equatorial belt and the tropics. In these zones there is a well marked alternation of dry and wet seasons, the latter associated with the passage of the overhead sun. Thus there may be two rainy maxima at the equatorward edge of the zones but these merge into a single rainy period further away from the equator. The amount and duration of rainfall both diminish with increasing latitude. Dry, trade wind conditions are characteristic of the winter. Temperatures remain fairly high throughout the year but both annual and diurnal temperature ranges increase with increasing latitude.

Arid subtropical zone
Zones extending polewards of the savannah to about 30° and including most of the earth's great hot deserts: the Sahara, Arabian, Arizona, Kalahari as well as those of Australia and South America. These are regions of subsiding air, often cloudless, very hot in summer, with large diurnal and annual temperature ranges. The winds are the trade winds, noted for their constancy. Rainfall is rare in the interior but

there may be short rainy seasons in the bordering areas of steppe. At the low-latitude boundary where this zone abuts the savannah, any rain will be confined to summer; near the poleward boundary any rain will occur in winter.

Warm temperate (transitional) zone
Also known as 'Mediterranean' type and typified by the area bordering that Sea, the type is also found in parts of California, central Chile, the extreme south of South Africa, and parts of southern Australia. It is a zone which comes within the arid subtropical regime in summer, but in winter, due to the equatorward shift of the subtropical high-pressure belt, experiences the cool, unsettled weather of the cool temperate zone. Summers are therefore dry and hot, whilst the winters may be wet and cool.

Cool temperate zone
These are the zones of the mobile westerlies: regions in which the weather is determined by the passage of frontal depressions and intervening cold anticyclones or ridges. There is no dry season and the winters can be cold, especially at locations well away from the benefits of a wind flow from the oceans. Winds are predominantly westerly and gales are frequent.

Boreal zone
This is a zone which occurs only in the northern hemisphere: it is well developed only over northern North America, Scandinavia and the former USSR. It is characterized by cool and moist summers and very cold winters. The large annual range of temperature is the dominant feature of this type.

Polar zones
Polewards of the Arctic and Antarctic Circles, the effects of season are extreme. In summer there may be three months with more than 20 hours of sunshine per day, whilst in winter there may be three months with 20 hours of darkness per day. Where the mean temperature of the warmest months rises above freezing-point some tundra vegetation is possible; i.e. mosses, lichens and grasses; elsewhere the surface is continuously under snow or ice and the ground permanently frozen.

Monsoon climate
On the eastern continental margins, the arid subtropical desert and Mediterranean types are replaced by areas of monsoon climate. The term derives from the Arabic word for season and was originally used to describe the winds of the Arabian Sea which blow for half the year from the north-east and for the other half from the south-west. The term is now used with reference to other markedly seasonal reversals of wind direction. The essential cause of these major wind changes is the differential heating of large land and sea masses, altering with season. Monsoon conditions are best exemplified over east and south-east Asia, and especially over the Indian sub-continent where the onset of the south-west monsoon of summer heralds the rainy season and the north-east monsoon of winter returns dry weather to most parts. In these areas the expression 'the monsoon' has come to be popularly used to denote the rains, without specific reference to the winds.

Monsoon conditions also occur, but to a lesser degree, in northern Australia, parts of western, southern and eastern Africa, and parts of North America and Chile.

20.4 THE CLIMATOLOGY OF SOME AIR ROUTES

The notes which follow deal briefly with the average seasonal weather characteristics of some regions of special importance to aviators but they do not constitute a treatise on route climatology; rather they should be regarded as brief cameos, highlighting just some of the more striking features; in the treatment of the different regions there is no attempt at even-handedness. Readers in the United Kingdom wishing to undertake an in-depth study of the climatology of any particular route or region are advised to consult the staff at the National Meteorological Library at Bracknell. Readers in other parts of the world may usually obtain similar assistance from the appropriate National Meteorological Service.

North polar regions

Within the Arctic Circle there are place to place and year to year variations which limit the usefulness of generalizations. Winters last five or six months but summer only about three months and changes are rapid during the short transitional seasons. A period of continuous darkness is centred around the winter solstice and one of continuous daylight around the summer solstice.

Synoptic situations. In winter, cyclonic activity is at its lowest, both arctic and polar fronts being far from the pole. Anticyclones are persistent. Depressions move north-eastwards into the Arctic Ocean in an almost continuous series between Greenland and Norway but east of Novaya Zemlya they stagnate and fill. Other small depressions form on the arctic front near the New Siberian Islands whence they move eastwards but generally they fill up before reaching Alaska. During summer, depressions reach most parts of the Arctic, especially the area from Iceland to Novaya Zemlya.

Temperature. In winter the sea in high latitudes is permanently frozen. Surrounding this ice there is a variable field of drift or pack ice. Air temperatures over the ice fields are near 0 °C even in summer; elsewhere the summer is mild and even warm over land. Inland, the variation of temperature from summer to winter can be considerable.

In winter the arctic troposphere is, on the whole, considerably colder than that of the ICAO standard atmosphere (ISA) and stratospheric temperatures are also somewhat colder than standard. In summer mean tropospheric temperatures are close to ISA but stratospheric temperatures are usually higher.

Snow. The main period for snow is from November to April but in the far north it may occur at any season and near the poles practically all precipitation falls as snow. Thunderstorms and hail are almost unknown except far from the pole where they are infrequent summer phenomena.

Cloud. With the exception of most of the Greenland, Norwegian, Barents and Kara Seas, conditions are usually much more cloudy in summer than in winter, when clear skies often prevail. Seasonal variation is well marked in the north and over the pack ice; the frequency of clear days is also quite high there during winter. In the north region and over pack ice, overcast days are frequent in summer when low stratus cloud is extensive. Most of the sea areas are always cloudy or overcast. During bad weather the cloud base is near the surface and tops frequently exceed 18 000 ft.

Visibility.   In the absence of fog and precipitation, visibility is usually exceptionally good. However, even a moderate wind reduces visibility drastically in blowing and/or falling snow giving rise to blizzard conditions. Advection fog is common; radiation fog is confined to inland Alaska, Canada and Siberia. Over the open sea, over pack ice and in coastal districts, fog is infrequent in winter but is very common in summer, occurring on average on one day in two. Inland, the occurrence of summer fogs is rare. Radiation fog is most frequent inland in autumn and winter but over open sea, pack ice and coasts it is much less frequent at this season than in summer. Ice fog is peculiar to the Arctic. It occurs mainly over land areas but sometimes over the pack ice also. It is usually shallow with good vertical visibility but horizontal visibilities can be very poor. Disturbance by aircraft and ground vehicles has been known to cause ice fog to form on aerodromes.

Ice accretion on aircraft.   This appears to be less of a problem in the Arctic than in temperate latitudes. Clear ice, although infrequent, is most likely in cloud over mountain ranges. Rain ice may also be encountered; in the north this is likely to be very infrequent and confined to summer. In the south its frequency may be greater, especially over land, but it is probable only in winter. Rime is common. Severe icing is not often reported. Once icing has occurred it can persist long after the aircraft has left the icing region.

North Atlantic

This region is concerned, in the most part, with the disturbed regime of the so-called temperate climatic zone; in the south it is the region of the subtropical high-pressure belt with a semi-permanent anticyclone positioned between Bermuda and the Azores.

Winter.   The outstanding feature is the prevalence of cyclonic activity. Most of the North American land mass is cold in winter and hence cold air from Canada is able to penetrate to quite low latitudes without much modification until, near the eastern seaboard of the USA, it comes into contact with warm, moist tropical air overlying the Gulf Stream between Florida and Bermuda. This well defined frontal zone represents the western end of the Atlantic polar front and is a fertile breeding ground for frontal depressions which stream away north-eastwards. The extent to which these depressions develop depends upon the precise shape of the upper air long wave pattern (cf. Fig. 107); if the pattern is favourable for development then the Grand Banks region near Newfoundland is commonly the site for the commencement of what is termed 'explosive deepening'. In this region the strong temperature contrast between the waters of the Gulf Stream and those of the cold Labrador current serves to amplify the thermal contrast which already exists across the polar front and favours vigorous development. It is explosive deepeners of this type (sometimes referred to as 'bombs' if the central pressure falls by 24 hPa or more in 24 hours) that account for some of the more stormy interludes experienced over north-west Europe and the eastern Atlantic; the storms of early 1990 over the British Isles were of this type. Only a few frontal lows deepen as dramatically as this but most deepen to some extent as they transfer north-eastwards towards high northern latitudes, many of them ending up as old, occluded systems slow-moving between southern Greenland and Norway. It is because so many lows end up in this area, or pass through it *en route* to the Arctic Ocean, that this is an area of low mean pressure — the so-called Icelandic low — on the mean pressure maps of Figs 111 and 113. While these frontal lows on the whole move towards the north-east, individual paths may deviate considerably, though nearly always with a component towards the east. Their speed of movement also varies greatly; 25–30 KT is fairly typical but speeds in excess of 60 KT are not unknown. Depressions also form on the arctic front, on secondary fronts over North America or in the polar air of northern waters.

Far to the south, mean pressure is at a maximum in the subtropical belt at about 30° N. This high undergoes some variation in both its position and intensity and is occasionally displaced by lows. At other times the subtropical high may link with North American highs or across Europe to the Asiatic high. The travelling depressions usually alternate with ridges of high pressure but discrete highs form from time to time in the polar air mass. Many of these are mobile systems but occasionally, when the Rossby wave pattern amplifies markedly, slow-moving 'blocking' highs may become established to persist as dominant features for a period of a week or two; in these circumstances the polar front becomes displaced either to higher latitudes or persists as a weak train of frontal wave depressions steered towards Mediterranean latitudes.

Cloud. Total cloud cover averages about 6 oktas over much of the area. Frontal cloud systems are horizontally extensive and commonly extend from near the surface to 20 000 ft, sometimes to over 30 000 ft. Convective clouds of polar air masses are normally well separated except where convergence occurs into a trough or polar low. Extensive sheets of stratocumulus are common in tropical air masses. Anticyclones are usually cloudless in their middle and upper levels but stratocumulus is often present over sea and coastal areas, trapped beneath the subsidence inversion.

Precipitation. Warm-front precipitation is often widespread but cold-frontal belts tend to be narrower. Elsewhere, precipitation is generally of a showery type. To the north and north-west of the North Atlantic there is often snow down to the surface and snow showers are common in polar airstreams; snow may also be encountered in low-level flight through frontal zones.

Ice accretion. This occurs widely and through great depths in both frontal and convective clouds; it is frequently of moderate or severe intensity. It may also occur when an aircraft has descended rapidly and flies through rain or freezing rain at low level.

Visibility. Sea fog is widespread in warm-sector south-westerlies. Visibility may be poor over large areas in frontal rain and drizzle. In fresh polar air, visibility is very good outside of showers. Fog is particularly a feature of the Newfoundland Grand Banks area, where air warmed by its track over the Gulf Stream passes over the ice-cooled waters of the Labrador current; it often encroaches over adjacent coasts.

Summer. Cyclonic activity is, on the whole, less frequent and less intense at this season. The polar front is weaker and positioned further north: in the mean it extends from about Labrador to the north of Scotland. Polar air masses are less cold and hence less unstable to sea surface temperatures than is the case in winter, therefore convection cloud, showers and squalls are less common. South-westerly airstreams contain abundant stratiform cloud and average cloud amounts in such currents differ little from those of the winter. In tropical air advection fog is common and may be extensive; the western approaches to the British Isles are often affected, spring and early summer being the most vulnerable times. Although the height of the 0 °C isothermal surface is greater than in winter ice accretion remains an important problem.

Central Atlantic, West Africa, West Indies and South America

The weather over the open ocean is generally fine but westward-moving tropical systems cross this area in the (northern hemisphere) late summer and autumn; in an average year it may be possible to identify as many as 100 potential hurricane 'seedlings' amid the cloud clusters of the trade wind belt but only about 10 survive to become named tropical storms or fully fledged hurricanes. A hurricane may be up to 1500 km across and usually comprises a roughly circular, multiple canopy of high- and medium-level clouds with numerous huge embedded cumulonimbus. The hurricane centre is marked by a cloudless 'eye' in which the wind is calm. Zones of active convective weather extend outwards from the centre curving away in the upwind direction. Severe ice accretion and turbulence should be expected. In tropical depressions and tropical storms there is no eye and the associated weather phenomena are less intense. Most of these North Atlantic tropical cyclones appear to originate within the trade wind belt but a few may arise from belts of disturbed weather associated with easterly (i.e. westward-moving) waves in the ITCZ.

Off north-west Africa, the cool Canaries current flows towards the equator. Upwelling of cold subsurface water near the coast chills the air above and this extra cooling favours the formation of fog for some distance offshore. This fog can drift inland when there is an onshore wind.

The harmattan is a dry wind which blows over north-west Africa associated with the north-east trade. Over the Sahara it is a pronounced feature from November to April, the dry season in those latitudes. The duration of the harmattan period decreases southwards, the Guinea coast being affected only occasionally during temporary recessions of the south-west monsoon. The harmattan is dust-laden, often reducing visibility below 4000 m and, at times, even below 1000 m. The dust often reaches great heights and is found aloft where the trades overrun the lower-level monsoon air. In these circumstances visibility aloft may be seriously impaired at a time when surface visibility remains good.

In the West Indies the easterly trade winds blow throughout the year. Land- and sea-breezes occur on most days. In air moistened during a prolonged sea track, orographic cloud forms readily and windward slopes have rain in all months. In summer the rainfall is accentuated by convection and is then more evenly distributed. Hurricanes average about three per season, the majority between August and October. They move west or north-west; although some continue into Mexico and the southern States of the USA, most curve across the islands or Florida and pass into the North Atlantic.

The north and east coasts of South America as far as about 30° S have onshore winds throughout the year. These are the north-east and south-east trades. The ITCZ is rarely, if ever, bifurcated by equatorial westerlies in these longitudes. As the ocean currents off the whole coast are warm, fog and low cloud are not a characteristic. North of the equator the winter months are mostly dry and the summer wet. The Amazon basin has heavy rainfall with frequent thunderstorms although the southern winter and spring are somewhat drier in the lower basin. From the equator to 20° S there is abundant rainfall in the summer and autumn but little in winter and spring. The coastal strip from Bahia to Natal is exceptional, however, in having a marked winter (July) rainfall maximum even though there is little rain inland at that time. South of 20° S there is rain in all seasons from the trailing cold fronts of higher-latitude depressions. Northern Argentina experiences the *pampero*, a dusty, polar (southerly) wind which sets in with violent line-squalls. Southern Argentina is within the region affected by the travelling depressions but as their rain-bearing westerlies have to cross the Andes, where they shed abundant moisture, precipitation is light throughout the year. Cloud amounts are small and strong, dry, turbulent westerly winds are characteristic.

Western and central Europe
Frontal depressions and anticyclones alternate, sometimes rapidly, but at other times one major system will predominate for days at a time. The Alps constitute a major barrier to frontal movements; cold fronts are often delayed and broad belts of frontal/orographic cloud and precipitation may persist across France and southern Germany to Poland. Active secondary depressions frequently develop on these fronts, tending to run east-north-east or north-east along them until eventually one of these circulations drives the front south into the western Mediterranean. In summer, a combination of strong heating and a supply of moist unstable air sometimes results in the development of a large depression, typically over Bavaria, characterized by belts of thick cloud and thunderstorms separating areas of clear sky. In winter and spring, depressions tend to form between the Alps and middle Danube, the supply of warm, moist air being drawn from the central and eastern Mediterranean. Associated warm fronts give extensive low cloud over Germany and Poland and this sometimes extends across the Low Countries to eastern England. Precipitation is widespread and may reach the ground as snow in winter.

High-pressure systems give dry but often hazy conditions (due to smoke trapped beneath the temperature inversion) in summer and extensive stratocumulus sheets, often with peripheral drizzle, in winter.

Rainfall occurs at all seasons, being mostly cyclonic in origin in winter and convective in summer. Total amounts decrease from west to east across Europe although there is much orographic modulation of rainfall. Fogs and very low cloud are common in the cooler months whilst summer fogs are usually coastal or from urban smoke. Airframe icing is common at all levels in winter. The icing conditions are aggravated in convective cloud by widespread forced ascent over mountains.

Mediterranean
In winter, because the sea is warmer than the surrounding land, the Mediterranean is an area of relatively low pressure. Polar and tropical air masses enter the basin and frontal depressions form there. Lee depressions, formed by the diversion of airflow over and around mountains, are associated with the outbreaks of cold northerlies which follow European cold fronts, and are frequently vigorous. Large lee depressions form to the south-east of the Atlas Mountains and move north-eastwards into the Mediterranean during the cool season. Warm air masses, from Africa, are dry, hence warm fronts and warm sectors are inactive. The most vigorous bad weather occurs as a result of violent convection as polar air currents

cross the warm water. Summer is the dry season, but isolated summer thunderstorms do occur when overrunning of cooler air aloft is abetted by local convergence, as at sea-breeze fronts for instance. Visibility is excellent in winter, except in precipitation, but it is reduced by dust in summer.

Some local winds and weather. The *mistral* is a strong and sometimes violent northerly wind centred on the Rhône valley; its effect is to pour cold air into the Gulf of Lions. When it occurs there is often a depression over the Gulf of Genoa. Mistral conditions are turbulent and any low cloud is usually concentrated in the zone of the cold front which precedes the mistral and on any cold troughs which may form subsequently. The mistral is usually a cold season wind and it is enhanced by cold, downslope, katabatic winds which occur late in the night.

The *bora* is a cold, squally, and often very dry, downslope northerly of the eastern Adriatic; it can reach 70 KT with gusts exceeding 100 KT at Trieste. It is strongest and most frequent in winter and occurs when pressure is high over central Europe and the Balkans and low over the Mediterranean

The *sirocco* (or scirocco — pronounced 'shirocco') is a hot, dry, dust-laden southerly wind of the central Mediterranean. Other regional names for this wind include *chili* (Tunisia), *ghibli* (Libya) and *khamsin* (Egypt). Such winds occur ahead of eastward-moving desert depressions which are a typical feature of the transitional seasons, especially March to May. The air is very hot and dry and often produces sandstorms over the North African coastal strip but it is rapidly stabilized and moistened as it crosses the cooler sea and may give sea fog, low stratus and even drizzle when it reaches more northern waters.

Egypt to South Africa

In the northern winter a ridge of high pressure extends from the Azores anticyclone across north Africa to Egypt. Although the Mediterranean coast has a significant rainfall, there is little at Cairo and the belt from Cairo to about 6° N is almost rainless and usually cloudless. The prevailing surface winds are mostly northerlies and the air is often dust-laden. In July the ITCZ reaches its northern limit at nearly 20° N and is associated with severe duststorms (haboobs) which are frequent over Sudan at this season. The tropical rain belt extends from the equator to near Khartoum (16° N), where summer rainfall averages about 150 mm, but other seasons are entirely dry. Ethiopia also has a wet summer, the higher parts having very heavy falls with much thunder; at other times the country is mostly dry. Kenya, straddling the equator, has two wet seasons (March to May and November to December) associated with the transit of the ITCZ; intervening months are not entirely dry. In the southern summer the north to north-east winds of north Africa extend far south of the equator in association with the southward displacement of the ITCZ which in January lies across Zimbabwe. Thus, Tanzania, Malawi and Zimbabwe have most of their rain in the southern summer (November to April). There is much convection in the rain areas and thunderstorms are frequent. The central plains of Zimbabwe and occasionally the Transvaal are affected by the *guti*; moderate to strong south-easterly winds with very low stratiform cloud from the Mozambique Channel. The guti lasts for one to five days and occurs often in the dry season from April onwards. The Mozambique Channel is very occasionally influenced by tropical cyclones which originate east of the Seychelles between about 5° and 15° S; these usually travel south-west and then recurve to the south-east, seldom reaching the Seychelles but frequently affecting Madagascar, Mozambique, the Comoro Islands, Reunion and Mauritius. They are liable to occur from November to May and are most frequent from January to April.

Arabian peninsula and Gulf

In summer this area is almost entirely rainless and very hot. The interior is extremely dry but coastal areas can become oppressively humid wherever onshore breezes occur: one such area is the Arabian Gulf where persistent north-westerlies (the *shamal*) although starting off as very dry, dust-laden winds over Iraq, pick up much moisture during the long trajectory along the length of the Gulf before arriving at the north-west facing coasts. An exception to the overall summer cloudlessness occurs in the far south of the peninsula; in midsummer the ITCZ reaches Oman bringing extensive low cloud and drizzle to coastal areas exposed to the monsoon south-westerlies.

In winter, eastward moving depressions from the Mediterranean cross the northern parts of the peninsula and associated cold fronts and troughs may push far south to bring a little rain to the interior. Over higher ground north of about 25° N snow is not uncommon in the mid-winter months. Widespread duststorms may occur in southerly airstreams ahead of travelling depressions and violent but short-lived duststorms may accompany the passage of cold fronts.

Arabian Gulf to the Indian subcontinent

The dry north-east monsoon prevails from December to February with fine weather only occasionally interrupted by the arrival of shallow depressions or troughs from the north-west. In the transitional season from March to mid-June the weather is mainly hot, dry and dusty; some weak lows still reach northern India from the west at this time, these 'nor-westers' bringing severe squalls and duststorms to Bengal.

As the land mass warms, pressure begins to fall over Pakistan and north-west India. Air from the Arabian Sea is drawn inland in response to the pressure gradient, first in low latitudes and then progressively further north. The onset of the south-west monsoon at any place is a sudden event. Paradoxically it occurs in the south-east first, its average date of onset over the Andaman Islands being about 20 May and over Bombay at about 6 June. The monsoon air is very moist and is convectively unstable and thus heavy orographic and convectional rains become widespread. Severe turbulence occurs in these cloud systems. The monsoon and its weather just reach the coast of Baluchistan.

Tropical cyclones form over the Arabian Sea and more especially over the Bay of Bengal during the advance and retreat of the south-west monsoon, i.e. May to July and September to December. Occasionally, tropical systems reach the Bay of Bengal from the South China Sea via the Gulf of Thailand, developing into cyclones as they move north-westwards. Storm surges associated with some of the more severe cyclones over the Bay of Bengal have caused widespread inundation of low-lying areas around the Ganges delta and south-east Bangladesh.

Bay of Bengal to Singapore

During the north-east monsoon the Bay of Bengal enjoys the protection of mountains and there is little cloud and good visibility, but it reaches Malaysia after a long passage across the warm South China Sea. Large cumulus and cumulonimbus clouds form and there are heavy or torrential showers and frequent thunderstorms. The west coast of the Malaysian peninsula is generally less wet, receiving some protection from the highlands.

During the south-west monsoon, as already mentioned, the Bay has its cloudy, wet season with the complication of cyclones. North of Sumatra the coast is exposed to the unmodified monsoon weather but further south there is a degree of shelter. The western side of the Malay peninsula is now cloudier than the east and experiences far more rain. Rainfall is enhanced orographically during both monsoons, being heaviest and most extensive when synoptic or mesoscale convergent systems are present. Convection being the major producer of cloud and rain there is marked diurnal variation with a maximum incidence over land in the afternoon and early evening and over the sea late in the night. Sea-breezes are strong and sea-breeze frontal phenomena contribute importantly. In the south-west monsoon cumulonimbus clouds form over Sumatra by day; when the easterly sea-breezes die on the east coast these clouds drift eastwards and begin to decay but they become rejuvenated by night-time convection over the warm waters of the Malacca Straits and by convergence between the monsoon and land-breeze flows, enhanced by katabatic flow, from Sumatra and Malaysia. When the southern shear-line is close to Singapore these convergent systems are fed by low-level southerly or south-easterly winds. Lines of violent thunderstorms (called 'Sumatras') sweep across Malaysia and Singapore late in the night or in the early forenoon.

The northern shear-line moves south across Malaysia, introducing the north-east monsoon to the whole peninsula by November. The south-west monsoon occurs after this shear-line has retreated northwards in the northern spring and until the southern shear line is driven northwards by the south-east trades in July and August. On some occasions the equatorial westerlies disappear altogether and the ITCZ affects the area.

Singapore to Java and northern Australia
The climate is rainy equatorial except near Darwin where there is little rain from May to September. In January the northern shear-line is near the equator and the north-west monsoon, moist and unstable after a long sea track, covers much of the area. In July, Australia is in the belt of subtropical high pressure. The south-east trades blow from the continent and the south Pacific driving the southern shear-line and south-west monsoon northwards. During the south-west monsoon there is much convective cloud over the islands, with frequent heavy showers and thunderstorms but as their topography is extremely varied there are often marked contrasts of climate between windward and leeward exposures. Land- and sea-breezes are regular features. The south-east trade air from Australia is dry and dust-laden and brings a period of haze and reduced rainfall to islands south of about 5° S. Generally the wettest periods at any place occur when the ITCZ is present and active or during the passage of an active shear-line. Tropical cyclones develop in or near the Timor Sea from January to March. They usually move south-westwards at first and, after recurving south-eastwards, pass into north-west Australia. They produce heavy or torrential rain and gales or severe gales.

Remaining parts of Australia
In the southern winter the subtropical high dominates Australian weather except in the 'Mediterranean' zones of the far south. With this exception the weather is

mostly dry with little cloud. Although the primary frontal lows of temperate latitudes mostly pass well to south of the continent their troughs and secondaries bring periods of disturbed weather to the south where there is also marked orographic enhancement of rainfall. The western coast of Australia is also exposed to mostly weak frontal systems moving east from the Indian Ocean; they do not produce much precipitation but often introduce spells of cloudy and windy weather.

In the spring the northern shear-line moves southwards and the north-west monsoon develops over northern Australia where it arrives wet and unstable. The southern shear-line reaches about 15–20° S in January.

Throughout the southern summer heavy rain showers fall in the north but falls are much less in the interior, some central parts being arid throughout the year. Fully developed cyclones are rare over the continent but there is much day to day variability of weather near the coasts.

Australia to New Zealand
The area lies within the zone of disturbed westerlies for most of the year but comes under the influence of the subtropical anticyclone in summer. Depressions frequently move south-eastwards between or to the south of Australia and New Zealand, resulting in changeable weather. The cold fronts of these systems are usually well-developed and are followed by cold anticyclonic cells with temporarily improved weather. In summer on average, about five anticyclone cells per month move eastwards in the zone of the subtropical high; the intervening troughs and cols bring brief periods of variable weather. Tropical cyclones form over the western Pacific south of the equator; some recurve south-eastwards near Australia, bringing heavy rain to the east coast and crossing New Zealand as very deep extratropical depressions. Periods of bad weather are usually not prolonged at any time of the year and flying conditions are, on the whole, good. Severe turbulence is often experienced in the lee of the New Zealand mountains.

Singapore to Japan
The area lies under the influence of the Asiatic monsoons with two brief transitional seasons. The northern shear-line and occasionally, when there are no equatorial westerlies, the ITCZ, lie across the area, well north of Singapore in summer. In winter the northern shear-line reaches about 200 km south of Singapore at maximum southward penetration.

Winter. The outflow from the Asiatic anticyclone is north-westerly in the north and north-easterly (the north-east monsoon) in the south. The monsoon becomes established gradually during September and October in successive bursts of cold air behind cold fronts. The air, of Siberian origin, is initially cold and dry, but is warmed and moistened as it passes over the sea to Japan and thence southwards and south-westwards to Singapore. In the north bad weather is mainly confined to cold fronts and post-frontal zones. The western slopes of the mountains of Japan experience especially bad post-frontal weather. From January to April long periods of low stratus cloud and drizzle with mist or fog (the *Crachin*) affect the coast from Shanghai to the southern tip of Cambodia; in southern China it penetrates well inland. Remnants of cold fronts, appearing as lines of shear separating a fast airstream from a slower one, occur in the north-easterlies over the South China Sea and may spawn a line of towering cumulus or mesoscale cyclonic circulations with clusters of towering clouds. The winter monsoon is generally overrun at about 7000 ft by a deep westerly current with little medium or high cloud above.

Summer. In May tropical air begins to advance northwards, heralded by cyclonic activity and the widespread rains of China and Japan, often called the 'Plum rains'. The summer (south-west) monsoon is usually well established over China and Japan in July and August. The weather is mostly hot and sultry with much convection cloud and many thunderstorms but there are also some small depressions which produce widespread rain from layered cloud. Some fog occurs over the cold current off the north-west coast of Japan. The monsoon flow may extend as high as 15 000 ft; it is usually overlain by easterlies in the south and by westerlies north of about 25° N. The seas off China and coastal areas from about 15° N northwards experience typhoons from May to November with the main season July to September. Most of these recurve, to pass over or near Japan but an occasional one penetrates to the Gulf of Thailand.

20.5 USING CLIMATOLOGICAL DATA

Averages — a cautionary tale

The study of climatology has much to do with averages — but not *just* with averages, for simple averages on their own can be very misleading. If the data are available it is also desirable to consider extreme values and the frequency of values within particular ranges. The frequency distribution of many meteorological elements will be close to what is termed a 'normal' or 'Gaussian' distribution; such a distribution is represented by a bell-shaped curve where the mean value is also the most frequently observed value as well as the middle value.

For most places, maximum temperature is likely be of this type and the quoted average maximum temperature can then be interpreted also as the most probable value and the median value; i.e. the value which will be exceeded on half the occasions. With a different element such an assumption could be quite misleading. For instance, cloud amount may sometimes be represented by a U-shaped frequency distribution in which there is a high frequency of cloudless occurrences and a high frequency of overcast occurrences but relatively few instances in between: in this case to speak of 'a mean cloudiness of four oktas' would convey quite the wrong impression.

There are particular problems too with vector quantities: wind for instance, which comprise two variables, direction and speed. The vector mean of a sequence of strong westerly winds followed by an equally long sequence of equally strong easterlies will be zero, which is hardly a satisfactory description of the wind regime.

The value of an average will be improved if it is accompanied by some measure of the variability of the quantities which are averaged. Some idea of temperature variability, for example, will be given if the observed extreme minimum and maximum values are quoted as well as the mean value, but an even better idea can be gained if some formal statistical measure of the variability is known. If the frequency distribution of the element approximates to a Gaussian distribution (as temperature usually does), then the standard deviation (SD) provides such a measure; two thirds of the observations would be expected to lie within ±1 SD of the mean and nearly all observations within ± 3 SD of the mean. In the case of vector quantities the vector mean becomes a more meaningful quantity if the vector standard deviation (VSD) is also known: this latter is examined later.

Site-specific climatological tables

The meteorological services of the United Kingdom and of the United States of America both publish collections of tables for airfields in many parts of the world; similar tables may be available from other national meteorological services. The types of information contained in these data sets are given below together with some suggestions for using them. More extensive information may be available for some airfields.

Air temperature

Temperature statistics are usually based upon data assembled over a period of 30 years or more and are quoted for each calendar month. Occasionally, but mostly in older publications, a single 'mean temperature' figure will be given: this may be the average of 24 hourly readings through each day or the average of the daily maxima and minima. In any case it should be used with caution: in March, both Timbuktu and Singapore have the same mean temperature of 27.5 °C but their daily temperature regimes are very different, the former experiencing a daily temperature range of 20 degC whilst Singapore has a range of only 7 degC.

More usually, averages will be given for both the day maximum and the night minimum temperatures; reasonable estimates of average temperatures through the 24 hours can be made by interpolating between these values, remembering that the minimum usually occurs around dawn and the maximum in the early afternoon. It is fairly safe to assume that values of day maxima and night minima will be normally distributed. Additional values may be quoted for (a) the average monthly maximum and minimum; these may be regarded as typical values for abnormally hot days and cold nights, and (b) the highest and lowest values on record.

Surface wind

Wind data are not normally included in basic climatological tables but may be available, on request, for airfields manned by meteorological personnel and equipped with anemometers. The most convenient formats are frequency tables of direction and speed or wind-rose diagrams. Both should, ideally, be for months or seasons and for fixed times (say every three hours) rather than combined figures for all hours and all seasons. Such tables show at a glance the prevailing winds in different seasons as well as diurnal features such as sea-breezes. Information on gusts is not normally included but these data too may be available on request. At some airfields it will be found that prevailing winds and runway directions do not match: this is either because topography will not permit or because wind direction data from other places were used in planning runway orientation.

Rainfall

Many basic tables contain only rainfall amounts and sunshine-duration data but a useful, broad-brush impression may still be gleaned from them. Monthly average rainfall amount (which will include the water equivalent of any melted snow), the average number of days per month with a certain amount of rain and the greatest fall in 24 hours are the three items usually given. Some tables also quote the greatest recorded fall in one hour.

If a location is subject to heavy convective storms it is quite likely that the greatest 24–hour fall occurred within the space of only a few hours. It is also a fairly safe guess that the range of individual monthly totals includes some months with little or no rain and others with twice the average or more. At Heathrow, October is the wettest month with an average monthly fall of 57.8 mm but only 1.6 mm fell in 1978; by contrast the total was 174.8 mm in 1987. In arid regions the rainfall can be even more capricious: the average *annual* rainfall at Dakhla (Mauritania) is a mere 37 mm but 88 mm fell on one September day, and almost certainly this would have been a thunderstorm lasting only a few hours. Clearly, rainfall amount is not one of those elements where the frequency distribution can be assumed to be 'normal' and the same may be said of the number of days of rain. One very rough rule of thumb is that the number of days of rain in a month varies from one third to five thirds of the average number.

Humidity
Statistical tables commonly include monthly mean values of relative humidity, usually for two observation times: typical times might be 0700 and 1300 local time but there is considerable variation from country to country. The observations are usually at the same time throughout the year, hence in winter the first observation may represent conditions before sunrise whereas in summer it could be some hours after sunrise.

Sunshine
In evaluating sunshine data it is important to remember that the possible duration of sunshine will vary according to latitude and season. For this reason statistical summaries sometimes give the monthly duration as a percentage of the total possible. This is never likely to be as high as 100% even with completely cloudless skies since sunshine is not strong enough to register on standard recorders when the sun is close to the horizon; with anything over about 70% it is safe to infer that average cloudiness is small.

Low cloud and visibility
Frequency tables of the occurrence of low cloud and poor visibility, either separately or simultaneously, are prepared at many airfields and may be available on request.

State of ground
Information on the frequency of lying snow is usually readily obtainable but the statistics will probably relate to only one time of day, usually 0900 local time. Runway temperature data are not generally archived but records of the overnight grass minimum temperature may be available.

Airfield weather characteristics
Airfield weather notes and diagrams have been prepared for many sites: diagrams for United Kingdom airfields may be available for inspection at larger forecasting offices. If they are not available or if they seem unduly lacking in detail, a useful

appreciation of characteristics can be made from first principles; this is an excellent exercise in applied meteorology and if carried out logically can provide many of the answers required for planning purposes.

The topics which need to be addressed are:

(i)   Is the airport in a climatic region subject to marked seasonal changes (monsoons, wet and dry seasons)?

(ii)   Is the airport near the coast? If so, consider:
— land- and sea-breeze components in the surface wind,
— sea-breeze fronts within about 40 km of the coast, possibly with, showers if gradient wind and sea-breeze are in opposition,
— showers mainly inland when sea-breeze is not opposed by gradient wind with clearer zone near the coast,
— sea fog encroachment with onshore wind,
— line of cumulus offshore, possibly with showers where land-breeze opposes light gradient wind.

(iii)   Is the airport near a large city and in a 'saucer'? If so, consider:
— threat of smoke in stable situations.

(iv)   Is the airport near high ground? If so consider:
— upslope winds on sunny mornings,
— katabatic winds on clear nights,
— topographic control of wind directions, valley funnelling,
— orographic cloud and rain on windward slopes,
— rain shadow and protection from low cloud to lee of high ground.

(v)   Is the airport near a sand or dust source? If so, consider:
— threat of blowing dust and sandstorms.

(vi)   Is the airport near marshland, reservoirs, etc.? If so, consider:
— vulnerability to early formation of radiation fog,
— risk of lower stratus with fetch from moisture sources.

(vii)   Is the airport in an elevated position? If so, consider:
— liability to upslope and hill fog,
— increased incidence of low cloud,
— reduced incidence of radiation fog forming *in situ*,
— risk of deterioration in lifted fog from valleys after sunrise.

(viii)   Is the airport in an area particularly prone to severe local storms? If so, try to establish:
— history of lightning strikes?
— history of tornado formation?
— history of microbursts?

Route climatological data
The Meteorological Office and other National Meteorological Services hold climatological upper-air data in grid-point format, usually on computer media.

Upper winds
When presented in map form, upper-wind data are usually given in the form of streamlines and isotachs of vector mean winds. Alternatively, they may be shown as contours of the height of a constant-pressure surface. In this latter case it is necessary to obtain the mean speed from the contours by use of a geostrophic wind scale; vector mean winds may be thought of as flowing along the contours, their strength being inversely proportional to the contour spacing, ignoring any contour curvature. To interpret either type of format, a field of vector standard deviation (VSD) is also needed. Use of VSD is described at the end of this section. Wind-rose maps are also available for a few areas.

Upper temperatures
Air temperature data are usually presented in the form of maps of isotherms at standard pressure levels. Maps of the average heights of the 0 °C and −40 °C isothermal surfaces are often available and these may have value in long-term planning in relation to the possibility of airframe icing.

Surface temperature
Unless large-scale maps are available it is unusual to find maps of temperature at ground level because of the complications in depicting the spatial variations in areas of high relief. On small-scale maps it is customary to show isotherms of the temperature 'reduced to sea level'. Fig. 115 shows the global average temperature distribution in January; the representation of temperature across major mountain ranges is plainly unhelpful. Note also that maps of global distributions tend to be of

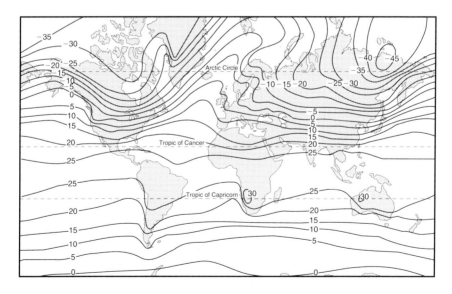

Figure 115.   Average temperature (°C) at mean sea level in January.

the average daily temperature and in order to learn something of the likely maxima and minima a further map is required showing the mean daily range of temperature. Fig. 116 is such a map, but this demonstrates yet another pitfall that should be watched for: it shows the mean range for *all* months of the year and may not necessarily be applicable to January. Such presentations may still be useful in providing a very-broad-scale perspective but for an indication of surface temperatures over a particular area it is better to have recourse to appropriate site-specific climatological tables.

Tropopause data
Mapping of tropopause height presents special problems: over broad belts centred on about latitude 40° there are commonly two overlapping tropopauses, polar and tropical. Contours of both surfaces could be shown on the same map by adopting different colours or styles of line but interpretation remains open to confusion and a more usual method is to show the average heights of one or both levels in thousands of feet or in flight levels, plotted at grid points; entries at each 10° of latitude and 30° of longitude give a satisfactory picture.

Vector standard deviation (VSD)
The vector mean wind is obtained by resolving a large number of observed winds along mutually perpendicular axes, taking a mean of the two components and combining these to give a resultant vector. This quantity shows the direction from which the wind probably blows most often, but not necessarily most of the time. The variation of observed wind vectors about their vector mean is measured by the vector standard deviation or VSD.

The technique of using vector mean wind and VSD is demonstrated for two different cases in Fig. 117. The given vector mean wind (OP) is drawn to scale on a polar diagram with the downstream end of the vector at the origin (O) and correctly

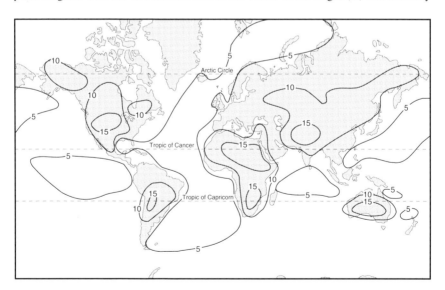

Figure 116.   Mean daily range of temperature (°C).

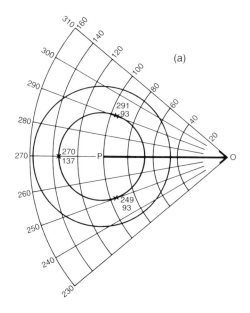

(a)

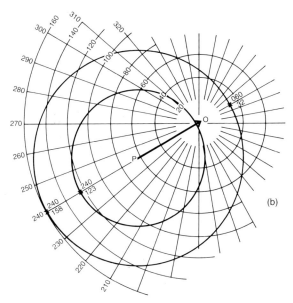

(b)

Figure 117.   Measurement of the variability of wind vectors, given the vector mean wind and the vector standard deviation (VSD). OP represents the vector mean wind; 62.5% of vector wind end-points lie within the inner circle (radius VSD) and 90% within the outer circle (radius 1.52 × VSD).

(a) January, FL300 at 30° N, 140° E, vector mean wind 270° 100 KT, VSD 37 KT.

(b) January, FL300 at 50° N, 40° W, vector mean wind 240° 63 KT, VSD 60 KT.

Some extreme cases are noted on the figures. Note that in case (b), where vector mean wind and VSD are of comparable magnitude, the 90% circle encompasses all directions.

oriented with respect to true north. A circle of radius given by the VSD is drawn about the upwind end of the vector (P). This circle encloses the end points of 62.5% of the population of wind vectors measured from the origin. The range of variation to be expected for a different proportion of cases can be estimated by changing the radius length by a factor as given in Table 17; for instance 90% of vectors would lie within the circle of radius 1.52 × VSD. The method assumes a fairly normally distributed wind regime; it would be unwise to use the technique where it was known, or suspected, that there was a bimodal wind distribution, such as might occur where there is a reversal of wind direction in a monsoon regime.

Charts showing global distributions of vector mean winds and vector standard deviations at various levels and seasons are contained in two Meteorological Office Geophysical Memoirs (Heastie and Stephenson 1960, Tucker 1960). More recent chart sets have not been published but a more extensive upper-wind climatology is now available in grid-point format and has been purchased by most airlines operating from the United Kingdom.

TABLE 17. *Percentage frequency of vector wind end-points occurring on or within circles of radius of (VSD × factor) centred on the upwind end-point of the vector mean wind.*

Percentage frequency	25.0	50.0	62.5	75.0	80.0	85.0	90.0	95.0	99.0
Factor		0.54	0.83	1.00	1.18	1.27	1.38	1.52	1.73	2.15

METEOROLOGICAL INFORMATION
FOR AVIATION

CHAPTER 21

METEOROLOGICAL INFORMATION
FOR CIVIL AVIATION

21.1 INTERNATIONAL ASPECTS

International organization for the provision of meteorological information for aviation was mentioned briefly in Section 14.1. The standard procedures necessary for the safe, economic and regular operation of international air services are formulated through the Meteorological Secretariat of the International Civil Aviation Organization (ICAO) and specified as Standards and Recommended Practices (SARPs) in Annex 3 (ICAO — Meteorological Services for International Aviation). ICAO works in close co-operation with the World Meteorological Organization (WMO) Commission for Aeronautical Meteorology (CAeM) to ensure common procedures and unnecessary duplication. Within each ICAO contracting state there is a nominated 'Meteorological Authority'; for the United Kingdom this Authority is the Directorate of International Policy and Co-ordination (INT8) of the Civil Aviation Authority (CAA); the day-to-day provision of meteorological services is undertaken by the Meteorological Office as the agent of the CAA.

21.2 UNITED KINGDOM ARRANGEMENTS
— AREA FORECASTS

Whilst always acting strictly in accordance with ICAO regulations and recommendations, the Meteorological Authority continues to keep procedures under review and is prepared to modify them from time to time as necessary to meet the ever-changing needs of the aviation community. Hence it would be out of place here to give more than a very general account of national arrangements and it should be borne in mind that those arrangements described hereunder are subject to change and that examples of forecast formats included in the Annex to this present work may not be representative of documentation in years to come.

WAFS charts
Flight planning charts giving forecast winds and temperatures and significant weather (SIGWX) are provided for designated areas of responsibility by Regional Area Forecast Centres (RAFCs) under the World Area Forecast System (WAFS). The charts are made available to United Kingdom users via ARTIFAX, a broadcast/dial-up facsimile facility run by the Meteorological Office under an agreement with the CAA. Charts are broadcast to a fixed schedule for flight documentation whilst some are available on a dial-up access. The latter are mainly for general aviation (GA) users.

RAFC charts are issued at 6-hourly intervals to be available to the user at least nine hours before the time of validity. Chart sets include a combined significant weather and tropopause/maximum wind chart as well as charts of wind and temperature at standard flight levels specified in the Annex.

The European RAFCs and the areas covered by their products are as follows:

Bracknell	(NAT)	Europe to North America,
Frankfurt	(EUR)	Europe and the Mediterranean,
	(MID)	Europe to the Far East
Paris	(AFI)	Europe to Africa
	(CAR/SAM)	Europe to Caribbean and northern South America.

ICAO recognizes three significant weather domains:

low level	the layer between flight levels 100 and 250
middle level	the layer between flight levels 250 and 450, and
high level	the layer between flight levels 450 and 600.

RAFC significant weather charts are usually for the middle level but for the NAT region middle and high levels are combined into a single chart to cater for SST traffic, and for the EUR region low and middle levels are combined.

Low-level weather charts
WAFS chart arrangements cover only those flights operating at FL100 and above. Within the United Kingdom separate forecast charts (Forms 215/415) are issued to provide for flights within the domain below FL100. An overlap is provided so that the forecast actually covers the height range from the surface to 15 000 ft. Heights on this chart are expressed in 'hundreds of feet above MSL', not 'flight level'. The difference may seem rather subtle but it avoids the awkward situation that can arise when the actual surface pressure is well above 1013 hPa: in such a case low cloud may have, say, a base of 'minus 200 ft' relative to the datum of 1013.2 hPa which is assumed when heights are expressed in flight levels.

The charts of forecast weather below 15 000 ft are fixed-time charts, covering the British Isles and near continent and issued 6-hourly; they are complemented by charts of winds and temperatures for different heights at selected locations. F215 gives low-level weather information over the United Kingdom and English Channel and is provided on the ARTIFAX broadcast to most civil aerodromes; F415 is for GA flights from the United Kingdom to Europe and is made available on the dial-up system. F214 and F414 are the corresponding spot-wind charts covering these areas

National forecast services — AIRMET
As the meteorological authority, the CAA regulates and funds forecasting services to civil aviation in the United Kingdom. To complement chart forms 214/215, the CAA has arranged the provision of the AIRMET service, which comprises regional and area text forecasts and a selection of TAFs and METARs. These data are available to users via telex, AFTN, telephone and facsimile.

The regional text forecasts are provided by Bracknell (CFO) (AIRMET SOUTH), Manchester (AIRMET NORTH) and Glasgow (AIRMET SCOTTISH). These regional forecasts are made available to aerodromes for ATC and Ops purposes as well as for flight planning by pilots; they are intended mostly for GA pilots, and as such are made available by telephone for convenience. The information includes details of the low-level wind and temperature, visibility, weather and cloud, as well as any warnings of expected hazards in the region. Recognising the GA requirements for local flying, area forecasts are provided for central and southern areas of England and the English Channel, in addition to the regional text. Another text message available by telephone provides an outlook for the following day for flying over the United Kingdom.

The telephone service arranged by the CAA is provided using a computer voice system; voice output is at a measured rate to facilitate copying. A special 'copy form' is obtainable which may be useful for copying any of the area forecasts.

Other area forecasts

Provision of the above-mentioned services ensures that the *en route* forecasting requirements of almost all branches of aviation can be met by routine output; inevitably there will be some occasions when this is not the case. If the requirements of a particular planned flight are not satisfactorily met by these routine arrangements then the onus is upon the pilot to seek advice from one of the aviation forecasting offices designated by the CAA and specified in CAP32 (*UK Air Pilot*), MET section (CAA 1993). Some situations when this may be necessary are:

(i)   A planned transAtlantic flight below FL250. A special low-level significant weather chart, together with winds and temperatures at suitable standard levels, can be prepared for an appropriate section of the NAT area. Since this will be a 'made-to-measure' chart package it is imperative that the Regional Centre at Bracknell is advised of the requirement well in advance, and certainly not less than four hours before the ETD.

(ii)   A planned flight below FL100 to a first stop beyond the limits of the routine low-level documentation. Again, advance notification to the nearest main forecast office (Bracknell, Manchester or Glasgow) is necessary. Arrangements may then be made for production of a dedicated flight forecast.

(iii) If, after full self-briefing from AIRMET or other routine output, the pilot still feels the need for some 'safety-related' clarification or amplification, he is entitled to access to a forecaster at one of the forecast offices listed in CAP32 (*UK Air Pilot*), MET section (CAA 1993).

(iv)   A forecast is required for some specialist general aviation activity (e.g. gliding, ballooning, microlighting, parachuting). Special forecasts may be made available to supplement the standard low-level documentation.

(v)   Forecasts are required for such non-standard services as aerial photography, test flying, and crop spraying or outlooks beyond the next day. The Meteorological Authority (CAA) has no obligation to fund services of this nature but forecasts may be obtained from the Meteorological Office by prior arrangement and on a repayment basis.

Facsimile and PC services

An automated facsimile system and a self-briefing PC system, have been developed for various customer services provided by the United Kingdom Meteorological Office. Under an agreement with the CAA these services are being provided to aviation users.

A range of standard aviation data provided by the CAA, and other products agreed with the CAA, are made available through a broadcast facsimile service (ARTIFAX) or on a dial-up system (METFAX) from which data may be selected as required. The systems enable users with group 3 facsimile equipment to receive the information they require for flight planning at their own convenience.

The PC system, called MIST (Meteorological Information Self-briefing Terminal), will enable those with personal PC systems to access data for planning flights at their convenience in the same way as the facsimile system. Both services will provide forecasts as well as TAF and METAR reports over the British Isles and near continent.

21.3 SITE-SPECIFIC FORECASTS AND 'ACTUALS'

Aerodrome forecasts and 'actuals'
Landing forecasts for individual aerodromes are prepared by designated meteorological forecast offices and are exchanged nationally and internationally in a coded (TAF) format. Weather observations, commonly referred to as 'actuals', are encoded in a METAR format. The two code forms have a common basic structure to facilitate interpretation. Within the United Kingdom, regular bulletins of TAFs and METARs received over the European MOTNE teleprinter network are disseminated over CAA-funded OPMET broadcasts.

TAFs are usually for a period of nine hours and are issued every three hours; they describe the expected operationally significant variations of wind, visibility, weather and cloud throughout the period. For selected international aerodromes, longer 18-hour TAFs may be available; these are issued 6-hourly. METARs are, of course, only available when an aerodrome is open and an observing watch is being maintained; they are usually issued half-hourly, but only hourly reports may be available from military and some civil aerodromes. There is a procedure for the issue of special reports to air traffic control when changes since the last METAR exceed certain laid-down criteria, but in the United Kingdom 'SPECI' (Selected Special Reports) are not usually disseminated off the aerodrome.

A basic requirement for preflight briefing is that a TAF for the intended destination as well as TAFs for selected alternate airfields should be available. If available, METARs can be included for a destination and alternates up to 1000 n. mile from the departure aerodrome. Although a recent METAR may be of some value if the intended flight is of short duration, especially if a TREND is appended, it cannot be over-stressed that a pilot should never consider flying solely on 'actuals'.

In general, TAFs are prepared only for those aerodromes at which regular routine observations are provided by professional or certificated meteorological observers, and when recent reports are available to the forecaster. Occasionally forecasters are asked to prepare a TAF for an aerodrome or landing site from which there are no observations and the local weather characteristics of which are unknown. In these circumstances an area forecast for a limited radius around the airfield may be provided instead of a TAF, but usually only where pilots would have no access to the standard low-level self-briefing material (F214/215 or AIRMET) to interpolate for themselves the conditions at their ETA, e.g. when the pilot is inbound from overseas. Such a forecast will be in plain language for a period of no more than two hours and any cloud heights will be given as heights above sea level. This contrasts with the coded TAF, METAR and SPECI formats in which all heights are given above aerodrome level.

The TAF, METAR and SPECI were designed as 'self-evident' code forms and have been restructured from time to time to more closely meet the changing needs of the aviator; the versions which became current in July 1993 are included in the Annex.

METAR TRENDs

Short-term landing forecasts (TRENDs) are appended to the METARs of certain aerodromes which provide half-hourly METARs and which are approved by the CAA for the VOLMET broadcast. These are intended to meet the requirement of aircraft within about one hour's flying time from the aerodrome. The TREND is a concise statement of the expected changes of operational significance over the two-hour period following the time of the METAR report to which it is appended.

Aerodrome warnings

Airfield authorities (usually Air Traffic Control) receive aerodrome warnings, as appropriate, from the designated responsible meteorological forecast office. The warnings requirement is reviewed from time to time, typically twice a year, and may include prior warnings of such phenomena as strong winds and gales, thunderstorms, squalls, hail, snow, frost, and fog. The further dissemination of warnings to other airfield users is the subject of local airfield arrangements.

21.4 IN-FLIGHT INFORMATION

SIGMETs and SIGMET SSTs

SIGMET messages advise of the reported occurrence or warn of the expected occurrence of certain conditions which are considered to be potentially hazardous to aircraft in flight. The messages are issued by Meteorological Watch Offices supporting Flight Information Centres (FIC) and are applicable to part or the whole of the FIR concerned. In the United Kingdom the Central Forecasting Office at Bracknell issues SIGMETs for London FIR and Shanwick OCA and Glasgow Weather Centre has a similar responsibility for Scottish FIR. The FIC is responsible for forwarding the warnings to aircraft in flight. Messages prefixed SIGMET SST similarly warn of potentially hazardous in-flight conditions likely to occur at transonic levels and supersonic cruising levels along designated SST tracks.

The phenomena for which SIGMETs are issued are as follows:

TS OBSC — thunderstorm (including, if necessary, cumulonimbus cloud not accompanied by thunderstorm) obscured by haze or smoke or not readily visible due to darkness

TS EMBD — thunderstorm (including, if necessary, cumulonimbus cloud not accompanied by thunderstorm) embedded within cloud layers and not readily recognizable

TS FRQ — area of thunderstorms with little or no separation between adjacent storms

TS LSQ — thunderstorms along a line with little or no separation

TS OBSC HVYGR, TS EMBD HVYGR, TS FRQ HVYGR, TS LSQ HVYGR
  — heavy hail accompanying the above categories
TC   — tropical cyclone (name added)
SEV TURB — severe turbulence (not turbulence in convective clouds or associated with tropical cyclones)
SEV ICE   — severe icing (not icing in convective clouds or associated with tropical cyclones)
FZRA   — severe icing conditions caused by freezing rain
SEV MTW — marked mountain waves
HVY DS   — widespread duststorm
HVY SS   — widespread sandstorm
VA   — volcanic ash (volcano name added).

Additionally, for SIGMET SSTs, the following phenomena are included:

MOD TURB — moderate turbulence
MOD CAT — moderate clear air turbulence
ISOL CB   — isolated cumulonimbus
OCNL CB — occasional cumulonimbus
FRQ CB   — frequent cumulonimbus.

VOLMET broadcasts
These are ground-to-air VHF transmissions of meteorological reports and forecasts. In the United Kingdom, VOLMET transmissions are made from London Air Traffic Control Centre, separate broadcasts covering the British Isles and parts of the near continent. The transmissions are plain-language versions of latest METAR reports. TREND and RVR values may be added to some reports.

Up-to-date schedules will be found in CAP32 (*UK Air Pilot*), MET section (CAA 1993).

Vertical wind shear warnings
At certain airports a wind-shear alerting service is operated. Alert messages are given in ATIS (Automatic terminal information service) broadcasts or by R/T to all arriving and departing aircraft whenever low-level wind shear has been recently reported or when a potential wind-shear condition is considered to exist on the basis of certain meteorological criteria.

Marked temperature inversion warnings
At certain aerodromes, a warning of marked temperature inversion is issued whenever a temperature difference of 10 degC or more exists between the surface and any point up to 1000 ft above the aerodrome. Warnings are broadcast to arriving and departing aircraft via ATIS or by radio.

21.5 USER CO-OPERATION

The success of any system for providing meteorological services to aviation depends to a large extent upon the co-operation between the meteorologist and the users of the information — the aircrew and flight planners.

In the years immediately following World War II virtually every flying unit had the benefit of a resident meteorological office; a personal briefing from the duty forecaster prior to each flight was *de rigueur* and a constructive rapport was soon developed between forecaster and aviator. More recently, the boom in both general aviation and charter flights and the proliferation of flying units has coincided with a contraction of the numbers of forecast offices. Technological advance has kept pace and ensured that centralization of the meteorological service has not deprived the aviator of the information that he needs, but the inevitable loss of the personal contact between provider and user is regretted by both.

There are some practical ways in which aircrew can help to preserve a healthy rapport with the forecasters; early advice of unusual requirements has been mentioned above; careful attention to details of track, flight levels and time standard (all times preferably in UTC) when booking a forecast will preclude later argument; a thorough knowledge of the range of products which are routinely available may prevent misunderstandings.

It is, of course, equally incumbent upon the meteorologist to show consideration and understanding in his dealings with aircrew and to make allowances for the gulf of weather experience that separates the trainee pilot from the senior captain of a national airline. To maintain the bond between forecaster and aviator, it is expected of forecasters from the centralized forecasting offices in the United Kingdom that they should pay occasional visits to airfields, sometimes under the guise of official inspection visits or simply as liaison trips. Aircrew are to be encouraged to take whatever opportunities may arise in order for them to visit 'the Met. Office'. In this way the strong and long-standing association between aviation and meteorology may be preserved and a high standard of service maintained.

DERIVATION OF SOME FORMULAE
INTRODUCED IN THE TEXT

Characteristic gas equation

For a given mass of gas there is a fundamental relation between the pressure p, volume v and absolute (kelvin) temperature T of the form

$$pv = RT \qquad (A1)$$

where R is a constant for any one gas. Since for unit mass the density ρ is the reciprocal of the volume, the equation is equivalent to

$$p = R\rho T \qquad (A2)$$

which is the more convenient form for meteorological applications. The value of R for dry air is 2.87 when p is in hectopascals, ρ in kg m^{-3} and T in kelvin; in SI units (i.e. with p in pascals) it is 2.87×10^2. Equation (A2) leads to expressions for the densities of dry and moist air (Section 4.2).

Pressure and height

A second fundamental equation in meteorology derives from the rule stated in Section 2.1 that the pressure at any level in the atmosphere is equal to the weight of air above that level in a column of unit cross-section. In Fig. A1, which represents a column of air standing on the ground, consider a layer extending from height z where the pressure is p, to height $z + dz$ where the pressure is denoted by $p + dp$. The pressure on the upper surface of the layer is less than the pressure on the lower surface by the weight per unit area of the layer itself. The difference of pressure is $p - (p + dp)$ or $-dp$, and if ρ is the density of the layer, the mass per unit area is ρdz and the weight $g\rho\,dz$, where g is the acceleration due to gravity.

Therefore $g\rho\,dz = -dp$.

Eliminating the density by means of equation (A2), we obtain

$$dz = -(RT/gp)\,dp. \qquad (A3)$$

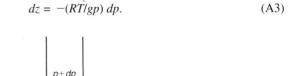

Figure A1.

This result shows how an increment of height dz is related to the corresponding increment of pressure dp, the negative sign indicating that pressure decreases with increase of height. Putting $g = 9.81$ m s^{-2}, we obtain the thickness dz in metres, thus:

$$dz = (2.87 \times 10^2)/(9.81) \times (T\,dp/p)$$

$$= 29.25\,(T\,dp/p).$$

Finally, for the thickness of a layer extending over a pressure range of 1 hPa, we may put $dp = 1$ to give

$$dz = 29.25T/p \text{ metres. (or } 96T/p \text{ feet).}$$

The height interval between two pressure levels p_1 and p_2 is obtained by integration of equation (A3). The result takes a simple form when the temperature is constant, thus

$$\int_{h_1}^{h_2} dz = -RT/g \int_{p_1}^{p_2} dp/p$$

whence $h_2 - h_1 = RT/g\,(\log_e p_1 - \log_e p_2)$.

Converting natural logarithms to base 10 logarithms gives:

$$h_2 - h_1 = 67.4T\,(\log p_1 - \log p_2) \text{ metres}$$

$$\text{or } h_2 - h_1 = 221.1T\,(\log p_1 - \log p_2) \text{ feet.}$$

Adiabatic relations
An equation given in Section 3.5 states the relation between the changes in pressure and temperature of a mass of air which is thermally insulated from its surroundings. This result is derived from the first law of thermodynamics which is an expression of the conservation of energy and the equivalence of energy and heat. It may be stated as follows:

If an amount of heat is taken up by a gas, some is converted into internal energy and the remainder is used up in work done on the environment as the gas expands.

The internal energy refers to the kinetic energy of the molecules and is known to be proportional to the kelvin temperature; for a given rise of temperature, the increase of the internal energy is therefore proportional to the change of temperature. If the rise of temperature is accompanied by expansion, then work is done in pushing back the environment so that some of the heat supplied is consumed in this way; or if the gas contracts, work is done on the gas by the environment and an additional amount of heat is made available. Thus, for a given

347

increase of temperature a definite amount of heat is taken up in changing the internal energy, while a variable amount (which may even be negative) is taken up in changing the volume. By the definition of specific heat we may write:

heat supplied = (specific heat) × (increase of temperature).

In the special case when the volume remains constant, all the heat goes to raising the temperature. The specific heat is then written as c_v to draw attention to the constancy of volume; it is called the specific heat at constant volume. Another special case arises if the pressure is kept constant; some heat is now consumed by the work done in expansion, so the specific heat has a value greater than c_v; it is denoted by c_p and is called the specific heat at constant pressure. Thus for a small rise of temperature dT the heat dQ taken in should be equated to $c_v dT$ if the volume is constant, or to $c_p dT$ if the pressure is constant.

Next, consider the work done by the gas as it expands and pushes back the environment. If, in a cylinder of cross-section A (Fig. A2) the expansion pushes a piston outwards through a small distance dx, the work done (force × distance) is $pA.dx$ or pdv, where dv is the increase in volume. Thus, of an amount of heat dQ applied to the gas, an amount $c_v dT$ is accounted for by the increase of temperature and an amount pdv by the change in volume. The law of conservation is therefore expressed by the equation

$$dQ = c_v\, dT + pdv. \tag{A4}$$

From equation (A1), by making a small variation, we obtain

$$pdv + vdp = RdT. \tag{A5}$$

Therefore equation (A4) becomes

$$dQ = (c_v + R\,)dT - vdp. \tag{A6}$$

Now an adiabatic change is by definition one in which no heat is supplied or removed; in this case dQ is zero and equation (A6) gives

$$(c_v + R\,)dT = vdp = (RT/p)dp$$

or

$$dT/T = R/(c_v + R).dp/p. \tag{A7}$$

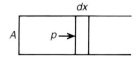

Figure A2.

Then by integration from pressure p_0 to p_1, corresponding to temperatures T_0 and T_1 we obtain the 'adiabatic' equation

$$\log T_0 - \log T_1 = R/(c_v + R) \, (\log p_0 - \log p_1). \tag{A8}$$

Again, from equation (A6), if the pressure is for the moment assumed constant so that $dp = 0$, then dQ, as we have seen, may be replaced by $c_p \, dT$ and we have

$$c_p \, dT = (c_v + R) \, dT,$$

or
$$R = c_p - c_v. \tag{A9}$$

The first factor on the right of equation (A8) then becomes $(c_p - c_v)/c_p$, or if the ratio of the specific heats, c_p/c_v, is put equal to γ the factor becomes $(\gamma - 1)/\gamma$. The value of γ for dry air is 1.402 so that equation (A8) becomes, finally

$$\log T_0 - \log T_1 = 0.287 \, (\log p_0 - \log p_1). \tag{A10}$$

Potential temperature
This has been defined in Section 3.5 as the temperature acquired by a parcel of air when its pressure is changed adiabatically to 1000 hPa. Let it be denoted by θ and let p_0 in equation (A10) refer to 1000 hPa. Then

$$\log \theta = \log T + 0.287 \, (\log p_0 - \log p) \tag{A11}$$

or
$$\theta = T \, (1000/p)^{0.287}$$

where T and p now denote the initial temperature and pressure of the air.

Dry adiabatic lapse rate (Section 3.5)
Equation (A7) may be rewritten as

$$dT/T = (\gamma - 1)/\gamma . dp/p. \tag{A12}$$

It determines the change in temperature dT resulting from a small change in pressure dp when the process is carried out adiabatically. This result will now be applied to the adiabatic ascent of a parcel of dry air. On substituting for dp/p from equation (A3) and dividing by dz, we find

$$dT/dz = -(\gamma - 1)/\gamma . g/R. \tag{A13}$$

The expression on the left is the rate of change of temperature with height in air ascending adiabatically, in other words it is the dry adiabatic lapse rate and its value as given on the right is seen to be constant. With the figures already used, this constant value becomes 0.287/96 degC per foot or, to a close approximation, 3 degC per 1000 ft (9.8 degC per km): the negative sign in equation (A13) shows that the temperature decreases with increasing height.

349

A discrepancy in the above argument should be noted. Whereas equation (A12) describes the conditions within an isolated parcel of air, equation (A3) concerns the relationship between pressure and height in the environment. Thus in combining these equations in order to derive equation (A13) it has been tacitly assumed that the conditions of the ascending parcel are the same as those of the environment at each level. This is true of the pressure but not in general of the temperature which, after a large displacement, may differ considerably from that of the environment at the same level. The formula for the adiabatic lapse rate is therefore strictly true only at the start of the displacement, but in practice its use does not seriously affect the computed temperature provided the change in height is less than about 10 000 ft. For changes greater than this, equation (A10) should be used.

The derivation of an expression for the saturated adiabatic lapse rate is much more complicated and will not be given here.

Entropy (Section 3.6)
We have seen that if a small variation takes place in the state of a gas, the amount of heat taken up is given by equation (A4). Now suppose the state of the gas changes by a finite amount. Since any two of the variables p, v and T are sufficient to define the state, we may represent the change on, for example, a $p - v$ diagram (Fig. A3) by a continuous line from the point A representing the initial state (p_1, v_1) to the point B representing the final state (p_2, v_2). Any intermediate point P on the curve AB represents the intermediate state (p, v) given by the co-ordinates of that point. In order to find the total amount of heat taken up by the gas in passing from the state A to the state B, the expression (A4) must be summed for all stages represented by the path curve AB. Thus the total amount of heat taken up is given by

$$Q_2 - Q_1 = c_v (T_2 - T_1) + \int_{v_1}^{v_2} p\,dv. \tag{A14}$$

Now pdv is represented by the element of area in the column under PP′, so that the integral on the right of equation (A14) is equal to the whole area ABCD enclosed between the curve AB and the v-axis; this area is clearly dependent on the shape of

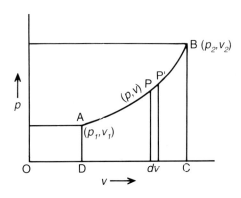

Figure A3.

350

the curve AB as well as on the actual positions of A and B themselves. Hence the amount of heat which must be supplied when the gas changes from the state $p_1 v_1$ to any other state $p_2 v_2$ depends on the precise manner in which the transition is brought about at each stage. This property of the amount of heat taken up is very inconvenient for purposes of calculation — it would be more convenient to have a related quantity whose value depends only on the initial and final points of the transition. Actually it is easy to derive such a quantity. All we need do is to divide equation (A4) throughout by the temperature before integrating. Thus

$$dQ/T = c_v \, dT/T + p \, dv/T$$

which by use of equation (A1) becomes

$$dQ/T = c_v \, dT/T + R \, dv/v$$

whence
$$\int_{Q_1}^{Q_2} dQ/T = c_v \log(T_2/T_1) + R \log(v_2/v_1). \tag{A15}$$

Hence the result of integrating dQ/T is to obtain an expression which depends only on the initial and final states of the gas and not at all on the intermediate stages. The expression dQ/T is written as dS, where S is termed the entropy. Thus from equation (A15) the general expression for the entropy of unit mass of gas is obtained as

$$S = c_v \log T + R \log v + \text{constant} \tag{A16}$$

where the constant depends on the temperature and volume in a state of zero entropy.

Thus the change of entropy, which may be defined as the sum of successive small heat increments each divided by the corresponding kelvin temperature, possesses the required property of depending only on the state of the gas and not on how that state was reached. Further, if a process takes place adiabatically, $dQ = 0$; it follows then that $dS=0$ so that the entropy is constant and the process is said to be isentropic. Consequently the dry adiabatic lines are lines of equal entropy and are therefore represented as a set of parallel straight lines on the tephigram.

Another expression for the entropy of dry air can be given in terms of potential temperature. From equation (11) we obtain

$$\log \theta = \log T - (\gamma - 1)/\gamma . \log p + \text{constant}.$$

By use of equation (A1) and by putting $\gamma = c_p/c_v$ this becomes

$$\log \theta = \log T - (c_p - c_v) \, c_p . \log T/v + \text{constant}$$

or
$$c_p \log \theta = c_v \log T + R \log v + \text{constant}.$$

Therefore $S = c_p \, \log \, \theta$, apart from an additive constant. Thus entropy is proportional to the logarithm of the potential temperature. The dry adiabatics on the tephigram are normally shown for every 10 degC of potential temperature, the position of any line being determined by its entropy, which is on a linear scale.

Humidity mixing ratio and dew-point (Section 6.1)
Consider a volume v containing 1 kg of dry air and r kg of water vapour. If the total pressure is p and the vapour pressure e, then the gas equation for the dry air alone is

$$(p - e)v = RT.$$

R_w, the gas constant for water vapour, is 4.615 and the corresponding equation for water vapour becomes

$$ev = r R_w T = 1.6rRT \text{ (approx.)}$$

and the humidity mixing ratio is given by

$$r = 0.622e/(p - e). \tag{A17}$$

For saturated air, e becomes the saturation vapour pressure e_s. Since the value of e_s is known experimentally for any temperature, it follows that the saturation mixing ratio at any pressure and temperature is obtainable from equation (A17) when e is replaced by e_s. Further, as the humidity mixing ratio is the saturation mixing ratio at the dew-point temperature, the dew-point temperature is partly dependent on pressure. In unsaturated adiabatic ascent, the humidity mixing ratio remains constant while both temperature and dew-point decrease, as may be verified from the tephigram.

Coriolis force (Section 5.2)
In deriving the formula for the geostrophic wind the direction and magnitude of the Coriolis force was assumed. To prove this result it is necessary first to consider how the rotation of the earth affects any part of its surface. The earth rotates about its polar axis from west to east with angular velocity denoted by Ω. The linear velocity of a point P in latitude ϕ (Fig. A4) is therefore $\Omega R \cos\phi$ and the velocity at a near point A in latitude $\phi + d\phi$ is $\Omega R \cos\phi + d(\Omega R \cos\phi)$. Thus the velocity at A relative to that at P is $\Omega R d (\cos\phi)$ or $-\Omega R \sin\phi.d\phi$ and similarly the relative velocity at A' in latitude $\phi - d\phi$ is $+\Omega R \sin\phi.d \phi$. Since the distance from P to A or A' along the earth's surface is $R\, d\phi$, it follows that the surface in the

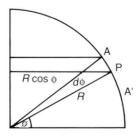

Figure A4.

neighbourhood of P rotates counter-clockwise about the vertical at P with angular velocity $\Omega\sin\phi$.

Let us now consider air moving horizontally over the earth in northern latitude ϕ with velocity V in a direction OA which is fixed in space (Fig. A5); in a small time dt the air travels a distance OA equal to Vdt. Meanwhile the rotation of the tangent plane to the earth's surface at O with angular velocity $\Omega\sin\phi$ carries the point A to A′, where the angle AOA′ is $\Omega\sin\phi.dt$. While moving along OA in space, the air therefore travels a distance represented by A′A (in that direction) across the earth's surface; this distance equals $Vdt.\Omega\sin\phi.dt$ or $\Omega\sin\phi.V(dt)^2$. Since the motion at O is directed along OA, the transverse motion may be regarded as accelerated from rest. If we denote this acceleration by f, the usual formula gives

$$A'A = f(dt)^2/2$$

whence $$f = 2\Omega V \sin\phi.$$

This is the Coriolis acceleration; its direction is seen to be perpendicular to and to the right of the wind velocity. In the southern hemisphere the corresponding latitude is to be taken as negative so that the directions of the rotation and of the Coriolis acceleration are reversed.

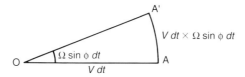

Figure A5

353

APPENDIX II

CONVERSION TABLES

TABLE I — *Conversion of degrees Celsius to Fahrenheit*

°C	.0	.2	.5	.8	°C	.0	.2	.5	.8
	degrees Fahrenheit					*degrees Fahrenheit*			
40	104	104	105	105	0	32	32	33	33
					−0	32	32	31	31
39	102	103	103	104	−1	30	30	29	29
38	100	101	101	101	−2	28	28	27	27
37	99	99	99	100	−3	27	26	26	25
36	97	97	98	98	−4	25	24	24	23
35	95	95	96	96	−5	23	23	22	22
34	93	94	94	95	−6	21	21	20	20
33	91	92	92	93	−7	19	19	19	18
32	90	90	91	91	−8	18	17	17	16
31	88	88	89	89	−9	16	15	15	14
30	86	86	87	87	−10	14	14	13	13
29	84	85	85	86	−11	12	12	11	11
28	82	83	83	84	−12	10	10	9	9
27	81	81	81	82	−13	9	8	8	7
26	79	79	80	80	−14	7	6	6	5
25	77	77	78	78	−15	5	5	4	4
24	75	75	76	77	−16	3	3	2	2
23	73	74	74	75	−17	1	1	1	0
22	72	72	73	73	−18	0	−1	−1	−2
21	70	70	71	71	−19	−2	−3	−3	−4
20	68	68	69	69	−20	−4	−4	−5	−5
19	66	67	67	68	−21	−6	−6	−7	−7
18	64	65	65	66	−22	−8	−8	−9	−9
17	63	63	63	64	−23	−9	−10	−10	−11
16	61	61	62	62	−24	−11	−12	−12	−13
15	59	59	60	60	−25	−13	−13	−14	−14
14	57	58	58	59	−26	−15	−15	−16	−16
13	55	56	56	57	−27	−17	−17	−17	−18
12	54	54	55	55	−28	−18	−19	−19	−20
11	52	52	53	53	−29	−20	−21	−21	−22
10	50	50	51	51	−30	−22	−22	−23	−23
9	48	49	49	50	−31	−24	−24	−25	−25
8	46	47	47	48	−32	−26	−26	−27	−27
7	45	45	45	46	−33	−27	−28	−28	−29
6	43	43	44	44	−34	−29	−30	−30	−31
5	41	41	42	42	−35	−31	−31	−32	−32
4	39	40	40	41	−36	−33	−33	−34	−34
3	37	38	38	39	−37	−35	−35	−35	−36
2	36	36	37	37	−38	−36	−37	−37	−38
1	34	34	35	35	−39	−38	−39	−39	−40

TABLE II. *Conversion of knots to metres per second*

1 knot = 0.51479 metres per second

Knots	0	1	2	3	4	5	6	7	8	9
					metres per second					
0	0.0	0.5	1.0	1.5	2.1	2.6	3.1	3.6	4.1	4.6
10	5.1	5.7	6.2	6.7	7.2	7.7	8.2	8.8	9.3	9.8
20	10.3	10.8	11.3	11.8	12.4	12.9	13.4	13.9	14.4	14.9
30	15.4	16.0	16.5	17.0	17.5	18.0	18.5	19.0	19.6	20.1
40	20.6	21.1	21.6	22.1	22.7	23.2	23.7	24.2	24.7	25.2
50	25.7	26.3	26.8	27.3	27.8	28.3	28.8	29.3	29.9	30.4
60	30.9	31.4	31.9	32.4	32.9	33.5	34.0	34.5	35.0	35.5
70	36.0	36.6	37.1	37.6	38.1	38.6	39.1	39.6	40.2	40.7
80	41.2	41.7	42.2	42.7	43.2	43.8	44.3	44.8	45.3	45.8
90	46.3	46.8	47.4	47.9	48.4	48.9	49.4	49.9	50.4	51.0
100	51.5	52.0	52.5	53.0	53.5	54.1	54.6	55.1	55.6	56.1

TABLE III. *Conversion of inches to millimetres*

1 inch = 25.4 millimetres

Inches	.0	.1	.2	.3	.4	.5	.6	.7	.8	.9
					millimetres					
0.0	0	3	5	8	10	13	15	18	20	23
1.0	25	28	30	33	36	38	41	43	46	48
2.0	51	53	56	58	61	64	66	69	71	74
3.0	76	79	81	84	86	89	91	94	97	99
4.0	102	104	107	109	112	114	117	119	122	124
5.0	127	130	132	135	137	140	142	145	147	150
6.0	152	155	157	160	163	165	168	170	173	175
7.0	178	180	183	185	188	191	193	196	198	201
8.0	203	206	208	211	213	216	218	221	224	226
9.0	229	231	234	236	239	241	244	246	249	251
10.0	254	257	259	262	264	267	269	272	274	277

TABLE IV. *Conversion of feet to metres*

1 foot = 0.3048 metres

1000's of feet	.0	.1	.2	.3	.4	.5	.6	.7	.8	.9
					metres					
0	0	305	610	915	1219	1524	1829	2134	2438	2743
10	3048	3352	3657	3962	4267	4572	4877	5182	5486	5791
20	6096	6401	6706	7011	7351	7620	7924	8229	8534	8839
					kilometres					
30	9.1	9.5	9.8	10.1	10.4	10.7	11.0	11.3	11.6	11.9
40	12.2	12.5	12.8	13.1	13.4	13.7	14.0	14.3	14.6	14.9
50	15.2	15.5	15.9	16.2	16.5	16.8	17.1	17.4	17.7	18.0
60	18.3	18.6	18.9	19.2	19.5	19.8	20.1	20.4	20.7	21.0
70	21.3	21.6	22.0	22.3	22.6	22.9	23.2	23.5	23.8	24.1
80	24.4	24.7	25.0	25.3	25.6	25.9	26.2	26.5	26.8	27.1
90	27.4	27.7	28.0	28.4	28.7	29.0	29.3	29.6	29.9	30.2
100	30.5									

Note: Metres are rounded off to the nearest whole metre; kilometres are rounded off to the nearest tenth of a kilometre; 500 feet = 152 metres.

355

REFERENCES AND BIBLIOGRAPHY

Bagnold, R.A., 1941: The physics of blown sand and desert dunes. London, Methuen.

Barry, R.G. and Chorley, R.J., 1992: Atmosphere, weather and climate. London, Routledge.

Boucher, 1975: Global climate. London, English University Press.

Bradbury, T, 1989: Meteorology and flight. London, Black.

Browning, K.A. *et al.* 1976: Structure of an evolving hailstorm. *Mon Weather Rev*, **104**, 603–610.

CAA, 1991: The effect of thunderstorms and associated turbulence on aircraft operations. London, Civil Aviation Authority, Aeronautical Information Circular No. 117/1991.

CAA, 1991: Piston engine icing. London, Civil Aviation Authority, Safety Sense Leaflet No. 14.

CAA, 1992a: Low altitude wind shear. London, Civil Aviation Authority, Aeronautical Information Circular No. 48/1992.

CAA, 1992b: Wake turbulence. London, Civil Aviation Authority, Aeronautical Information Circular No. 122/1992.

CAA, 1993: United Kingdom Air Pilot. London, Civil Aviation Authority, CAP32.

Chandler,T.J. and Gregory, S, 1976: Climate of the British Isles. London, Longman.

Crutcher, H.L. and Quayle, R.G., 1974: Mariners worldwide climate guide to tropical storms at sea. Washington, Naval Weather Service.

Farman, J.C., Gardiner, B.G. and Shanklin, J.D., 1985: Large losses of total ozone in Antarctica reveal seasonal ClO_x/NO_x interaction. *Nature*, **315**, 207–210.

Heastie, H. and Stephenson, P.M., 1960: Upper winds over the world, parts I and II. *Geophys Mem, Meteorol Off*, No. 103.

Henderson-Sellers, A., 1986: Contemporary climatology. Harlow, Longman.

ICAO, 1964: Manual of the ICAO standard atmosphere, 2nd edition. Montreal, International Civil Aviation Organization.

ICAO, 1989: Procedures for air navigation services. ICAO abbreviations and codes (PANS-ABC), 4th edition. Montreal, International Civil Aviation Organization, Doc 8400/4).

ICAO, 1992: Meteorological Services for international air navigation, Annex 3, 11th edition. Montreal, International Civil Aviation Organization.

IPCC, 1990: Climate change, The IPCC scientific assessment. Cambridge University Press.

Lorenc, A.C., Bell, R.S., Davies, T. and Shutts, G.J., 1988: Numerical forecast studies of the October 1987 storm over southern England. *Meteorol Mag*, **117**, 118–130.

McCallum, E., 1990: The Burns' Day storm. *Weather*, **45**, 166–173.

McCallum, E., 1992: The importance of satellite imagery to the man–machine mix. *Weather*, **47**, 34–49.

McCallum, E. and Norris, W.J.T., 1990: The storms of January and February 1990. *Meteorol Mag*, **119**, 201–210.

McCarthy, J. and Serafin, R., 1984: The microburst: hazard to aircraft. *Weatherwise*, **37**, 120–127.

McIlveen, J.F.R., 1986: Basic meteorology. A physical outline. Wokingham, Van Nostrand Reinhold.

Meteorological Office, 1982a: Observer's Handbook. London, HMSO.

Meteorological Office, 1982b: Cloud types for observers. London, HMSO.

Meteorological Office, 1982c: Handbook of meteorological instruments. London, HMSO.

Meteorological Office, 1993: Handbook of meteorological telecommunications. Bracknell, Meteorological Office.

Middleton, W.E.K., 1952: Vision through the atmosphere. Toronto University Press.

Piggott, D., 1988: Understanding flying weather. London, Black.

Scorer, R.S., 1963: Atmospheric turbulence and its relation to aircraft. Proc Symp RAE Farnborough, November 1961. London, HMSO.

Tucker, G.B., 1960: Upper winds over the world, part III. *Geophys Mem, Meteorol Off*, No. 105.

Wallington, C.E., 1977: Meteorology for glider pilots. London, Murray.

Watson, and Lyall, 1985: Heaven's breath: a natural history of the wind. London, Hodder and Stoughton.

Welch, A., 1973: Pilot's weather. London, Murray.

WMO, 1975: International cloud atlas, Volume I. Geneva, World Meteorological Organization, Publication No. 407.

WMO, 1982: Guide on the global data-processing system. Geneva, World Meteorological Organization, Publication No. 305.

WMO, 1984: Manual on codes, volume II — Regional codes and national coding practice. Geneva, World Meteorological Organization, Publication No. 306.

WMO, 1988: Manual on codes, volume I — International codes. Geneva, World Meteorological Organization, Publication No. 306.

WMO, 1992: Weather reporting, Volume A — observing stations. Geneva, World Meteorological Organization, Publication No. 9.

Woodroffe, 1990: Forecasting the storm of 8 November 1989. *Meteorol Mag*, **119**, 129–140.

ANNEX

This section contains examples of synoptic charts, forecast products that might be given as flight documentation, and some codes and forms. Much contained here is liable to change, in contrast with the rest of the book. It has been collected here because it is an easily found location for reference and also to ease the production of future editions.

Codes and coding

Example standard low-level forecasts

Example WAFS forecast charts, valid 0000 UTC on 8 May 1992

Significant weather, tropopause and maximum wind:

Upper wind and temperature:

Plotted synoptic chart examples:

Page 388   August, 0600 UTC; occluding fronts moving across British Isles. Evidence of medium-level instability above col over Low Countries.

Page 389   January, 0600 UTC; polar continental air mass moving into the British Isles.

Tephigram

Page 390   Blank tephigram

Guidance on the decoding of a SYNOP message

SYNOP is an all-figure code message for exchange of surface weather data between meteorological stations. Although these reports are not usually seen by aviators, they can be obtained from the meteorological data banks, and the guidance below will assist in the extraction of those elements usually available in a METAR. Note that sea-level pressure (QFF in a SYNOP) is not evaluated in the same way as the QNH quoted in a METAR, but usually the difference between the two values is small, and only rarely would exceed 1 hPa.

Each SYNOP group usually contains five figures, but if elements are not observed, the figures will be replaced by solidii (/) or the group may be missing; hence care must be taken in identifying by their 'indicator' those containing the items of interest to aviation. Automatic weather stations usually only have the means to report wind, temperature and pressure.

Example

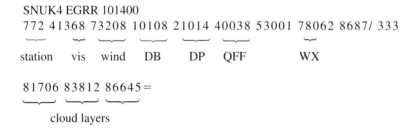

    SNUK4 EGRR 101400
    772 41368 73208 10108 21014 40038 53001 78062 8687/ 333

    station   vis   wind   DB   DP   QFF   WX

    81706 83812 86645 =

       cloud layers

The header line identifies the SYNOP bulletin by its number, meteorological collecting centre, and date/hour of the observation.

First group — station number (3 figures). However, in an international bulletin, this may be prefixed by two additional figures Global Block Number), e.g. 03 for British Isles, 06 for Low Countries, 07 for France.

Second group — the last two figures give the horizontal (surface) visibility. Up to 50, it is expressed directly in hundreds of metres; above 50 (and up to 80), subtract 50 and the result will be the visibility in kilometres, e.g. '35' = 3500 m, '56' = 6 km, '80' = 30 km, '00' = <100 m.

Third group — the last four figures give surface wind direction and speed (averaged over 10 minutes), in tens of degrees true from north and in knots, e.g. '3105' = 310 deg 05 kt; '0322' = 030 deg 22 kt; '0000' = calm.

Subsequent groups are identified by an initial 'indicator' figure.

The '1' group: the last three figures give the surface air (dry-bulb) temperature in degrees Celsius and tenths, preceded by either '0' or '1', to indicate positive or negative temperature respectively, e.g. '10067' = PS 6.7 °C, '10102' = PS 10.2 °C, '11102' = MS 10.2 °C.

The '2' group: similar to the '1' group, but giving dew-point temperature.

The '4' group gives the QFF in hectopascals and tenths. If 1000 hPa or higher, the thousands figure will be missing, e.g.'49986' = 998.6 hPa; '40092' = 1009.2 hPa.

The '7' group: the two figures immediately following the 7 report 'present' weather — see attached table for decode. If '00', '01', '02', '03', or the group is missing, there is no significant weather. Prior to July 1993 these code figures appeared with the letter code in the METAR weather group.

The '8' group(s) provide information on cloud. Those appearing after the indicator group '333' report significant layers in ascending order of height; following each 8 are encoded (respectively) the amount in oktas (one figure), the cloud type (one figure), and the base height above station level (two figure).
Cloud-type code figures '9' and '8' indicate (respectively) cumulonimbus and cumulus ('7' = ST, '6' = SC, '5' = NS, '4' = AS, '3' = AC). Cloud-base code figures up to 50 express the height directly in 100s of feet; above 50, subtract 50, and the height will be in thousands of feet, e.g. '84915' = 4/8 CB base 1500 ft; '88365' = 8/8 AC base 15 000 ft.
If the cloud amount code figure is '9', then cloud is not discernible.
Be aware that the code regulations allow the '333' and the groups following to be omitted from a report, even if cloud is present. Although for aviation purposes the information is not as precise, refer then to the single 8-group, the one usually appearing immediately before the '333'.
The first figure after the 8 gives the total amount of all low cloud in oktas (or of medium cloud if no low cloud is present), then the next three figures report (respectively) the predominant low, medium and high cloud in terms of genus, species and variety, e.g. '2' = TCU, '3' and '9' = CB. For an approximate height of the lowest reported cloud, refer to the code figure immediately before the visibility in the second group, namely

'0' = <150 ft; '1' = 150–299 ft; '2' = 300–599 ft; '3' = 600–999 ft; '4' = 1000–1999 ft; '5' = 2000–2999 ft; '6' = 3000–4999 ft.

If it appears that all 8-groups are missing, check the figure for the total amount of cloud covering sky immediately before the wind in the third group: if '0', sky is clear; if '9', cloud is not discernible (sky obscured).

Decode of the example SYNOP (only aviation weather information extracted)

SNUK4 EGRR 101400
772 41368 73208 10108 21014 40038 53001 78062 8687/ 333 81706
83812 86645=

Report at 1400 UTC on the 10th for station '772' — London (Heathrow) Airport:

Visibility '68' = 18 km; wind '3208' = 320 deg 08 kt;
temperature '0108' = PS 10.8 °C; dew-point '1014' = MS 1.4 °C;
QFF '0038' = 1003.8 hPa; present weather '80' = shower of slight rain ;
cloud '81706 83812 86645' = 1/8 ST 600 ft, 3/8 CU 1200 ft, 6/8 SC 4500 ft.

Guidance on the decoding of a METAR message

The METAR equivalent of the above SYNOP would appear in a bulletin in the
form:

SAUK31 EGGY 101350
EGLL 32008KT 9999 –SHRA SCT006 SCT012 BKN045 11/M01 Q1003=

Decode for SYNOP 'present weather' code figures (simplified version).

00	⎫	26	Recent snow or rain and snow
01	⎪ Not significant		shower
02	⎬ to aviation	27	Recent hail
03	⎭	28	Recent fog
04	Smoke or volcanic ash	29	Recent thunderstorm
05	Haze	30	⎫ Dust/sand storm,
06	Dust in suspension	31	⎬ slight or moderate
07	Dust or sand raised by wind	32	⎭
08	Well developed dust or sand whirl	33	⎫ Dust/sand storm,
09	Adjacent or recent dust/sand storm	34	⎬ severe
10	Mist	35	⎭
11	Shallow fog (patches)	36	Drifting snow, slight or moderate
12	Shallow fog (continuous)	37	Drifting snow, heavy
13	Lightning seen, no thunder	38	Blowing snow, slight or moderate
14	Precipitation not reaching ground	39	Blowing snow, heavy
15	Distant precipitation	40	Fog in vicinity
16	Adjacent precipitation	41	Fog patches
17	Thunder heard, no precipitation	42	Fog, sky discernible, thinning
18	Squall	43	Fog, sky obscured, thinning
19	Funnel cloud (tornado/waterspout)	44	Fog, sky discernible, not changing
20	Recent drizzle or snow grains	45	Fog, sky obscured, not changing
21	Recent rain	46	Fog, sky discernible, thickening
22	Recent snow	47	Fog, sky obscured, thickening
23	Recent rain and snow mixed	48	Freezing fog (sky discernible)
24	Recent freezing drizzle or rain	49	Freezing fog (sky obscured)
25	Recent rain shower	50	Drizzle, intermittent, slight

51	Drizzle, continuous, slight	78	Snow crystals
52	Drizzle, intermittent, moderate	79	Ice pellets
53	Drizzle, continuous, moderate	80	Shower of rain, slight
54	Drizzle, intermittent, heavy	81	Shower of rain, moderate or heavy
55	Drizzle, continuous, heavy	82	Shower of rain, violent
56	Freezing drizzle, slight	83	Shower of rain and snow, slight
57	Freezing drizzle, moderate or heavy	84	Shower of rain and snow, moderate or heavy
58	Drizzle and rain, slight	85	Shower of snow, slight
59	Drizzle and rain, moderate or heavy	86	Shower of snow, moderate or heavy
60	Rain, intermittent, slight	87	Small hail or snow pellets, slight
61	Rain, continuous, slight	88	Small hail or snow pellets moderate or heavy
62	Rain, intermittent, moderate	89	Shower of hail, slight
63	Rain, continuous, moderate	90	Shower of hail, moderate or heavy
64	Rain, intermittent, heavy	91	Rain, slight; recent thunder
65	Rain, continuous, heavy	92	Rain, moderate or heavy; recent thunder
66	Freezing rain, slight	93	Snow or hail, slight; recent thunder
67	Freezing rain, moderate or heavy	94	Snow or hail, moderate or heavy; recent thunder
68	Rain (or drizzle) and snow, slight	95	Thunderstorm with rain and/or snow
69	Rain (or drizzle) and snow, moderate or heavy	96	Thunderstorm with hail
70	Snow, intermittent, slight	97	Thunderstorm with rain and/or snow, heavy
71	Snow, continuous, slight	98	Thunderstorm with dust/sand storm
72	Snow, intermittent, moderate	99	Thunderstorm with hail, heavy
73	Snow, continuous, moderate		
74	Snow, intermittent, heavy		
75	Snow, continuous, heavy		
76	Diamond dust		
77	Snow grains		

Guidance on the decoding of a plotted synoptic observation

The model below shows the relative positions of the various elements of a station plot. Figure values are plotted for VV, N$_s$, h$_s$h$_s$, TT, T$_d$T$_d$, f'f', PPP and ppp; symbols are used for the remaining elements.

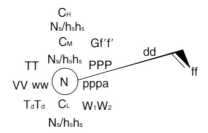

Code figures and symbols

N   Total amount of cloud covering sky

amount of sky covered	0	1/8	2/8	3/8	4/8	5/8	6/8	7/8	8/8	sky obscured
symbol	○	◐	◐	◐	◐	◐	◐	◐	●	⊗

ddff   Wind velocity
The wind direction is shown by the shaft of an arrow flying with the wind. The speed is indicated by feathers and solid pennants. A full-length feather can be regarded as 10 kt, a half-feather 5 kt and a pennant 50 kt. Calm is represented by a complete circle surrounding the station circle, variable by a broken circle, and 1 or 2 kt by a shaft with no feathers. Gust speeds (f'f'), preceded by 'G', may be found plotted above the QFF.

VV   Visibility
Up to 50, plotted in hundreds of metres; then up to 80, subtracting 50 gives the visibility in kilometres. Above 80 the steps are in 5 km. When <100 m 'F', followed by the visibility in metres, may be plotted instead of '00'.

ww   Present weather
Identify the 'ww' code figures appropriate to the symbol from the following table (first figure from beginning of row, second from column); then refer to the SYNOP decode on pages 362/3.

ww	0	1	2	3	4	5	6	7	8	9
0					⌐∿		S	$⁄ℓ	⧟	(⌿→)
1	⁼	⁼⁼	⁼⁼	⌇	⦁	)•(	(•)	⌿	▽	)(
2	’]	•]	⋆]	⋆]	∿]	▽]	⋆▽]	△]	⁼]	⌿]
3	⌿|	⌿→	|⌿→	⌿→|	⌿→	|⌿→	⌿+	+⌿+	++	⧺
4	(⁼)	∵	⁼|	⁼|	⁼⁼	⁼	|⁼	|⁼	⨛	⨛
5	’	’’	⸴	’’	⸴	’’’	∿	∿	⸴•	⸴•
6	•	••	⸽	⸽∴	⸽	❖	◡	◡	⸽⋆	⋆⸽⋆
7	⋆	⋆⋆	⋆⋆	⋆⋆	⋆⋆⋆	⋆⋆⋆	↔	⊸	⋆⊸	△
8	•▽	•▽	⸽▽	⸽⋆▽	⸽⋆▽	⋆▽	⋆▽	△▽	△▽	▲▽
9	▲▽	⌿]•	⌿]⸽	⌿]⋆⁄△	⌿]⋆⁄△	⋆⌿	△⌿	⌿	⌿→⌿	△⌿

W₁W₂ Past weather

This refers to the previous 6 hours if on the 00, 06, 12 or 18 UTC charts; to the previous 3 hours if on the 03, 09, 15 or 21 UTC charts; to the previous hour if on charts for other times. A single symbol means that particular weather has occurred for part of the time; two identical symbols means that it has been continuous; two different symbols means that each has occurred, the first being predominant.

W₁W₂	
⌿→	Sand-/dust-storm
⁼	Fog
’	Drizzle
•	Rain
⋆	Snow, or rain and snow
▽	Shower
⌿	Thunderstorm

365

$C_LC_MC_H$ Cloud types

C_L		C_M		C_H	
◌	small Cu	⟋	thin As	⌐	strands of Ci
△	moderate or large Cu	⟋	thick As or Ns	⌐	dense Ci
🜂	Cb without anvil	ᴟ	Ac	⌐?	dense Ci in form of anvil
⌂	Sc formed by the spreading of Cu	𝒢	patches Ac	⟋	Ci in hooks invading the sky
⌄	Sc	⟅	Ac in bands growing denser	2⏤	Ci and/or Cs continuous veil below 45°
—	St	⋉	Ac from spreading Cu or Cb	2	Ci and/or Cs continuous veil above 45°
---	St fra or Cu fra (St or Cu fractus)	⟆⟆	Ac in layers or with As or Ns or opaque Ac	2⸲	veil of Ci over whole sky
⌣	Cu and Sc	M	Ac castellanus	⸲	Cs not covering whole sky
🜃	Cb with anvil	𝒢	Ac in chaotic layers	⟲	Cc predominating

N_s **Amount of individual cloud layer** with base h_sh_s, expressed in oktas. The base of medium-level cloud (C_M) is plotted below the station circle when it is below 8000 ft and if no low cloud (C_L) is reported.

h_sh_s **Height of base of cloud layer above station level**.
Up to 50, plotted in hundreds of feet; above 50 and up to 80, subtracting 50 gives the base in thousands of feet; above 80 the steps are of 5000 ft.

TT **Dry-bulb temperature** ⎱
T_dT_d **Dew-point temperature** ⎰ Plotted in whole degrees Celsius with a minus sign for sub-zero temperatures

PPP **MSL pressure (QFF)**: only tens, units and tenths figures plotted, e.g. '894' = 989.4 hPa; '094' = 1009.4 hPa

ppp **Pressure tendency**: change in pressure during preceding 3 hours. Usually units and tens figures plotted, with tens only as necessary, e.g. '03' = change of 0.3 hPa; '101' = change of 10.1 hPa.

a   Characteristic or direction of pressure tendency

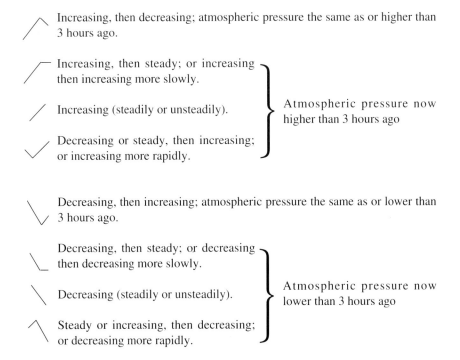

Increasing, then decreasing; atmospheric pressure the same as or higher than 3 hours ago.

Increasing, then steady; or increasing then increasing more slowly.

Increasing (steadily or unsteadily).

Decreasing or steady, then increasing; or increasing more rapidly.

} Atmospheric pressure now higher than 3 hours ago

Decreasing, then increasing; atmospheric pressure the same as or lower than 3 hours ago.

Decreasing, then steady; or decreasing then decreasing more slowly.

Decreasing (steadily or unsteadily).

Steady or increasing, then decreasing; or decreasing more rapidly.

} Atmospheric pressure now lower than 3 hours ago

If no symbol, and tendency figure '00' then atmospheric pressure steady, same as 3 hours ago.

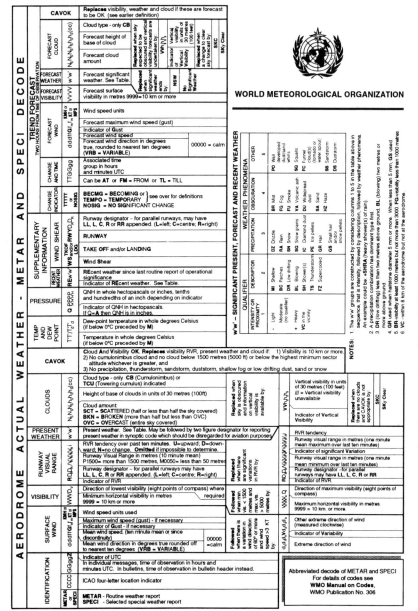

AERODROME ACTUAL WEATHER – METAR AND SPECI DECODE

TREND FORECAST (TWO HOURS FROM TIME OF OBSERVATION)

CAVOK		Replaces visibility, weather and cloud if these are forecast to be OK (see earlier definition)
FORECAST CLOUD	$N_sN_sN_sh_sh_sh_s(cc)$	Cloud type - only **CB**
		Forecast height of base of cloud
		Forecast cloud amount
FORECAST WEATHER	$w'w'$	Forecast significant weather. See Table.
FORECAST VISIBILITY	VVVV	Forecast surface visibility in metres 9999 = 10 km or more
FORECAST WIND	$dddff(G f_m f_m)$ $\frac{MN/ KT or}{MPS}$	Wind speed units
		Forecast maximum wind speed (gust)
		Indicator of Gust
		Forecast wind speed
		Forecast wind direction in degrees true, rounded to nearest ten degrees (**VRB** = **VARIABLE**) 00000 = calm
CHANGE AND TIME	$TTGGgg$	Associated time group in hours and minutes UTC
		Can be **AT** or **FM** = FROM or **TL** = TILL
CHANGE INDICATOR	$TTTT$ or $NOSIG$	**BECMG** = BECOMING or **TEMPO** = TEMPORARY } see over for definitions **NOSIG** = NO SIGNIFICANT CHANGE

Replaced when sky expected to be obscured and vertical visibility forecasts are undertaken by $VVh_sh_sh_s$ Indicator of Vertical Visibility — Vertical visibility in units of 30 metres (100 feet) — Replaced when a change to clear sky forecast by **SKC** Sky Clear

Replaced when significant weather ends by **NSW** = No Significant Weather

SUPPLEMENTARY INFORMATION

WIND SHEAR	WS $\frac{TKOF}{RWYD_RD_R}$ or LDG	Runway designator – for parallel runways, may have **LL, L, C, R** or **RR** appended. (L=left; C=centre; R=right)
		RUNWAY
		TAKE OFF and/or **LANDING**
		Wind Shear
RECENT WEATHER	$REw'w'$	REcent weather since last routine report of operational significance
		Indicator of REcent weather. See Table.
PRESSURE	$Q PPPP$	QNH in whole hectopascals or inches, tenths and hundredths of an inch depending on indicator
		Indicator of QNH in hectopascals. If **Q**=**A** then QNH is in inches.
TEMP AND DEW POINT	$T'T'/T'_dT'_d$	Dew-point temperature in whole degrees Celsius (if below 0°C preceded by **M**)
		Temperature in whole degrees Celsius (if below 0°C preceded by **M**)
CAVOK		Cloud And Visibility OK. Replaces visibility RVR, present weather and cloud if: 1) Visibility is 10 km or more. 2) No cumulonimbus cloud and no cloud below 1500 metres (5000 ft) or below the highest minimum sector altitude whichever is greater, and 3) No precipitation, thunderstorm, sandstorm, duststorm, shallow fog or low drifting dust, sand or snow
CLOUDS	$N_sN_sN_sh_sh_sh_s(cc)$	Cloud type - only **CB** (Cumulonimbus) or **TCU** (Towering cumulus) indicated
		Height of base of clouds in units of 30 metres (100ft)
		Cloud amount: **SCT** = SCATTERED (half or less than half the sky covered) **BKN** = BROKEN (more than half but less than OVC) **OVC** = OVERCAST (entire sky covered)
PRESENT WEATHER	$w'w'$	Present weather. See Table. May be followed by two figure designator for reporting present weather in synoptic code which should be disregarded for aviation purposes
RUNWAY VISUAL RANGE	$RD_RD_R/V_RV_RV_RV_Ri$	RVR tendency over past ten minutes. U=upward; D=downward; N=no change. Omitted if impossible to determine.
		Runway Visual Range in metres (10 minute mean) P1500= more than 1500 metres, M0050= less than 50 metres
		Runway designator – for parallel runways may have **LL, L, C, R** or **RR** appended. (L=left; C=centre; R=right)
		Indicator of RVR
VISIBILITY	$VVVVD_v$	Direction of lowest visibility (eight points of compass) where required Minimum horizontal visibility in metres 9999 = 10 km or more
SURFACE WIND	$dddff(G f_m f_m)$ $\frac{MN/ KT or}{MPS}$	Wind speed units used
		Maximum wind speed (gust) - if necessary
		Indicator of Gust - if necessary
		Mean wind speed. (ten minute mean or since discontinuity) 00000 =calm
		Mean wind direction in degrees true rounded off to nearest ten degrees (**VRB** = **VARIABLE**)
IDENTIFICATION	$CCCC GGggZ$	Indicator of UTC
		In individual messages, time of observation in hours and minutes UTC. In bulletins, time of observation in bulletin header instead.
		ICAO four-letter location indicator

METAR or **SPECI**

METAR - Routine weather report
SPECI - Selected special weather report

Replaced when sky is obscured and information on vertical visibility is available by: $VVh_sh_sh_s$ — /// = Vertical visibility unavailable — Indicator of Vertical Visibility — Replaced when there are no clouds and CAVOK is not appropriate by: **SKC** Sky Clear

Replaced when there are significant variations in RVR by $RD_RD_R/V_RV_RV_RV_RVV_RV_RV_RV_Ri$ — RVR tendency — Runway visual range in metres (one minute mean maximum over last ten minutes) — Indicator of significant Variation — Runway visual range in metres (one minute mean minimum over last ten minutes) — Runway designator –for parallel runways may have **LL, L, C, R** or **RR** — Indicator of RVR.

Followed when min vis. < 1500 metres and max vis. > 5000 metres by: $VVVV_v Q$ — Direction of maximum visibility (eight points of compass) — Maximum horizontal visibility in metres. 9999 = 10 km. or more.

Followed when there is a variation in wind direction of 60° or more and wind speed >3 KT by: $d_nd_nd_nVd_xd_xd_x$ — Other extreme direction of wind (measured clockwise) — Indicator of Variability — Extreme direction of wind

WORLD METEOROLOGICAL ORGANIZATION

w'w' – SIGNIFICANT PRESENT, FORECAST AND RECENT WEATHER

WEATHER PHENOMENA

QUALIFIER		PRECIPITATION	OBSCURATION	OTHER
INTENSITY OR PROXIMITY 1	DESCRIPTOR 2	3	4	5
- Light	**MI** Shallow	**DZ** Drizzle	**BR** Mist	**PO** Well developed dust/sand whirls
(no qualifier) Moderate	**BC** Patches	**RA** Rain	**FG** Fog	
+ Heavy	**DR** Low drifting	**SN** Snow	**FU** Smoke	**SQ** Squalls
VC in the vicinity	**BL** Blowing	**SG** Snow grains	**VA** Volcanic ash	**FC** Funnel cloud(s) (tornado or water spout)
	SH Shower(s)	**IC** Diamond dust	**DU** Widespread dust	
	TS Thunderstorm	**PE** Ice pellets	**SA** Sand	**SS** Sandstorm
	FZ Supercooled	**GR** Hail	**HZ** Haze	**DS** Duststorm
		GS Small hail and/or snow pellets		

NOTES:
1. The w'w' groups are constructed by considering columns 1 to 5 in the table above in sequence, that is intensity, followed by description, followed by weather phenomena. An example could be +SHRA (heavy shower(s) of rain).
2. A precipitation combination has dominant type first.
3. DR (low drifting) less than two metres above ground, BL (blowing) two metres or more above ground.
4. GR used when hailstone diameter 5 mm or more. When less than 5 mm, GS used.
5. BR-visibility at least 1000 metres but not more than 3000 FG-visibility less than 1000 metres.
6. VC –within 8 km of the aerodrome but not at the aerodrome

Abbreviated decode of METAR and SPECI
For details of codes see
WMO Manual on Codes,
WMO Publication No. 306

Aerodrome actual weather — METAR and SPECI decode

AERODROME FORECAST - TAF DECODE

IDENTIFICATION

TAF	TAF - Name for an Aerodrome Forecast
CCCC	ICAO four-letter location indicator
YYGGggZ	Date and time of origin of forecast in UTC
	Indicator of UTC
$G_1G_1G_2G_2$	Beginning G_1G_1 and end G_2G_2 of forecast period in hours UTC

FORECAST SURFACE WIND

$dddff G_f f_m$ — KMH or KT or MPS

- Wind speed units used
- Maximum wind speed (gust)
- Indicator of Gust
- Mean wind speed
- Mean wind direction in degrees true rounded to nearest ten degrees. **(VRB = VARIABLE)** 00000 = calm

FORECAST VISIBILITY

VVVV — Minimum horizontal visibility in metres 9999 = 10 km or more

FORECAST SIGNIFICANT WEATHER

w'w' — Forecast significant weather (see table on other side)

Replaced when significant weather phenomenon forecast to end by:
NSW — No Significant Weather

FORECAST CLOUD AMOUNT AND HEIGHT

$N_sN_sN_sh_sh_sh_s(cc)$

- Cloud type - only CB (cumulonimbus)
- Height of base of cloud in units of 30 metres (100 feet)
- Cloud amount:
  - **SCT = SCATTERED** (half or less than half the sky covered)
  - **BKN = BROKEN** (more than half but less than OVC)
  - **OVC = OVERCAST** (entire sky covered)

Replaced when sky is expected to be obscured and information on vertical visibility is available by:
$VVh_sh_sh_s$ — Vertical visibility in units of 30 metres (100 feet)
- Indicator of Vertical Visibility

Replaced when clear sky is forecast by:
SKC — Sky Clear

Replaced if agreed regionally, when no CB and no cloud below 1500 m (5000 ft) or below the highest minimum sector altitude, whichever is greater are forecast and CAVOK and SKC are not appropriate by:
NSC — No Significant Cloud

CAVOK — Cloud And Visibility OK. **Replaces** visibility, weather and cloud if:
1) Visibility is forecast to be 10 km or more
2) No cumulonimbus cloud and no other cloud forecast below 1500 metres (5000 ft) or below the highest minimum sector altitude whichever is greater, and
3) No precipitation, thunderstorm, sandstorm, duststorm, shallow fog or low drifting dust, sand or snow forecast

THESE GROUPS ONLY USED IF AGREED REGIONALLY

FORECAST TEMPERATURE
(TT_FT_F/G_FG_FZ)
- Indicator of forecast Temperature
- Forecast temperature at G_FG_F. Temperatures below 0°C preceded by **M**.
- Time UTC to which forecast temperature refers

FORECAST ICING
$(6I_ch_ch_ch_cl_c)$
- Indicator of UTC [Indicator of forecast icing]
- Type of icing (see below)
- Base of layer of icing in units of 30 metres (100 feet)
- Thickness of layer (thousands of feet) with code figure 0 = up to top of clouds

FORECAST TURBULENCE
$(5Bh_Bh_Bh_Bt_B)$
- Indicator of forecast turbulence
- Type of turbulence (see below)
- Base of layer of turbulence in units of 30 metres (100 feet)
- Thickness of layer (thousands of feet) with code figure 0 = up to top of clouds

SIGNIFICANT CHANGES IN FORECAST CONDITIONS INDICATED BY:

PROBABILITY
- **PROB** C_2C_2 — **PROB**ability. Only 30 or 40 used, indicating 30% or 40%

Probability is used to indicate the probability of occurrence of:
a) an alternative element or elements
b) temporary fluctuations

TIME
GGG_eG_e — Beginning GG and end G_eG_e of forecast period in hours UTC

CHANGE
TTTTT — Type of significant change:
BECMG - BECOMING, used where changes are expected to reach or pass through specified values at a regular or irregular rate.
TEMPO - TEMPORARY fluctuations of less than one hour and in aggregate less than half the period indicated by GGG_eG_e

Both replaced if one set of weather conditions is expected to change more or less completely to a different set of conditions, thus indicating the beginning of another self-contained part of the forecast, by:
TTGG — This takes the form **FM**GG where FM is the abbreviation for from and GG is time to the nearest hour UTC. All conditions before this group are superseded by conditions indicated after the group.

TIME
GGG_eG_e — Beginning GG and end G_eG_e of forecast period in hours UTC

	0	1	2	3	4	5	6	7	8	9
I_c	no icing	light icing	light icing in cloud	light icing in precipitation	moderate icing	moderate icing in cloud	moderate icing in precipitation	severe icing	severe icing in cloud	severe icing in precipitation
B	no turbulence	light turbulence	moderate turbulence in clear air, infrequent	moderate turbulence in clear air, frequent	moderate turbulence in cloud, infrequent	moderate turbulence in cloud, frequent	severe turbulence in clear air, infrequent	severe turbulence in clear air, frequent	severe turbulence in cloud, infrequent	severe turbulence in cloud, frequent

Aerodrome forecast — TAF decode

Abbreviated decode of TAF
For details of codes see
WMO Manual on Codes,
WMO Publication No. 306

The Met.Office

EXPLANATION NOTES FOR METFORM 215 –
CHART OF FORECAST WEATHER BELOW 15000 FT

Metform 215 is a forecast form which has been introduced to replace written low-level area and route fore-casts for flights within the United Kingdom and to the very near Continent.The form covers in-flight con-ditions from the surface to 15000 ft and comprises three sections; a forecast chart of the UK low-level weather for a fixed time and a surface chart for the outlook section, a tabular section containing complete descriptive text for the various weather zones, and an outlook with the main synoptic features for the next six hours.
Following its trial introduction in June 1992 the Metform 215T met with unanimous approval and the CAA decided to introduce it permanently from 1993.

INFORMATION GIVEN

a) Charts

i) Top left-hand side

- The weather chart shows the forecast position and direction and speed of movement of surface fronts and pressure centres for the fixed time shown in the chart's legend. All features are given identifying letters to enable their subsequent movements to be followed on the outlook chart.
- Freezing levels (0 °C) are shown in boxes as thousands of feet, at appropriate places on the chart.
- Zones of distinct weather are enclosed by continuous scalloped lines, each zone being identified by a number within a circle.

ii) Top right-hand side

- A surface forecast chart 'Outlook' showing the expected positions of the principal synoptic features and surface isobars at the end of the outlook period of six hours. NO weather zones are given on the outlook chart.

b) Tabular Forecast

- Each zone, identified by its number on the weather chart, is self contained with each zone being dealt with separately and completely. The text contains the main zone weather (visibility, weather, cloud) during the period of validity followed by local variants within the zone, together with appropriate warnings and remarks.

c) Outlook

The outlook text describes the principal weather changes expected during the six-hour outlook period.

ISSUE TIMES

Time when chart becomes available	Validity time	Period of validity	Outlook to
0500 UTC	0900 UTC	0600-1200 UTC	1800 UTC
1100 UTC	1500 UTC	1200-1800 UTC	0000 UTC
1700 UTC	2100 UTC	1800-0000 UTC	0600 UTC
2300 UTC	0300 UTC	0000-0600 UTC	1200 UTC

The time when the Metform is issued by the Met. Office and the date are shown at the bottom of the form.

AMENDMENTS

- An amended Metform 215 is indicated by the word AMENDED at the top of the form.
- Minor amendments are issued as a separate amending text appended at the bottom of the form, which may be reduced slightly in size to accommodate the extra text.

May 1993

Form 216 — explanatory notes for FORM 215 — Chart of forecast weather below 15 000 ft

The Met.Office

EXPLANATION NOTES FOR METFORM 215 – CHART OF FORECAST WEATHER BELOW 15000 FT

Pressure centres and fronts.

The surface position of pressure centres is shown by **X** for a low centre and ○ for a high centre. The letters **L** or **H**, as appropriate, together with the central pressure in millibars are shown adjacent to the position.

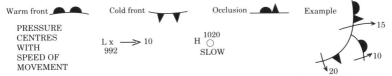

PRESSURE
CENTRES
WITH
SPEED OF
MOVEMENT

L x ⟶ 10
992

H ○ 1020
SLOW

The direction and speed of movement (in knots) of centres and fronts is given. Letters are allocated to surface fronts for identification purposes for movements on the outlook chart. Movements of less than 5 knots are shown as 'SLOW'.

Abbreviations used in the tabular section

GEN – general

LOC – locally	**WDSPR** – widespread	**N** – north
ISOL – isolated	**E** – east	**S** – south
OCNL – occasionally	**W** – west	**COT** – coast
FRQ – frequent	**EMBD** – embedded	

Surface visibility is expressed in metres (M) or kilometres (KM), with the changeover at 5KM

Weather:-

RA – rain	**DZ** – drizzle	**TS** – thunderstorms
SH – showers	**FZ** – freezing	

Other phenomena are written in full and may be a combination.

Cloud:-

ST – stratus	**SC** – stratocumulus	**CU** – cumulus
CB – cumulonimbus	**AC** – altocumulus	**AS** – altostratus
LYR – layers	**NS** – nimbostratus	

amounts are in oktas with base followed by tops and turbulence and ice if applicable.

MOD – moderate	**SEV** – severe	**BLW** – below

Hill fog is not used but Cloud covering hills was thought to be more informative and implies visibility <200M, CB and TS imply severe turbulence and icing.

Tolerance:-

Single numerical values given for any element represent the most probable mean in a range of values covering approximately + or -25%.

The complementary form F214 provides spot winds over a similar area.

May 1993

Form 216 — explanatory notes for FORM 215 (continued)

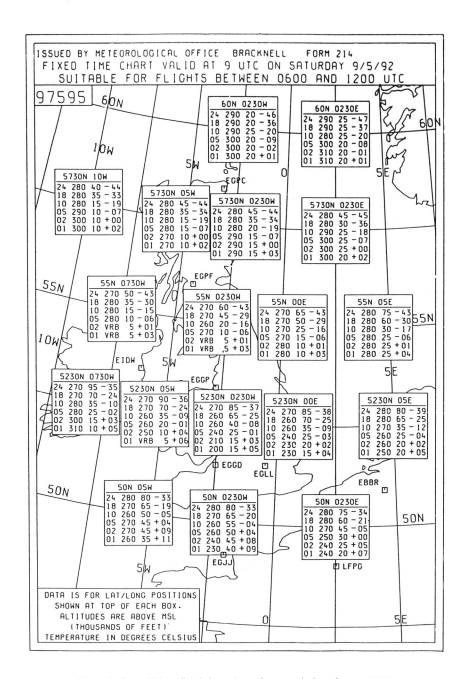

Example Form 214 — fixed-time chart of upper winds and temperature

372

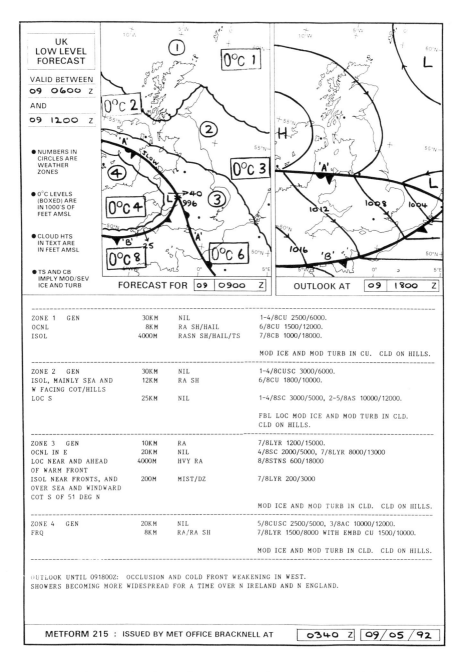

ZONE 1 GEN	30KM	NIL	1-4/8CU 2500/6000.
OCNL	8KM	RA SH/HAIL	6/8CU 1500/12000.
ISOL	4000M	RASN SH/HAIL/TS	7/8CB 1000/18000.
			MOD ICE AND MOD TURB IN CU. CLD ON HILLS.
ZONE 2 GEN	30KM	NIL	1-4/8CUSC 3000/6000.
ISOL, MAINLY SEA AND W FACING COT/HILLS	12KM	RA SH	6/8CU 1800/10000.
LOC S	25KM	NIL	1-4/8SC 3000/5000, 2-5/8AS 10000/12000.
			FBL LOC MOD ICE AND MOD TURB IN CLD. CLD ON HILLS.
ZONE 3 GEN	10KM	RA	7/8LYR 1200/15000.
OCNL IN E	20KM	NIL	4/8SC 2000/5000, 7/8LYR 8000/13000
LOC NEAR AND AHEAD OF WARM FRONT	4000M	HVY RA	8/8STNS 600/18000
ISOL NEAR FRONTS, AND OVER SEA AND WINDWARD COT S OF 51 DEG N	200M	MIST/DZ	7/8LYR 200/3000
			MOD ICE AND MOD TURB IN CLD. CLD ON HILLS.
ZONE 4 GEN	20KM	NIL	5/8CUSC 2500/5000, 3/8AC 10000/12000.
FRQ	8KM	RA/RA SH	7/8LYR 1500/8000 WITH EMBD CU 1500/10000.
			MOD ICE AND MOD TURB IN CLD. CLD ON HILLS.

OUTLOOK UNTIL 091800Z: OCCLUSION AND COLD FRONT WEAKENING IN WEST.
SHOWERS BECOMING MORE WIDESPREAD FOR A TIME OVER N IRELAND AND N ENGLAND.

METFORM 215 : ISSUED BY MET OFFICE BRACKNELL AT 0340 Z 09/05/92

Example Form 215 — fixed-time chart of weather below 15 000 ft

```
===========================================================================
                    GLIDING  FORECAST
                 FOR MONDAY 04 MAY 1992.
===========================================================================
Met Nr: 1-8                   Prepared at EGRRYMYX.
Recipient:                    Site:
EAST SUSSEX GLIDING CLUB      BRIGHTON, HASTINGS,  (WED, SAT, SUN & PH)
                              AND TUNBRIDGE WELLS.
LONDON GLIDING CLUB           CHILTERNS.
KENT GLIDING CLUB             CHALLOCK, Nr ASHFORD (WED, SAT, SUN & PH)
WYCOMBE GLIDING CLUB          BOOKER AIRFIELD.
LASHAM GLIDING CLUB           LASHAM AIRFIELD.
ENSTONE GLIDING CLUB          ENSTONE AREA.
POPHAM MICROLIGHT SCHOOL      POPHAM AIRFIELD.
BATH & WILTS GLIDING CLUB     KEEVIL. (SAT, SUN & PH)
---------------------------------------------------------------------------
Period:  DAWN  TO  DUSK
---------------------------------------------------------------------------
      ALL HEIGHTS ABOVE MEAN SEA LEVEL   -   ALL TIMES UTC
NOTE: THIS FORECAST TO BE USED IN CONJUNCTION WITH AIRMET
===========================================================================
THERMAL  ACTIVITY  MOD TO AROUND 4500FT LATE MORNING
     AND AFTERNOON; TRIGGER TEMP PS12C.   DYING AFTER ABOUT 1500Z.
---------------------------------------------------------------------------
INVERSIONS  SLIGHT AT 5500FT AND 10000FT
     WITH SHALLOW SURFACE INVERSION INLAND AT FIRST.
---------------------------------------------------------------------------
SURFACE WIND
     WESTSOUTHWESTERLY 05KT, BUT VARIABLE OR CALM AT TIMES
---------------------------------------------------------------------------
LEE WAVES NIL.
---------------------------------------------------------------------------
SEA BREEZE EFFECTS WEAK SEA BREEZE AFTER 0900Z,
     CONFINED TO THE SOUTH COAST AND NOT PENETRATING FAR INLAND.
---------------------------------------------------------------------------
LOWEST FORECAST PRESSURE (QNH)
EAST SUSSEX GLIDING CLUB:  1025MB
LONDON GLIDING CLUB     :  1024MB
KENT GLIDING CLUB       :  1025MB
WYCOMBE GLIDING CLUB    :  1024MB
LASHAM GLIDING CLUB     :  1024MB
ENSTONE GLIDING CLUB    :  1024MB
POPHAM MICROLIGHT SCHOOL:  1024MB
BATH AND WILTS G.C.     :  1024MB
```

Example of gliding forecast

```
========================================================================
          BALLOONING  FORECAST
========================================================================
                       NOTE
THIS FORECAST IS PROVIDED AS A SUPPLEMENT TO, AND NOT A SUBSTITUTE FOR,
                "AIRMET" OR CHART FORMS 214/215.

========================================================================
AREA :      SOUTHEAST AND CENTRAL SOUTHERN ENGLAND
PERIOD :    DAWN TO MIDDAY, MONDAY 4TH MAY 1992.
========================================================================

WINDS : (DEGREES TRUE AND KNOTS)
     SURFACE :   VRB 05KT, BUT CALM AT TIMES.

    THERMALS :   WEAK TO 4500FT, TRIGGER TEMP PS12.

  INVERSIONS :   SLIGHT AT 5500FT AND 10000FT.

 SEA BREEZES :   WEAK SEA BREEZES AFTER 0900Z, CONFINED TO SOUTH COAST.

   LEE WAVES :   NIL.

LOWEST PRESSURE (QNH) : 1025MB.

SURFACE AIR TEMPERATURE:
          0600:   PS05C.
          0900:   PS09C.
          1200:   PS14C.

OUTLOOK UNTIL DUSK: THERMALS BECOMING MODERATE.

========================================================================
ISSUED AT:  040300Z.
========================================================================
TIME GMT    AREA  OF  INTEREST
```

Example of ballooning forecast

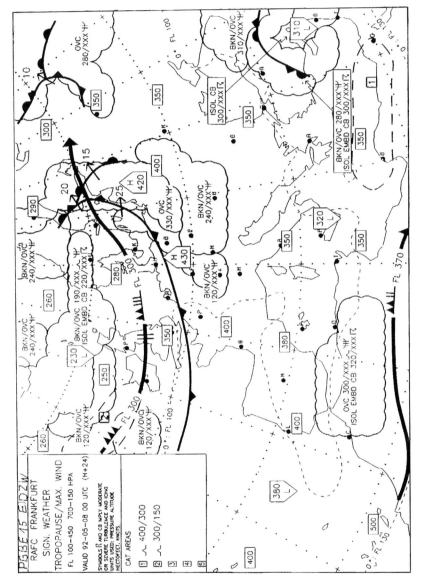

Example forecast significant weather/tropopause/maximum wind chart: European (EUR) area — FL100 to FL450

376

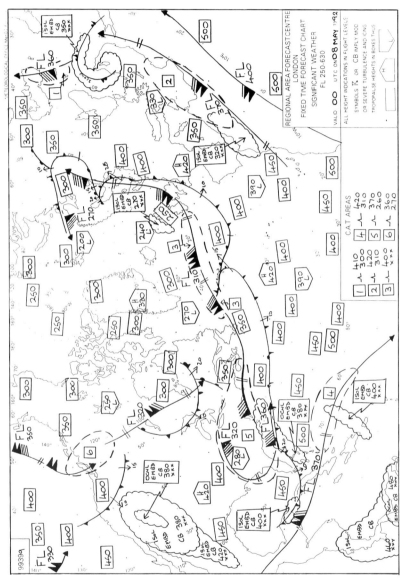

Example forecast significant weather/tropopause/maximum wind chart: North Atlantic (NAT) area — FL250 to FL630

377

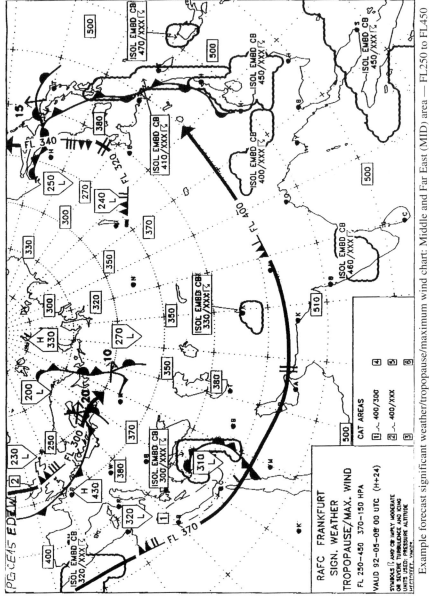

Example forecast significant weather/tropopause/maximum wind chart: Middle and Far East (MID) area — FL250 to FL450

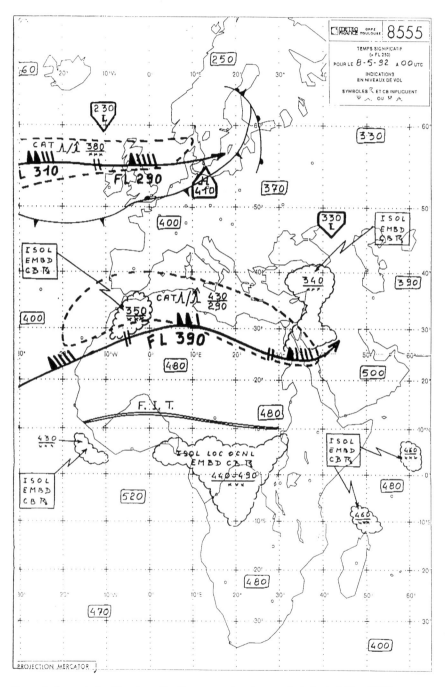

Example forecast significant weather/tropopause/maximum wind chart: Africa (AFI) area — above FL250

379

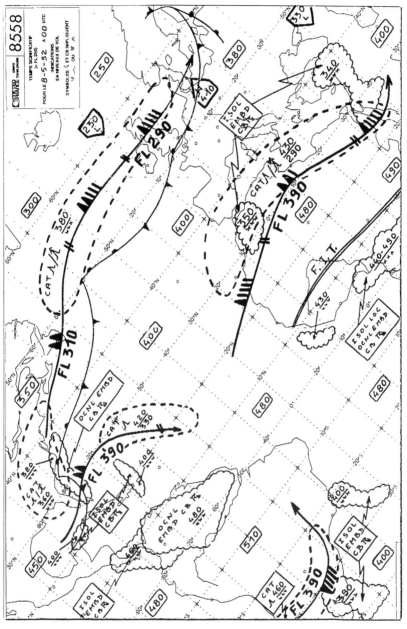

Example forecast significant weather/tropopause/maximum wind chart: Caribbean and South America (CAR/SAM) area — above FL250

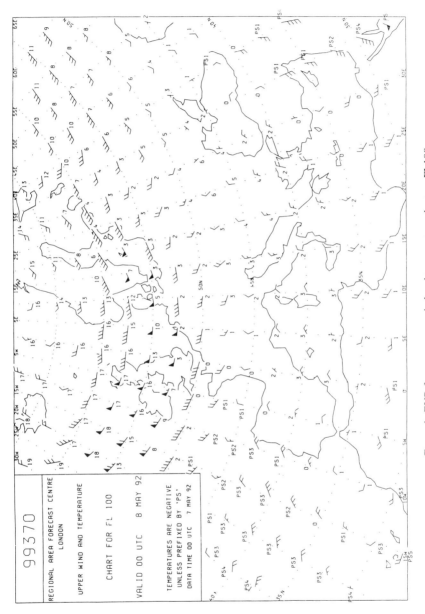

Example EUR forecast upper wind and temperature chart — FL100

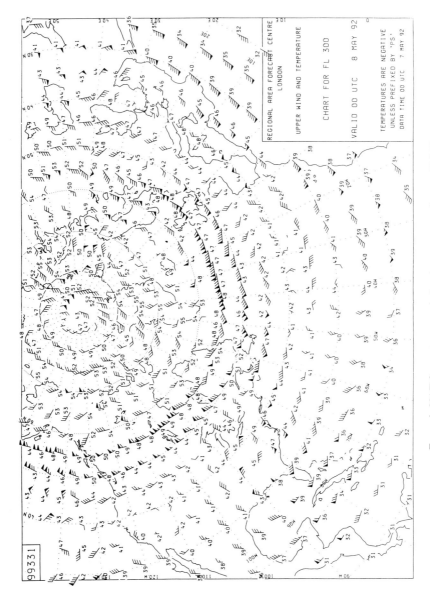

Example NAT forecast upper wind and temperature chart — FL300

Example MID forecast upper wind and temperature chart — FL340

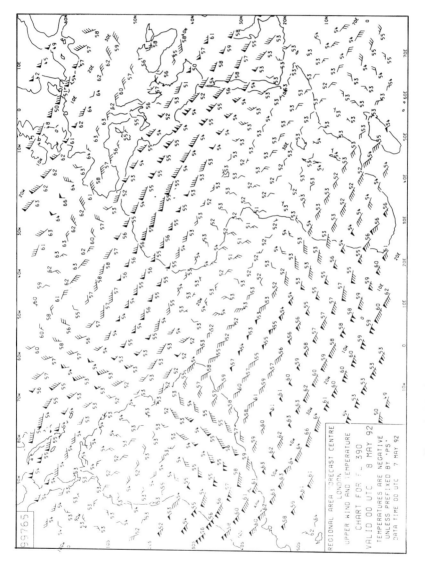

Example AFI/CAR/SAM forecast upper wind and temperature chart — FL390

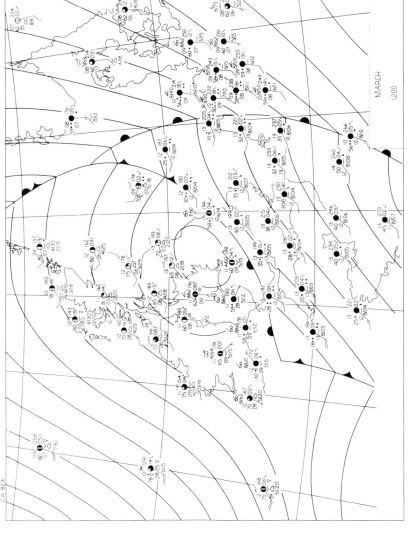

Plotted synoptic chart example, 1: March, 1200 UTC: shallow secondary wave depression on cold front crossing England and Wales.

385

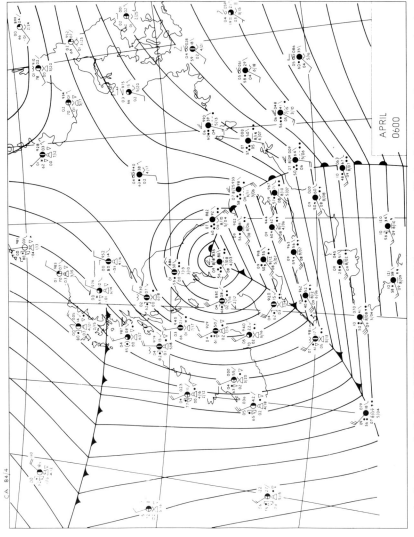

CA 84/4

APRIL
0600

Plotted synoptic chart example, 2: April, 0600 UTC; intense frontal depression over England with arctic air mass moving into Scotland.

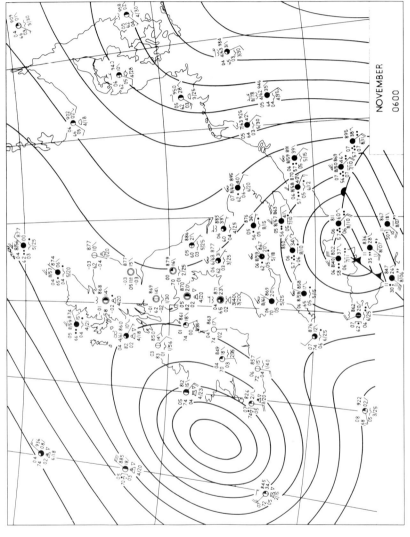

Plotted synoptic chart example. 3: November, 0600 UTC; frontal depression over northern France and deeper non-frontal depression to the west of Ireland.

387

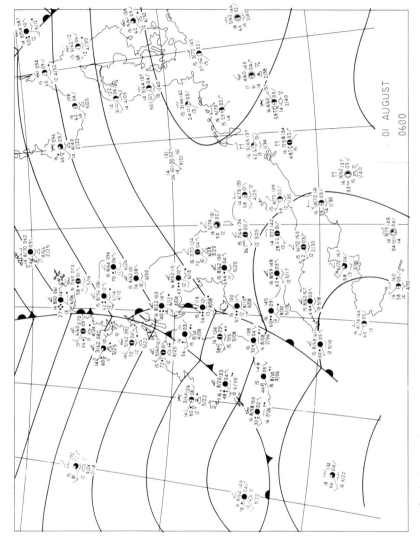

Plotted synoptic chart example, 4: August, 0600 UTC; occluding fronts moving across British Isles. Evidence of medium-level instability above col over Low Countries.

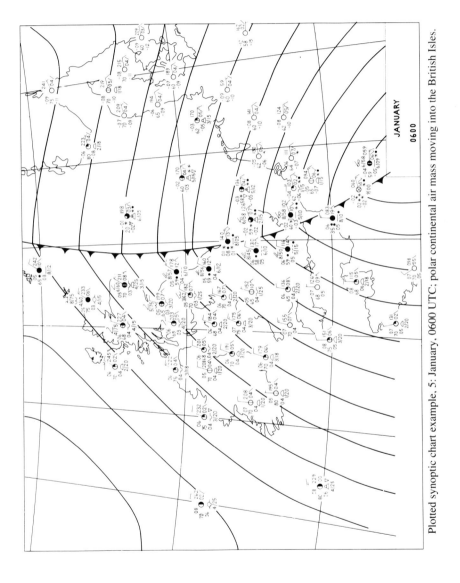

Plotted synoptic chart example, 5 January, 0600 UTC; polar continental air mass moving into the British Isles.

389

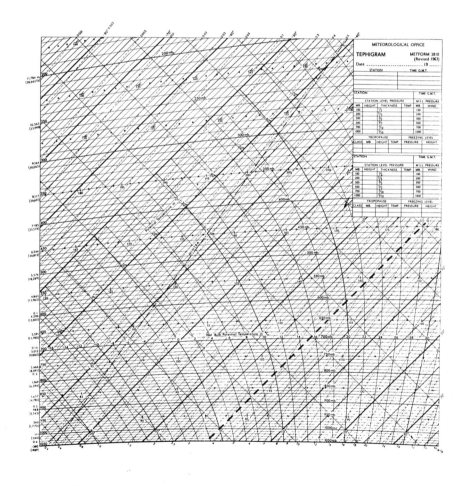

Tephigram (blank)

390

INDEX

Entries in bold type refer to the first page of sections in which the topic is discussed at length

Visibility — *continued*
    meter, 201
    observations, 200
    reduced by smoke, 152
    reduced by solid matter, 152
    slant, 142
    topography, effect on, 146
Visual range, 139
Volcanic ash, 152
VOLMET, 344

WAFS products, 291, 339
Warm,
    sector, 250
    temperate climatic zone, 318
Warmings, stratospheric, 159
Warnings, 343
    marked temperature inversion, 344
    vertical wind shear, 344
Water drop,
    supercooled, 89
    terminal velocity, 93
Waterspout, 268
Wave,
    cloud, 71
    easterly, 322
    long, 278
    mountain (standing, lee), 70
    polar-front, 245
Weather,
    air-mass, 234, 295
    air route, 319
    observation, 202
    radar, 115, 118
    station, automatic, 204
Wedge of high pressure, 10
Wet-bulb,
    potential temperature, 92
    temperature, 89
    thermometer, 89

Wind, **42**
    ageostrophic, 76
    anabatic, 60
    contours related to, 63
    cyclostrophic, 51, 65
    diurnal variation, 57
    earth's rotation, effect of, 47
    equivalent head/tailwind, 85
    föhn, 58
    force, 184
    free atmosphere, 63
    friction, effect on, 53
    funnel, 58
    geostrophic, 47
    gradient, 51, 65
    gustiness, 53
    heat transference by, 84
    isobars related to, 46
    katabatic, 60
    local variation, causes of, 298
    measurement, 183
    observation, 183
    pressure related to, 45
    ravine, 61
    shear, 77, 203
    surface, 53
    thermal, 65
    topography, effect of, 68
    tornado, 51
    trade, 302
    tropical cyclone, 51
    turbulence, caused by, 53
    upper, 6
        determination of, 206, 210
    valley, 60
    variation with height, 67
Wing-tip trails, 58
World Meteorological Organization,
    225, 339

Zone, climatic, 317

Printed in the United Kingdom for HMSO
Dd 296966 C21 4/94 0296966 12521